T5-AFZ-828

THE GRAIN TRADE:
How It Works

THE GRAIN TRADE:
How It Works

A DESCRIPTIVE STUDY
BY

James S. Schonberg

AN EXPOSITION-UNIVERSITY BOOK

EXPOSITION PRESS • NEW YORK

Dedicated to Free Enterprise

EXPOSITION PRESS INC., 386 Fourth Avenue, New York 16, N.Y.

FIRST EDITION

Library of Congress catalog card number: 56–10301.

Preface

This book has been written to assemble in one publication the many materials about the operation of the grain trade. Much has been written and said about the many separate aspects of the business of marketing grain. It seems worth while to bring as much as possible of this together so that it can be seen as a whole.

There is much romance surrounding the grain trade, especially the pricing and trading of grain, and much misunderstanding of the different jobs that need to be done. Among the many people who handle the trading in grain there is a great deal of direct and personal contact, which has resulted in one of the most remarkable codes of ethics and unwritten law in the whole area of commerce.

The grain business is highly technical. Some of its areas requiring extensive technical knowledge are the storing and conditioning of grains, each of which is a living and distinctly different being; the grading and sorting of the many lots of grain, each one a bit different from the other; the transportation of grain, with the various means of shipping and the huge complex of freight rates that surround our railroad system; and the intricacies of price interrelationship in time and space.

Grain is bought from farmers in tremendous quantities and numerous small lots at harvest time, held in widely separated concentration points, distributed to the places and at the times indicated by consumption needs, and certified for quality throughout. During all of these operations the risks of major price changes are carried by people other than those who own the grain. This system of shifting price risk, developed over the past 100 years, has made the trading of grain unique, has since spread to other commodities, and has resulted in much of the misunderstanding that surrounds the grain trade.

I have taken the position of an observer, avoiding controversial issues except when necessary for illustration. It has not been my intention to present an economic treatise on the trade or to discuss national policies. The views are not to be considered as interpretations of exchange rules or regulations, as they are not official in any way. The object has been to present information that is likely to be helpful to those interested in the grain trade. It is for those who are engaged in one segment of the trade and are not familiar with the workings of other branches, producers who would like to know what happens to their grain after they sell it and how the price is established even before the crop is planted, consumers who can buy as far ahead as they wish, county agents who work with farmers, legislators who form our farm policy, foreign buyers of our grain, instructors and students in our schools, and those who trade in grain and desire information.

The large yearly enrollment in the Grain Exchange Institute, Inc., course held in Chicago is evidence that knowledge of grain-trade practices is sought. It was because of this course, the Chicago Board of Trade Symposia, and the Uhlmann Awards Contests that I decided to assemble this book.

The system of grain handling is presented from a Chicago viewpoint; Chicago is one of the largest cash-grain markets and the center of the price-risk transference operations. For trading purposes the country east of the Rocky Mountains is divided into several sections, with Chicago located in the Central States. Other trading areas are the East, the Northwest, and the Southwest. These areas function as a unit because grain grown in its western portions finds market outlets all the way east. The Pacific Coast and Rocky Mountain States are a separate and distinct trading section, although their grain is sometimes shipped east and competes otherwise in foreign markets with grain grown east of the Rocky Mountains. Geographical boundaries differing from trading areas are designated for grain production and consumption purposes and for the railroad freight-rate structure.

In each kind of grain there are different varieties of seed which are grouped into classes and sub-classes as determined by a Federal grading agency, and each lot of grain has a numerical grade designation according to its quality factors. The quantity of grain handled and traded is measured by weight expressed in bushels according to a specific number of pounds for each grain per standard bushel measurement. Because of these standardizations it has been possible to handle the great bulk of grain and to develop the marketing and trading system as it is today. This has made possible the trading in futures-delivery contracts, the center of the grain-pricing system.

In order to cover the subject completely there is some repetition of material contained in other chapters. Chapter III goes somewhat ahead of the sequence and into technicalities in order to explain some of the fundamentals necessary for comprehending individual branches of the business covered in later chapters.

I am indebted to Dr. Thomas A. Hieronymus, Assistant Professor of Agricultural Economics, College of Agriculture, University of Illinois, for his review and criticism of the manuscript. Appreciation is also expressed to others for their help and guidance in the publication of the book—Mr. F. C. Bisson, Director of Marketing Research and Information, Chicago Board of Trade; Mr. Willis B. Combs, Marketing Specialist, United States Department of Agriculture Extension Service; Mr. Clarence C. Fivian, Vice-President of the Continental Grain Co.; Mr. Clarence M. Galvin, crop reporter and partner, Francis I. du Pont & Co.; Mr. Everett B. Harris, Secretary of the Chicago Board of Trade and later President of the Chicago Mercantile Exchange; Mr. I. M. Herndon, Manager of the Transportation Department, Chicago Board of Trade; Mr. Allan Q. Moore, Vice-President, Pillsbury Mills, Inc.; Mr. Robert F. Straub, President, Bunge Corporation; Mr. Richard F. Uhlmann, President, Uhlmann Grain Co.; Mr. Lee H. Wagner, Vice-President, Norris Grain Co.; Mr. Charles M. Walker (deceased), President, Grain Exchange Institute, Inc.

JAMES S. SCHONBERG

Contents

I THE WORLD'S GRAIN AND ITS TRADING

Grain's Relation to World Food Crops	3
The Development of Agriculture	6
Futures	10
The Chicago Board of Trade	12
The Commodity Exchange Authority	16
Supervision of Customers' Funds	19
Deliveries	21
Futures as a Guide to Pricing	22
Chicago Exchange Rules and Regulations	23

II THE OPERATION OF A FUTURES MARKET

Clearing Futures Trades	25
Handling Futures Business	27
Futures Commission-Merchant Operations	28
Futures Orders	29
Customers' Accounts	31
Settlement-Department Clearing	32
Execution of Futures Orders	35
Futures Quotations	37
The Relation of Other Futures Markets to Chicago	38

III CASH GRAIN AND FUTURES

Scope	40
Individual Risks	43
Cash Basis	44
Hedges	45
When Cash Grain Is Bought	47
When Cash Grain Is Sold	48
Inverse Carrying Charges	48
Competition	49
Use of Futures	52
Futures Carrying Charges	53
Equalization of Areas	54

IV WORLD PRODUCTION AND TRADE OF PRINCIPAL GRAINS

World Grain Résumé 56
Wheat 59
Corn 71
Oats 75
Barley 77
Rye 78
Grain Sorghums 80
Lard 81
Soybeans 82
Crude Soybean Oil 85
Soybean Meal 86

V GROWING, MARKETING AND MERCHANDISING

Farming Hazards 89
Fertilizers 91
Advancement in Farming Methods 92
Sale of Crops 94
Harvest Movement 96
Country Elevators 99
Sales to Terminals 101
Terminal or Processor Buying and Hedging 103
Storing and Selling Terminal Grain 104
Buying Grain From Terminals 108
Export Grain 109

VI TRANSPORTATION

Trucks 114
Railroads 115
(Freight-Traffic Territories, 116. Gateway Rates, 116.)
The Great Lakes 119
Inland Waterways 120
"Illinois Proportional" 122
Transit-Balance Rates 123
Tariffs 123
Loading Cars 124

Freight Bills 124
Milling in Transit 125
Grain Movements 125
Imports 126
Export 126
(Ocean Transportation, 127.)
Freight Rates 128
Other Charges 129
Summary 130

VII STORAGE
Kinds and Places 132
Farm Bin Storage 134
Farm Storage vs. Elevator Storage 136
Off-farm Storage Capacity 138
Corn Cribs 138
The Country Elevator 140
Drying Grain 144
Terminal Elevators 145
Barge Elevators 149
Eastern Lake Elevators 150
Export Elevators 150
Vessel Storage 151
Emergency Storage 152
Laws 152
Exchange Regulations 155
Weighing 156

VIII INSPECTION
Purpose 158
The United States Grain Standards Act 158
Licensed Inspectors 159
Appeal 159
Sampling Methods 160
(Carlots, Trucks and Wagons, 161. Bins in Elevators, 162. Cargo Grain, 162.)
Analysis 163

Grading Factors 164
(Test Weight per Bushel, 165. Moisture-testing, 166. Dockage, 167. Damaged Grain, 167. Damage in Wheat, 168. Unfit for Mixing, 168. Hidden Infestation, 169. Damage in Corn and Soybeans, 169.)
Classes 169
Inspection Service 171
Inspection in Canada 172
Sales on Special Qualifications 175
Other Commodities 176
(Lard, 176. Crude Soybean Oil, 177. Soybean Meal, 178.)
Board of Trade Sampling 179

IX PURCHASING AND PROCESSING
Purchasing Grain From Country Locations 180
Terminal-Elevator Buying 183
Processor Buying 185
Wheat-Flour Milling 188
Rye Milling 194
Wet Corn Processing 195
Dry-Process Milling of Corn 199
Oats Milling 200
Barley Malt 202
Pearling Barley 205
Soybean Processing 206
Feed Manufacturing 213

X STATISTICS AND NEWS
Crop Reports 217
Procedure in Making a Crop Report 223
Other Government Reports 227
Grain Exchange Prices 229
Grain Exchange Statistics 232
Private Statistical Agencies 233
Canadian Data 235
World Data 236
Weather 238
Widespread Uses of Grain Information 242

XI EXPORTING
Exports as a Balancing Item 245
Routine of the Export Business 251
Types of Export Firms 253
Contracts 255
(N.Y.P.E. Contract, 255. N.E.A.G.A. Contract, 256. L.C.T.A. Contract, 257.)
Insurance 258
Vessels 258
(Cargoes, 258. Parcels, 260.)
Out-turn 261
Export Ports 262
Inspection 268
Selling Abroad 269

XII MECHANICS AND BEHAVIOR OF THE MARKET
Transference of Risk 276
Open Interest vs. Stocks of Grain 280
Percentage of Hedging, Spreading and Speculation in Open Interest 288
(Hedging Percentages, 289. Speculative Percentages, 297. Hedges vs. Speculation, 297.)
Exchange Floor Trading 299
Off-the-Floor Customer Activities 302
Behavior of the Market 303

XIII SPREADING
As a Gauge for Distribution 310
Market Adjustment to World Levels 311
(Degree of Scarcity Governs Inverse Carrying Charges, 312. References, 314.)
Relation to Government Program 315
Handling Spreading (Changing Hedges) 315
Odd-Lot Spreading 317
Execution of Orders 318
Inter-market Spreads 319
Foreign Inter-market Spreads 323
Importing Spreads 324
Grain vs. Products 327

XIV SUMMARY
Services 332
Services Used and Operations Performed 333
(By Country and Terminal Elevators, 333. By Moderate-sized Firms and Dealers, 336. By Large Grain Firms, 337. By Grain Firms Generally, 337.)
Factions Consolidate Trade 338
Value of Futures 338
Banks 341
Speculation 341

INDEX 343

List of Figures

1.	Map: World Acreage of Principal Grain Crops	5
2.	Map: World Wheat Production	61
3.	Movement of Corn	73
4.	Horses and Mules, and Tractors, on Farms	93
5.	Farm Output and Labor Input	95
6.	Uses of Cropland Harvested	187
7.	Trends in Our Eating Habits	189
8.	Open Interest in Wheat Futures vs. Stocks of Wheat	279
9.	Wheat Commitments at Four Leading Markets	281
10.	Wheat Prices and Loan Rates	283
11.	Wheat: Open Interest and "Visible Supply"	285
12.	Soybeans: Open Interest, Stocks, Prices	287
13.	Wheat: World Supply and Price, 1923–40	305
14.	Cotton: Price vs. Carryover	307
15.	Wheat: Price vs. Carryover	308
16.	Hog-Corn Price Ratio and Hog Slaughter	330

Table

I.	Open-Interest Semi-monthly Averages (C.E.A. 1950 Report)	290
II.	Occupation Analysis of Wheat and Corn Futures Accounts	293
III.	Average Month-End Commitments in 1948 (C.E.A. Report)	294
IV.	Open-Commitment Semi-monthly Averages (C.E.A. 1951 Report)	295

THE GRAIN TRADE:
How It Works

CHAPTER I

The World's Grain and Its Trading

Grain's Relation to World Food Crops

Grains are the most important crops grown in the world, and almost half of all the acreage of crops is devoted to their production. Cultivated land throughout the world amounts to nearly 2,500,000,000 acres. This is about 7½% of the earth's 32,600,000,000 acres of land. Probably another 7½% of this land is used for such agricultural purposes as permanent meadows and pastures. The total acreage of wheat, rice, corn, oats, barley, and rye is about 1,200,000,000 acres. Wheat, rye, and rice, grown on over 40% of the world's grain acreage, are utilized mainly for human consumption, whereas corn, oats, and barley, grown on less than 40%, are used mostly for feeding livestock.

Even though rice occupies only about one fifth of the grain areas, it is the leading food of about half of the people of the world. More than 90% of the rice is grown in southern and eastern Asia and adjoining islands. Asia, excluding the U.S.S.R., has more than half of the world's population, with less than one third of the world's cultivated land area. Cultivated land per person in China is .29 of an acre, and in India it is .98 of an acre, whereas in the United States it is 3.13 acres per person.[1]

Exclusive of the Soviet Union, Europe, which covers less than 5% of the earth's surface and has more than 15% of its population, is one of the most highly developed agricultural

[1] United States Department of Agriculture Miscellaneous Publication No. 705, Oct., 1949.

and industrial regions of the world. Its population is about 370,000,000, having more than doubled during the past 100 years. Grain is the leading crop of Europe, with wheat ranking first among the principal grains, and oats, rye, barley, and corn following respectively. Potatoes are grown on a large scale as a feed crop and are also a very popular food.

The Soviet Union wheat acreage exceeds that of rye, but the latter is the largest of any country, varying from 60% to 70% of the world's total, whereas wheat is about one fourth the world total. For all crops, it is second in the world in the number of cultivated acres, and India is third. Both are only slightly below the United States.

The United States not only has the largest area of cultivated land in the world but also has extensive areas of permanent meadows, pastures, and range lands which are used for grazing livestock. The abundant supply of meat products derived from the livestock industry plus the crops produced on cultivated land gives the United States a well balanced agriculture, which only a few countries are fortunate enough to have. The population has increased nearly 100% in the past 50 years, while the cultivated land has increased only about 10%. This greater population pressure upon the food supply has been more than offset by improved methods of farming, from which have resulted increased yields per acre of crops as well as larger outputs of products per animal unit.[2]

It was during the past century that the grain trade developed as we now know it. In our own country and in other export nations the populations had to be fed. At the same time, surpluses were provided for shipment in international trade to deficit nations who could pay for importations. Wheat is by far the most important food product in international trade. It is a commodity that does not deteriorate readily in storage or in transit; it can be moved easily and is readily standardized so that it can be purchased from distant markets with confidence.

---

[2] U.S.D.A. Miscellaneous Publication No. 665, June, 1948.

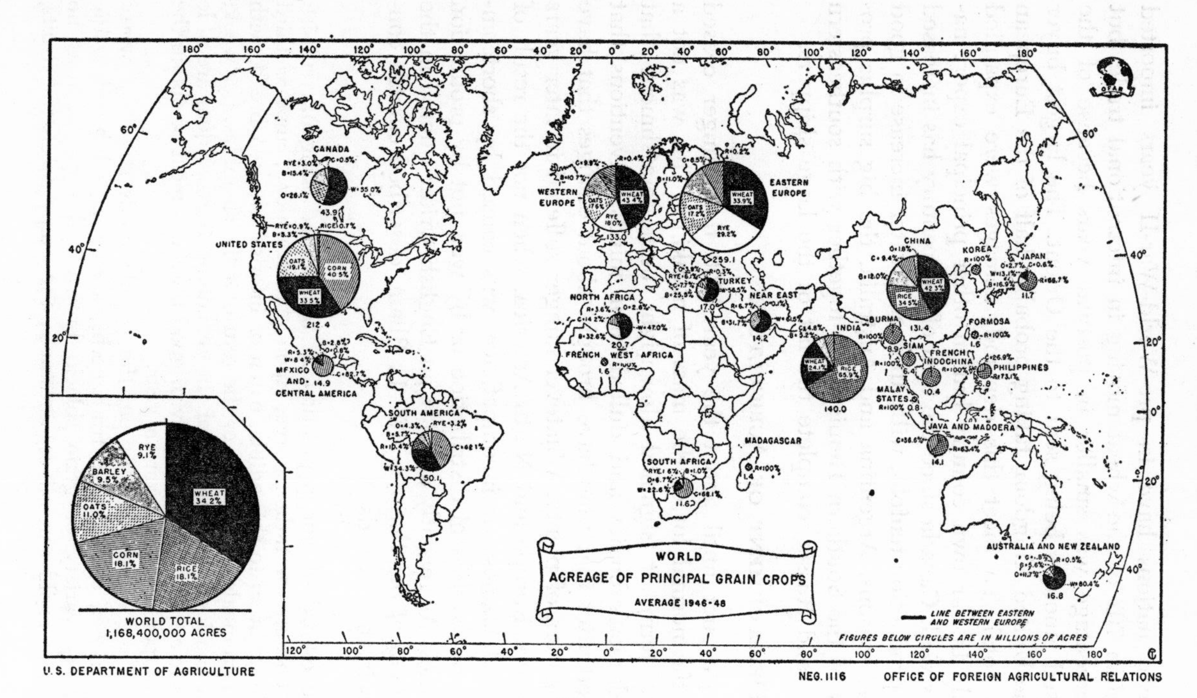
WORLD
ACREAGE OF PRINCIPAL GRAIN CROPS
AVERAGE 1946-48
CANADA
43.9
UNITED STATES
212.4
MEXICO AND CENTRAL AMERICA
14.9
SOUTH AMERICA
50.1
WESTERN EUROPE
133.0
EASTERN EUROPE
259.1
NORTH AFRICA
20.7
FRENCH WEST AFRICA
1.6
TURKEY
17.0
NEAR EAST
14.2
SOUTH AFRICA
MADAGASCAR
1.4
INDIA
140.0
BURMA
8.9
SIAM
6.4
FRENCH INDOCHINA
10.4
MALAY STATES
0.8
CHINA
131.4
KOREA
JAPAN
11.7
FORMOSA
1.6
PHILIPPINES
6.8
JAVA AND MADOERA
14.1
AUSTRALIA AND NEW ZEALAND
16.8
WHEAT 34.2%
RICE 18.1%
CORN 18.1%
OATS 11.0%
BARLEY 9.5%
RYE 9.1%
WORLD TOTAL
1,168,400,000 ACRES
LINE BETWEEN EASTERN AND WESTERN EUROPE
FIGURES BELOW CIRCLES ARE IN MILLIONS OF ACRES
U. S. DEPARTMENT OF AGRICULTURE
NEG. 1116
OFFICE OF FOREIGN AGRICULTURAL RELATIONS

FIGURE 1

European nations have in pre-World-War-II years imported more than 70% of the wheat moving in international trade, but the percentage was smaller in postwar years because of the increased amounts being sent to the Orient. The largest buyer was the United Kingdom, taking probably half of the European import total. To meet this demand, acreages were expanded not only in our own country but in other principal export nations as well. Canada since the turn of the century has increased wheat production tenfold, with an even greater increase in good growing seasons. Argentina and Australia, the big surplus producers of the Southern Hemisphere, together with southeastern Europe and Russia, complete the list of the large shippers.

The Development of Agriculture

It was not until about the year 1800 that hunger ceased to be the normal lot of the mass of mankind. This was not a relative term; it signified downright undernourishment that stunted men's bodies and dulled their minds. Inventions that occurred after that time have brought about changes that have led to an era of plenty. Whatever hunger suffered in later years in Western Europe and North America, when not the result of individual laziness or incompetence, was caused by shortcomings of our system of distribution or by war, not by production difficulties. As recently as 1844 an English writer quoted in the *Dictionary of the Farm*, by W. L. Rham, described current conditions in these words:

> Fully one-third of our population in the United Kingdom subsist, almost entirely, or rather starve, upon potatoes alone; another third have, in addition to this edible, oaten or inferior wheaten bread, with one or two meals of fat pork, or the refuse of the shambles, per week; while a considerable majority of the remaining third seldom are able to procure an ample daily supply of good butcher's meat or obtain the luxury of poultry from year to year.
>
> On the continent of Europe, the population is still in a worse condition: fish, soups made from herbs, a stuff called bread, made from every variety of grain, black, brown and sour, such as no Englishman could eat; olives, chestnuts, the pulpy saccharine fruits,

roots, stalks, and leaves and not infrequently, the bark of trees; sawdust, blubber, train oil with frogs and snails, make up a good part of the food of the greater portion of the inhabitants of Europe.

Unsatisfactory as this menu would appear to modern tastes, it would have appeared epicurean to the man of an earlier day. In those times bread was the chief, if not the only, food of mankind, for wheat has existed throughout history and grows in most parts of the world. At different times of the year in different parts of the world the bread diet was supplemented by meat, milk, fish, and other animal products. All livestock was slaughtered in the fall, except for a few animals saved for breeding. The meat was preserved by salting it. The grain grown barely sufficed for man's own food and could not be spared for livestock.

William Farr, in the *Journal of the Royal Statistical Society*, in 1846 wrote as follows:

> In the eleventh and twelfth centuries, famine is recorded every fourteen years, on an average, and the people suffered twenty years of famine in two hundred years. In the thirteenth century the list exhibits the same proportion of famine; the addition of five years of high prices makes the proportion greater. Upon the whole, scarcities decreased during the three following centuries; but the average from 1201 to 1600 is the same, namely, seven famines and ten years of famine in a century.

The physical aspects of famine were no more terrible than the intellectual and moral effects. Cannibalism and infanticide were not unheard of, nor was the conservation of the food supply by driving out the weaker members of the population of a city to starve beyond the city walls.

Europe and other parts of the world fared no better than England. China and India were, by reason of their intermittent rainfall and inefficient methods of agriculture, particularly subject to famine, and still are. Russia, also, up to 1921 was frequently visited by famine.

However, with the exception of Russia and the potato famine in Ireland in 1846, no major famine resulting from natural causes is recorded in Western and Central Europe or in North America since 1800. Wars have brought food shortages, but these have been purely man-made.

Few agricultural workers in organized society from the beginning of history until the breakdown of the feudal system were free men. They cultivated as they were told and received from the product of their labor only enough to maintain and reproduce themselves. "Eighteenth century wheat was cut in the Scriptural way, by a sickle held by the laborer in one hand, while he grasped a few heads of wheat in the other," says J. Russell Smith in *The World's Food Resources*. The same writer reports the invention of the cradle for harvesting wheat in 1806, in New England, but man still depended on hand labor for his "staff of life."[3]

In 1800 there were about 375,000 people west of the Appalachians in farmlands so rich that, spurred by tales brought back by the returning travelers, a million more joined them during the next twenty years. So great was the exodus that some seaboard states tried to stem it by legislation. The Napoleonic Wars and attendant hard times laid a heavy hand on Europe. With wheat at $3.50 a bushel in England, food exports from the United States boomed. The War of 1812 paralyzed trade, commerce, and agriculture along the seaboard. Wheat sold at $1.50 a bushel in New York. Across the Alleghenies there was an abundance, but transportation costs over the mountains were prohibitive.

Two solutions to the marketing problem that thus arose had been given to the country a few years before, and this crisis brought them into sharp public focus. In 1804 George Renick fattened a herd of cattle in Ohio and started driving them eastward. He succeeded in driving the corn-fed herd 300 miles over the mountains to Baltimore with an average loss of less than 100 pounds per head. The experiment proved extremely profitable. When the East became hard-pressed for food, many

[3] International Harvester Co., *Food in War and Peace,* 1943.

others followed this example. Corn could not be carried to the eastern market except at prohibitive cost, but it could be fed to livestock and the animals could be driven to Atlantic ports and sold at fantastic prices. The second solution was the invention of the steamboat in 1807, making practical the shipment of produce to the East by way of the Mississippi River and the Gulf of Mexico. James Watt late in the previous century had invented the steam engine, which was a tremendous impetus to the growth of the factory system. The eastern states gave their chief attention to industry and commerce, looking to the Middle West for food. By 1820 the Mississippi Valley was firmly established as the granary of the nation. The world needed food; the Middle West had it. Trade, commerce, and industry, firmly grounded on an agricultural foundation, grew and raised the United States to world power.[4]

In 1828, three years before the reaper was invented, there were only two or three railroads in the country, none more than a few miles long. By 1869 the expansion of the railroad system had resulted in the opening of the first transcontinental line.

The first plows were crooked sticks, and wood was used in all plows until around 1800. Inventions for harnessing horses and oxen were slow. The Romans, instead of using shoulder collars and traces, fastened the tongues of the plows to straps around the horse's neck. As soon as the horse began to draw his load the strap about his neck tightened, interfering with both circulation and breathing. The Romans tipped and often covered their heavy wooden plows with iron. Between 1820 and 1830 farmers in the United States rather suddenly abandoned wooden plows and adopted those of cast iron.

The invention of the reaper in 1831 by Cyrus McCormick solved the harvesting problem and changed farming from drudgery into a business calling for mind as much as muscle and yielding substantial results for reasonable labor. The mower was invented about three years later; the threshing machine

---

[4] Corn Industries Research Foundation, *Corn in Industry,* 1937.

followed in 1834, and then the first combine in 1836. Grain drills, permitting more efficient planting than hand sowing, came in the 1840's. Within one decade the time required to harvest an acre of wheat was reduced from 37 hours to 11½ hours and in a century to only half an hour. The total labor time for producing an acre of wheat starting with the breaking of the ground with a plow and two oxen took 64½ hours in 1830 and was reduced to 2 hours 24 minutes in 1930. The total labor time for an acre of corn produced by aid of horses instead of oxen was reduced from 38¾ hours in 1830 to 5 hours 21 minutes a century later by the aid of machinery.

As the American frontier was pushed back, inventions quickly followed. In 1837 the self-scouring steel plow made possible the cultivation of the rich, sticky prairie lands. Other principal developments contributing to the new era were the perfection of the Bessemer process in 1856, followed by the open-hearth furnace in 1867, the sand blast in 1870, the telegraph in 1844, the telephone in 1876, the dynamo in 1867, and the internal-combustion engine, the development of which was made possible by the discovery of oil in Pennsylvania in 1845. Standardization of parts, which made mass production possible, began during the Civil War with the manufacture of guns for the army. Modern industry was not possible prior to that time, when it took the production of one farm worker to supply the needs for himself and four other persons, whereas now his efforts support eighteen others.

Futures

We have come a long way in a century and a half. Man is no longer a slave to the production of necessities for subsistence. Common man has time for leisure and the luxuries of life.

The system of futures trading upon which the grain trade depends for pricing is a continuation of the system of spreading the risk among the consumers in these days of expanded availability of food, just as the risk of procurement had been spread among the consumers from primitive days when each man sought his own food. No one has controlled the price of food for long. In the present day, food is concentrated in production and storage areas and the consumers are diversified, contrary to earlier days, when food had to originate close to the consumers and was not stored in abundance. In primitive days, when the storehouse of the supply of food was widespread in the fields, it was each man's task to secure his food through his ability to hunt, and that was tantamount to ownership; he was in control of his individual requirements. Now, stocks of grain, the principal food, are concentrated in commercial channels and merchants distribute them to meet widespread individual requirements.

While the grain is held in storage, what has not been sold ahead for later consumption is secured against price change through the use of futures contracts. Speculators, scattered widely and representative of consumers who will later use the grain, carry the burden of the price risk; yet actual ownership of the grain rests with the merchants. This follows the same pattern as in other industries of an age with specialized production and diversified distribution. Every endeavor, whether agricultural, commercial, industrial, or medical, has its specialists, and it cannot be otherwise now when no one produces all of his own necessities of life, contrary to former times, when he was required to do so.

Futures trading has attained a high degree of efficiency, and use of the system has spread to many commodities. Each exchange on which trading is conducted has its special rules and style of trading as well as different conditions governing fulfillment by delivery at consummation of contracts. Available facilities and the trade practices for handling each commodity govern the prescribed basis of tender from seller to buyer, and they often govern the method of shipment after delivery has been made. One thing they all have in common is that before delivery is made, either party to the contract has the privilege of offsetting his purchases by a sale or offsetting his sale by a purchase, and then settling the contract by payment or collection of the money difference between the purchase price and the sale price. This relieves the obligation of taking delivery, in the case of a buyer, or of making delivery, in the case of a seller. The United States Supreme Court has ruled on this point.

Once futures contracts are entered into on established rules of an exchange the conditions prevail until maturity. The same grades of grain prevail, so that, while the seller has a choice, he must deliver a grade among those prescribed at the outset. The time of delivery during the contract expiration month is also at the choice of the seller; and the location, where there are several, may be selected by him. The Federal Government has established grading standards for grain and some other commodities; from these the exchanges select grades that may be delivered on futures contracts. Where no official standards exist for a commodity, they are set forth in the contract. There may be tolerances in conditions because of the peculiarities natural to the commodity, but these provisions are contained in the contract. The vital features of the contract remain uniform all during its trading life. At times it becomes necessary to alter the conditions under which a grain may be traded for future delivery; such alterations occur when any of the vital factors are changed. The new contract almost always takes effect at the beginning of trading in a new delivery month; but if it becomes necessary to change a futures contract after trading has started, the exchange designates the existing contract as "old" and the one under the new terms as "new."

The Chicago Board of Trade

During a period of development accompanying new inventions which changed customs and the mode of living in the United States, in the last half of the nineteenth century the Board of Trade of the City of Chicago started futures trading as the need for it arose in the natural evolution of the system of handling grain. Chicago's, however, was not the first grain exchange in the United States, for the St. Louis Merchants Exchange had been organized in 1836, twelve years before the

Board of Trade in Chicago. Grain production was mounting in the Midwest in the decades following the many inventions in farm machinery, and Chicago was particularly affected by the construction of the Illinois and Michigan Canal, which was opened in April, 1848. It is recorded that Thomas Richmond, an elevator operator, and W. L. Whitney, a grain broker, had discussed the feasibility of establishing a board of trade in Chicago. They consulted other businessmen, and at the first meeting to consider the matter, formally on March 13, 1848, a resolution was passed that the rapidly developing trade in Chicago called for the formation of a board of trade. A constitution was adopted and a committee appointed to draw up bylaws, which were passed on April 3 by the 82 members.

In that same year other events, no doubt, promoted this movement. The peace treaty with Mexico was ratified; Wisconsin entered the Union; gold was discovered in California. The first telegram received in Chicago came from Milwaukee on January 15; a contract was let for twenty-five miles of railroad to be added to the seven miles begun the preceding year by the Galena & Chicago Union Railroad, and the Southwest plank road, the first such road in Illinois, was begun in May. The first ocean-going steamship, the *Propeller Ireland,* arrived from Montreal ready for a return trip to Liverpool. The first United States Court was established in Chicago in July. The first locomotive, the *Pioneer,* owned by the G. & C. U., arrived by sailing vessel in October and brought the first wheat hauled by rail into Chicago on November 20, and the year 1848 also saw the building of the first stockyards in Chicago. All of these were important events for the grain business, for they meant rapid communication via telegraph, better roads, cheaper water transportation, a railroad going west, and the lure of gold in California bringing more settlers to the Middle West.

Chicago had had a poor start. Historians just twenty-five years before the formation of the Board of Trade had written very discouragingly of its possibilities. In 1829 there was a population of 100, including settlers, half-breeds, and three or four French traders. Not until 1836 were troops withdrawn from Fort Dearborn, at which time the reservation became part of Chicago.

Transportation was the problem in those days. New Orleans on the Mississippi River had been a natural outlet for mid-western grain, but the Erie Canal in New York was opened in 1825 and the Welland Canal around Niagara Falls in 1833, both providing outlets to the East. Water was the logical means of transportation at that time. The Illinois-Michigan Canal to connect the Illinois River and Lake Michigan at Chicago was talked of for years but was not opened until 1848. In fact, it was the commission for the canal that laid out a plan for a town just north and west of Fort Dearborn on the muddy banks of the Chicago River.

The first cargo of grain shipped by lake from Chicago was loaded from Newberry & Dole's warehouse on the north bank of the river in 1839. It was a flat warehouse, and the grain was loaded on the brig *Osceola* by means of a chute.

It was calculated in 1844, when prices were low, that the value of a wagonload of wheat was equal to the cost of hauling it sixty miles. Corn, being of less value per bushel, could not profitably be hauled long distances, and in most years arrivals in Chicago were little more than would satisfy local requirements. The opening of the Illinois-Michigan Canal had only moderate influence on the wheat business, but it resulted in a great increase in the amount of corn that came to and left Chicago by boat.

Numerous corn cribs sprung up along the canal and the Illinois River, and some very large and substantial stocks were accumulated in the years that followed. It was found advisable to hold much of the corn in cribs until late spring or even summer to permit it to dry thoroughly before shelling and shipping; some of the early shipments had spoiled while afloat on the waterways. It is evident that the element of speculation was large in connection with shipping corn by canal and river, because the dealers were unavoidably subjected to price declines on a large part of their stock. In such circumstances, it is not surprising that some dealers should hit upon the expedient of entering into "time contracts" with Chicago merchants. Some of these men would come to Chicago and hunt from office to office for men who would "buy the corn for May." Such a contract has been found to be recorded in the *Chicago Journal* of March 13, 1851, calling for the delivery of 3,000 bushels of corn in June at a price one cent lower than the quotation for corn on hand on March 13. A wheat trade was recorded in 1852. These trades came about from other contracts, recorded almost from the opening of the canal, known as "to arrive" contracts, and futures trading seems to have evolved from such contracts.

Speculative risks for wheat were also great in the early days of the exchange, particularly in wheat purchased after the close of navigation on the Great Lakes in the fall. Such grain could not be shipped until the following spring, and substantial stocks were accumulated during the winter.

In the 1850's other markets, like New York, used such contracts, their use doubtless stimulated by the Crimean War. One observer in Chicago commented in 1855, "The corn which was expected to pass this port before June had probably all changed hands once or twice by prospective contracts." Activity in time contracts increased later and was given great stimulus by the Civil War. In 1863 a rule passed by Board of Trade directors and followed in 1865 by others more comprehensive provided requirements for margins not to exceed 10% and included previous provisions for enforcement of verbal or written contracts with other members, as well as some standardization of delivery and payment.

It is difficult to determine when the actual transfer from time contracts to futures contracts was accomplished, but historians give 1875 as a likely guess. It is believed that the idea of transferring market risk from dealers to speculators without actual change of ownership of grain was not conceived for some time. In a lawsuit in New York it was suggested that the hedging of corn by country grain dealers became common some time in the

1870's and that the hedging of wheat was common by 1880. (The Chicago Fire in 1871 destroyed many grain-trade records covering Board of Trade activities.)

The handling of wheat developed along somewhat different lines, for its higher price permitted it to be hauled by other methods; much to the disappointment of grain dealers it continued to come in by wagon and only in small volume by canal. In 1849 Charles Walker built a grain warehouse at Babcock's Grove, now Lombard, 21 miles west of Chicago, terminus of the G. & C. U. R. R., and during the first week of its use 25,000 bushels of wheat were shipped to Chicago. Expansion of railroads was stimulated in 1850 when the United States Congress granted 2,500,000 acres for the construction of the Illinois Central Railroad. That same year saw the G. & C. U. R. R. extend its lines to Elgin and Aurora; and a 100,000-bushel elevator significantly increased Chicago storage. Telegraph communication was being extended both east and south, affording business increased facilities, and in 1858 the laying of the transatlantic cable aided business further.

In 1851 the Illinois legislature passed an act regulating issuance of grain warehouse receipts, and the grain trade, with Chicago, continued to grow in importance. In 1852 the first eastern railroad entered Chicago, and by the end of the year there were two eastern and two western railroads terminating in Chicago. While grain shipments from Chicago in 1848 were 2,750,000 bushels, by 1854 the total had reached 13,000,000.

The early days saw many disputes over warehousing that dragged on for years. Later, bucket shops were a great annoyance, and there was much litigation aimed at telegraph companies for furnishing Board of Trade quotations to them. "Bucket shops" were places which accepted bets on grain-price fluctuations as reported by the Exchange's ticker. Around the turn of the century they sprung up all over the country until one judge proclaimed, "Gambling in grains may be said to be the national pastime."

No grain was ever actually delivered on any contracts in a

bucket shop. None of the orders they received were executed on a legitimate exchange, and no commercial interests used bucket-shop facilities. Outsiders simply bet against the house on price changes. Most bucket shops hid in hole-in-the-wall dives, but others assumed quite an aura of respectability.

The Exchange attacked all these imitation institutions with vigor. Its first move was to remove its tickers from all such shops; obviously, if the bucket shops could not obtain Board of Trade quotations there could be no betting on those quotations. Finally the courts put an end to the bucket-shop menace.

Chicago started trading in numbers of pounds of grain per bushel in 1854, which replaced the system of "a bushel by measurement." Other practices for uniformity were instituted from time to time, including standard grades for wheat in 1856; but in the years that followed there were many changes, and now the trade uses Federal standards. Federally licensed inspectors are available in all important markets, with the service continually expanding. The Board of Trade Weighing Department was organized in 1857. The interchange of market reports with other cities was developed by 1858, and since 1880 the ticker has aided in disseminating prices.

The Commodity Exchange Authority

The exchanges do no trading themselves but as self-governing bodies provide rules and regulations for their members' conduct. The Chicago Board of Trade rules and regulations are made under authority granted in the Illinois State Charter passed by the legislature in 1859 and amended in 1945. It now also operates under the United States law originally enacted in 1922 and several times amended, now known as the Commodity Exchange Act, which authorizes certain practices, endorses others, and prohibits some by its authority. Under this authority the Secretary of Agriculture designates contract markets as such and licenses firms and brokers and exercises powers over nonmembers' using the futures markets. The law and its administrative rules and regulations are contained in a booklet of about

100 pages, which brings it up to date. From time to time additional regulations are issued that are often important in the daily conduct of the futures business.

One requirement is the daily reporting of trades, and strict supervision is exercised over individual traders if their volume is large. One person may not hold or control more than 2,000,000 bushels of grain in any one market or more than 3,000,000 bushels if it is "a spread," provided not more than 2,000,000 is in one future. The rye limitation is 500,000 bushels and soybeans 2,000,000. Trader's daily trades may not be in excess of these amounts. At times the Board of Trade has limited trading to liquidation or has asked individual traders to reduce their open trades. The Business Conduct Committee of the Exchange receives reports of what may be considered excessive dealings, and the committee is charged with the duty and authority to prevent manipulation of prices, etc. Hedges are exempt from C.E.A. limits on "positions" and daily trading in futures.

Reports must be made to the C.E.A. if 200,000 bushels or more are open in any one delivery month, in which case all delivery months in all markets of that grain must be reported. This includes hedging and spreading as well as speculative trading. Reports are also required on other commodities when amounts reach C.E.A. published limits. On occasion they may ask commission firms for special, full, or partial reports of all traders' commitments in one or more grains. Regular reports must be given to the C.E.A. by those who hold reporting amounts, but only on days when trades are made; these reports in addition to the reporting trader's own commitments include trades of all accounts controlled by him. Also, firms having open trades on their books for accounts with reporting amounts must report them weekly to the C.E.A.

In an endeavor to explain the volume of trading and open interest in futures for all traders' accounts combined (as published in the daily C.E.A. statement), let us go to the beginning, when the first trade is made in a new future month on an exchange—the first day of trading in the new month in the pit. If A buys 5,000 bushels and B sells it, the volume of trade and open interest is 5,000 bushels. If two others make like trades, volume and open-interest total will be 10,000 bushels, and so on. Each time there is a new buyer and a new seller the open interest increases by the amount in which they trade. In this report the total of all buyers added together is the volume of trade for the day. The total of those who sold would record the same figure.

Let us go back to the original trade, in which A bought 5,000 bushels and B sold it, and the open interest was therefore 5,000 bushels. The only way that those 5,000 bushels can be eliminated is by both reversing—that is, B buying 5,000 bushels and A selling them. Then there would be no open interest at all. In the complexities of trading, we know that A and B keep their trades open for different lengths of time. If A, who has bought, retains it for a long time, but B soon buys 5,000 bushels previously sold and makes his trade with C, the open interest stands as follows: A has bought and C has sold, with B eliminated, and the total open interest is still 5,000 bushels. Finally, all who have bought must sell, or take delivery, and all those who have sold must buy, or make delivery. Another way of interpreting open interest in futures is to explain that deliveries of the commodity in an amount equal to the open interest would entirely eliminate the latter.

Supervision of Customers' Funds

The Commodity Exchange Authority promulgates many other requirements for conduct of the business. One important section of the rules and regulations is section 1.20:

> All money received by a futures commission merchant to margin, guarantee, or secure the trades or contracts of commodity customers and all money accruing to such customers as the result of such trades or contracts shall be separately accounted for and be segregated as belonging to such customers. Such funds, when deposited with

any bank or trust company, shall be deposited under an account name which will clearly show that they are customer's funds segregated as required by the Commodity Exchange Act, and under a written agreement with such bank or trust company waiving any claim, lien, or right of set-off of any nature, which such bank or trust company might otherwise have or obtain against such funds. An executed copy of such agreement shall be kept as a permanent record by the futures commission merchant. If such funds are deposited with a clearing organization of a contract market, they shall be deposited under an account name which will clearly show that they are customer's funds segregated as required by the Commodity Exchange Act. Under no circumstances shall any portion of a commodity customer's funds be obligated to the clearing organization of a contract market, or to any member of a contract market, except to margin, guarantee, secure, transfer, adjust, or settle trades and contracts made in behalf of such commodity customers.[5]

They further state that if an account should show a debit, other customers' funds cannot be used to offset this debit. However, the commission house can place their own funds with those of customers for such purposes, and must keep a permanent record of all such amounts. Under certain conditions loans can be made against warehouse receipts with these funds. Also, the funds may be invested in Government securities, with the interest earned and price appreciation going to or loss sustained by the commission merchant.

If a firm trades in futures for itself or its officers as speculation or hedging, it must be given the same treatment as other customers under Board of Trade or C.E.A. rules. Concerning margins on futures trades, the Commodity Exchange Authority has no jurisdiction. They are concerned, however, that no customers' funds shall be used except to margin, etc., customers' trades. Margins are regulated by the exchanges, but when customers' funds are received for this purpose they must be handled under the C.E.A. requirements of segregation.

---

[5] Commodity Exchange Act of 1936; formerly the Grain Futures Act of 1922.

Deliveries

One exchange rule, conforming to C.E.A. requirements, is that there shall be no settlement of open futures positions during the last seven business days of a trading month except by delivery of grain under the rules of the exchange on which the futures trade was made. You can, however, during the seven days make an exchange of futures against a bonafide cash trade in any position suitable to both buyer and seller in order to close part or all of your futures contracts. The buyer, of course, can insist on regular delivery.

The seven-day period for delivery of grain after pit trading ceases gives the seller time to bring grain to Chicago, if necessary, or to arrange completion on whatever terms are required by the contract. The seller must make good on his contract by furnishing the cash commodity, provided he has not bought in futures as an offset while pit trading was still permitted. The "long" who receives delivery may make whatever disposition he wishes of the commodity, including selling it to one who may again deliver it in satisfaction of a sale of futures; often arrivals in the spot market are purchased by those who use them for delivery purposes. Grain held in storage and not immediately required to fill other intended applications may also be sold to those who need it to make deliveries; when demand is strong, sale of such grain may be made at a price higher than that with which it can be replaced for the original commercial use. Late-month pit trading may adjust the futures price to a level that will attract the commodity to market for delivery purposes, or it may induce those who have bought the futures to liquidate their holdings. Prices may have risen to a level that, compared to other values, would be considered too hazardous to maintain ownership. It may be that the same commodity could be purchased cheaper elsewhere, or be purchased cheaper for a later position, so that if the "long" took delivery he would find that others could undersell him.

Actual delivery on a futures contract of sale is accomplished by tender of a notice of intention to deliver with payment for the document of title to the commodity following. Payment for grain is made the next banking business day after the tender of notice is given, except that track deliveries of grain need not be paid for until the grain is unloaded from the railroad car (80 per cent is paid if the car is diverted to a different elevator). Even though the notice of intention is presented to the Clearing House, which passes it to the oldest "long" clearing firm on their books, payment is made direct by the receiver of the notice to the issuer of the notice.

Futures as a Guide to Pricing

The whole grain trade is a closely knit system in which the futures trading is the guide, and each interest watches the price level as it affects that interest. From those who follow it in order to decide upon the right crops to grow or when to sell what they have produced to those who use it in securing supplies to process for consumption, all have the opportunity to transfer risk of price change through use of futures.

Futures quotations are disseminated rapidly throughout the nation by means of the fastest kind of communication. Quotation tickers carry each price change throughout the length and breadth of the United States and into Canada. The telegraph, by both private and public wires, as well as radio, telephone, and cable systems, sends price changes to numerous locations at home and abroad. The quotations of various futures trading centers are immediately recorded in all other markets, so that a price move in one may be reflected in the others, insofar as it affects individual conditions. Each futures market represents the factors of the trade in its own area, and prices move with regard to those forces, although not with complete independence, because competition becomes active when prices make trading attractive. There is a constant change in value between grades and classes of the same kind of grain in different areas and between grades and classes of grain in one area. In the case of wheat, price often determines whether spring or winter flour will be sold; and within each kind of flour, changing prices for varying protein content again influences decisions. Other processed and unprocessed grains are similarly affected by futures prices. In feeds, the price of one will cause it to be used more abundantly, if relatively cheap, and others less so, if comparatively high. And general feed-grain prices largely govern livestock and poultry production quantities.

All these factors, and many more, are price-making influences. Each affects the futures market in its area, and each futures market another, so that in culmination the effect on prices is quickly recorded and is known far and wide. The reason for a price change may not be known at the time that quotations change, and even when the news that influences the market is published, its market significance may not be generally understood; but the constant absorption of all the complex influences is recorded in the price level. It may be a question of whether the news makes the price or the price makes the news. In fact, one influences the other, because changing prices will induce either buying or selling. It may be a change in the weather, in farmer or commercial activity, in political events, or in other developments that exerts the influence. Members of the trade are constantly ferreting out all the news that is available and relaying it to those who are interested. Various agencies also inform members of the trade and the general public through their widespread news services.

Chicago Exchange Rules and Regulations

In its charter the Chicago Exchange is officially named the Board of Trade of the City of Chicago, and the preamble to its rules and regulations states: "The objects of the Association are: To maintain a commercial exchange; to promote uniformity in the customs and usages of merchants; to inculcate principles of justice and equity in trade; to acquire and disseminate valuable commercial and economic information; and, generally, to secure to its members the benefits of co-operation in the furtherance of their legitimate pursuits."

Most of the officers, the directors, and members of some committees are elected by the membership; others are elected by the Board of Directors or are appointed by the president. Some of the officers and most of the committee members serve without remuneration. The association has the right to admit such persons that they consider qualified. Corporations and partnerships may not become members, but by virtue of membership(s) held by their officer(s) or partner(s) they may enjoy certain privileges. The policy of the association is to encourage but not to compel the arbitration of disputes, and the Arbitration Committee hears evidence of members or non-members and files its award. Any interested party dissatisfied with an award may appeal to the Committee of Appeals. Awards are final and may be filed with the Circuit Court for enforcement.

Exchanges have a number of departments for grain and other commodity services—for weighing, sampling, inspection, statistics, warehousing, quotations, etc.—which are usually under the jurisdiction of a committee of members whose chairman is a director of the Exchange. Members of an exchange must abide by its rules and regulations; offienses may be punishable by suspension or expulsion.

CHAPTER II

The Operation of a Futures Market

Clearing Futures Trades

Trading in future delivery must take place only in the exchange hall during regular hours and in the pit assigned to that commodity, exceptions being the exchange of futures against cash trades, etc.,—so-called office trades. Futures trades in Chicago are cleared through the Clearing House, which is a corporation having its own charter, bylaws, and resolutions. The bylaws may not be changed without the consent of Board of Trade directors. Members of the Clearing House are individual members of the Board of Trade, corporations, and partnerships when they are admitted under the qualifications prescribed by the Clearing House after they are approved by the directors of the Exchange. Where a future-delivery contract is cleared through the Clearing House, the Clearing House is deemed substituted as seller to the buyer and also as buyer to the seller, and thereupon the Clearing House has all the rights and is subject to all of the liabilities of the original parties with respect to such a contract. Where a member buys and sells the same commodity for the same delivery and such contracts are cleared through the Clearing House, the purchases and sales are offset, so that the member is deemed a buyer from the Clearing House to the extent that his purchases exceed his sales, or a seller to the Clearing House to the extent that his sales exceed his purchases.

Trades for customers, either members or non-members of the association, are subject to Clearing House terms. Such trades may be offset against other trades, as between clearing members and the Clearing House. If the trade is not offset and a seller tenders a delivery notice to the Clearing House, the clearing member to whom such notice is passed is substituted as buyer in lieu of the Clearing House, and such a buyer must substitute the issuer of the notice as seller in lieu of the Clearing House. Payment for the commodity tendered by delivery notice is then made direct by buyer to seller.

With reference to "offsets," the Supreme Court of the United States wrote, in part, in its decision in the Christi Grain Case, written by Justice Oliver Wendell Holmes, on May 8, 1905, as follows:

> There is no doubt that a large part of those contracts is made for serious business purposes. Hedging for instance, as it is called, is a means by which collectors and exporters of grain and other products, and manufacturers who make contracts in advance for the sale of their goods, secure themselves against the fluctuations of the market by counter contracts for the purchase or sale, as the case may be, of an equal quantity of the product, or of the material of manufacture. It is none the less a serious business contract for a legitimate and useful purpose that it may be offset before the time of delivery in case delivery should not be needed or desired. . . . The sales in the pits are not pretended, but, as we have said, are meant and supposed to be binding. A setoff is in legal effect a delivery.

The Commodity Exchange Act (Section 5) authorizes the Secretary of Agriculture to direct and designate any board of trade as a contract market when, and only when, it complies with and carries out certain conditions and requirements. With reference to transactions for future delivery, among other things, a further requirement is "the manner in which said transactions are fulfilled, discharged or terminated." In Section 1.46 of the Rules and Regulations under the Act the Secretary of Agriculture provides for the application and closing out of offsetting long and short positions for future delivery. This shall be done the same day as purchase or sale is made against previously held short or long positions. They make certain exceptions: for "customers' accounts" of another futures commission merchant; hedging, as defined; and sales held for the purpose of making delivery when warehouse receipts accompany instructions to make delivery.

Handling Futures Business

Commission merchants who handle futures business make trades for members of the Exchange or for non-members in their own name and become liable as principals between themselves and the other parties to the trade. Minimum rates of commission are prescribed for services rendered, varying according to the category within which they fall. Services of clearing members range from clearing trades made by members (who may employ brokers) in the pits exclusively for their personal account and who are charged the lowest rates of commission, through services for members who trade otherwise for themselves or customers and are charged members' rates, to services for non-members, who pay full non-member rates. Except for "odd" or "job" lots originating within Chicago, the Chicago Board of Tráde minimum grain-commission rates are the same for customers anywhere within the United States or Canada but are higher if the orders originate elsewhere.

Some exchange members are members of the Clearing House as individuals for the purpose of clearing their own transactions. Corporations must have two members of the Exchange registered with the Exchange for the corporation in order to clear trades only for their own account, and four such registrations if they accept trades for others. Partnerships are required to have registered members in relation to the number of partners in the firm. A corporation or partnership trading in futures through a commission merchant, in order to be entitled to members' rates of commission, must, through one of its member officers or general partners, apply to the exchange for this purpose. When permission is granted, the firm then becomes subject to all the rules and regulations of the association that are applicable to members.

Futures Commission-Merchant Operations

Commission merchants, which may be referred to as brokerage houses, perform varied services; they may be engaged in both futures and cash commission businesses as well as operating elevators, conducting a merchandising trade, or being processors, etc. In futures, their scope of operations may be confined to one office or they may have a widespread system of offices and leased private telegraph wires stretching from coast to coast and even into Canada and Mexico. Some of these firms enter extensively into service to customers in foreign countries and often are members of many commodity and security exchanges. There are those who clear trades in many markets and others who clear on only one exchange but accept orders for execution as members or non-members elsewhere and rely upon reciprocal business for compensation. However, no agreement as to the amount of reciprocal business may be made. It is through the service of such firms that persons interested in grain or similarly traded commodities, or companies engaged in actually handling these commodities, make their contact with the futures-contract markets.

Usually a room is provided in the main office and in branch offices of the commission merchant for the convenience of customers, and also for solicitors to service their clientele. This "customers'" or "board" room has a quotation board which registers price changes in the markets. Quotations may be furnished by tickers, which rapidly record the fluctuations of some or all prices emanating from the various exchanges. These are posted on a blackboard. Some quotations are carried over the private wires of the firm. Another quotation system, conducted by means of electrically operated quotation boards serviced by an independent company directly from a central location to many firms and cities, registers both commodities and securities. Market news and general news is also made available through news tickers. The customers' room is readily accessible to the wire room so that orders may be transmitted instantly to the exchange for execution and for quick return of the report.

In the wire room in the city of the Exchange are employee telephone men who are in constant communication with each pit location, so that a moment after an order comes off a branch wire it is phoned to a position on the trading floor handy to the trading pit for that commodity. At each relay point on the wire system the order is electrically time-stamped so that a full record is kept of its progress. All changes in market quotations are quickly recorded and timed by Exchange-employed reporters in various pits and are kept as permanent records. Brokerage offices keep their time clocks synchronized with the ten-second changes of those on the Exchange. Except for the human element entering into the handling of the quotations and the fact that at times several trading months may be very active, the recording of quotations is done in a matter of seconds. Customers not in contact with wire offices may use the public telegraph or telephone direct to the commission merchant's office or to the Exchange trading floor at the expense of the commission firm.

Futures Orders

When futures orders are placed, customers specify the conditions on which they are to be executed. A "market order" is to be executed by purchase or sale as soon as it is received in the pit. Other orders may specify a time for filling, such as at the opening or closing of the market or at a specified time. Some orders are limited as to price and may not be filled except at that price or better. Any part of the order may be filled by the pit broker in multiples of trading units and immediately reported to the customer; no order may be entered except on that condition, for it cannot be accepted for "all or none" of the quantity specified.

A "stop order" or "stop loss order" is one which becomes

effective for buying or selling when the market reaches a specified price. Such an order to buy becomes a market order when the commodity sells (or is bid) at or above the stop price, and one to sell becomes so when the commodity sells (or is offered) at or below the stop price. Other orders may be contingent upon a price quoted for the same or another trading month, in the same market or elsewhere.

A "spread" order is for buying one future and selling another of the same or different commodity in the same or in another market. Spread orders may be "at the market" or at a guaranteed limit of difference. There are inter-month or inter-delivery spreads, and also inter-grain and inter-market spreads.

Sometimes a commission house will accept an order that is complicated to handle, with the understanding that they will do their best to fill it in accordance with the customer's instrucions, but that they cannot guarantee that quotations will not go against them. An example of this would be to buy or sell one of the several months traded in the pit at certain prices or at so much advance or decline from a previous quotation. The firm has a right to refuse any order that is complicated or that would jeopardize them in attempting to fill it.

All orders given for futures are good for the entire session of the day they are entered, but they may be canceled at any time. Orders may be given as "open" or as "good until they are filled or canceled," which may remain in force for a long time. It is customary for the commission merchant to send a mail reminder once a week calling the customer's attention to the fact that they have such an order on hand. Orders may also specify being in force for a portion of the session or to be canceled at a certain time. A "quick" order, sometimes designated "fill or kill"—meaning that if it cannot be filled immediately the order is canceled—is used in connection with spreading between markets, or for another desired purpose. These orders call for a reply that the execution has been made, a reply which also gives the price or states "unable" or "can't quick," and quotes the market price in the pit at that moment and also whether it is bid or offered.

CUSTOMERS' ACCOUNTS

Commission merchants are obligated to call their customers for a minimum initial margin deposit in accordance with exchange rules and regulations—which may be changed from time to time. Each commission firm may also set its own requirements, which may differ from one customer to another, but they must never be below exchange minimums. Exchange margin rates may differ for each commodity and for the purpose for which the futures trade is used—hedging, spreading, or speculating. Impairment of margins is permitted until they reach a maintenance level, at which point they are renewed to maintenance requirements. Equities resulting from changes in market prices are regarded as money equivalents in figuring margins and are available to be paid to customers before trades are closed. Exchanges have regulations pertaining to collateral or other deposits for margin purposes and for any special conditions pertaining to margins.

As market prices change, margin clerks in brokerage offices watch the accounts and call for additional margins when needed or, upon request, pay excess margins to customers. If additional margins are not forthcoming, the commission merchant will probably enter "stop loss" orders to close out existing trades, should prices reach about the point at which required funds in the account would be exhausted.

The commission merchant keeps grain-ledger accounts for all customers' purchases and sales. Customarily, purchases are entered in columns on the left-hand side of a page and termed "long," and sales to the right and termed "short." A purchase to close out an original sale, or a sale to close out a purchase, is entered on the same line as the offset. From this grain-ledger entry the clerk renders an "account purchase and sale" (p. and s.) showing debit or credit for the market difference of the commodity, and he charges commission according to the quantity of the commodity at the prescribed rates. This "account purchase and sale" is mailed to the customer the same day. Written confirmations of all trades are made to customers on the day of execution, in accordance with exchange rules, and they must show the commodity bought or sold, the amount, the price, the delivery month, and either the name or the words "name of other party to contract furnished on request." Upon the request of an interested party, the Exchange investigates conditions pertaining to trades. The amount of the "account purchase and sale" is posted in the customer's dollar account; and from this same "purchase and sale" the debit or credit for the market difference is posted to an "office account" for the commodity.

Settlement-Department Clearing

The office-account ledger entries, together with customers' trades remaining open when calculated to the settlement prices, will equal the amount of money which the commission merchant has paid to, or collected from, the Clearing House in daily accumulative totals.

As an internal safety check of a firm's customers' record books against records of trades made in the pits, the customers' trades on p. and s.'s are "marked off" against the same trades on the "settlement-department," or so-called "street," books. In other words, when trades are eliminated from the customers' record books, the same trades are eliminated from the firm's books. The customers' trades remaining open are checked periodically against those not marked off on the settlement-department books to determine the accuracy of the records at the time a "grain balance" is taken.

The settlement department keeps the records of trades as they come from the pits, and brings them to an official settlement price about equaling the market closing price each day. Any profits in these trades are collected from the Clearing House and losses paid to it at the end of the day. Pit purchases and sales offset each other on the settlement-department books, and the net long or short amount, combined with and adjusted to the net long or short carried from the previous day, is carried in balance with the Clearing House. Money differences resulting from price changes are settled according to the settling price. All money amounting to customers' profits and losses is determined by pit trades. Therefore, as every clearing member settles daily with the Clearing House, the commission merchant always has the net of his customer's trades in balance with the settlement department's books, which in turn are in balance with the Clearing House and the money settlement made with the latter.

Typical office routine is as follows. The settlement department receives trades from the pit brokers' trading cards as they come from the exchange trading floor. To verify telephone and trading-floor accuracy, all trades on the cards are identified with customers' orders that came off the telegraph wires. The orders then are entered in the customer's grain ledger and next go to typists, who type trade confirmations to be mailed to customers. The trades on the cards are entered in the settlement grain ledgers, where there is a running record for each commodity for each delivery month, with purchases on the left-hand page and sales on the right. The data, with one line for one contract, contains the price and the clearing firm from whom it was bought or to whom it was sold, with a column for purchase and sales account numbers when "marked off," and a column for the customer's account number to identify the trade. One purpose of these ledgers is to arrive at the trading position—the net amount of purchases or sales. If purchases exceed sales, the position is termed "long," or if sales exceed purchases it is termed "short."

This "long" or "short" position is the accumulation of purchases entered in the ledger from the start of trading in a future applied against the running total of the sales. The net long or short position of the settlement ledger agrees with the net long or short position of all customers open trades combined on the customers' grain-ledger books and also with the firm's position with the Clearing House. Check slips for each trade are exchanged with other clearing members to confirm pit trades and assure accurracy before clearing them with the Clearing House, which, when it accepts the cleared trades, assumes full responsibility in place of the other clearing member.

At the end of each day's business when clearing members submit their report to the Clearing House, the report is accompanied by a check for payment of the net amount due, which check is certified promptly on the next business day; or the clearing member collects the money due him from the Clearing House.

One sheet filed with the Clearing House for each delivery month for each grain is termed "purchase and sale sheet" and lists clearing members' names with quantities bought and sold and money to be paid or collected to bring these trades to the settlement price. On the same sheet is the net amount of that delivery cleared and carried over from the previous day and brought to the new settlement price. If the clearing firm has made or received and retained any tenders of delivery, adjustments are made in the long or short position (for the day of delivery) at the settlement price for the day of tender. If tenders are made, the amount is offset by a purchase from the Clearing House; if tenders are received (and retained), a sale to the Clearing House is entered on the books. If tenders are received and retendered during the same session, no entry is made on the clearing firm's books, for the pit sale of futures—which was necessary to accomplish the retender—eliminates the long position and the notice of tender (the same one as originally received on tender) is passed back to the Clearing House, which then gives it to another clearing firm.

A "recapitulation" of the purchase and sale sheets is made on a separate sheet, with the net money for all trades, including the carry-over from the previous day and also including the new long or short position for each delivery. Upon this "recap" the clearing firm calculates "standing" margins for the net of each commodity; all delivery months are brought to one net amount. Standing margins are those fixed by the Clearing Corporation and are separate from the margins that the Board of Trade requires commission merchants to secure from customers. The standing-margin money is deposited by the Clearing House in a bank designated by the clearing member, and the bank delivers a margin certificate for the amount to the clearing member. When standing margins are no longer needed to secure trades, the Clearing Corporation endorses the certificate so that the clearing member may deposit it in any bank to the credit of the segregated-fund account. Standing margins are not co-mingled with other funds in the Clearing House, but are security against clearing members' trades, should they fail to meet their obligations otherwise. Government securities purchased with segregated funds may be used for standing margins when held in escrow in a bank.

During a session of the Exchange, either the Clearing House or a clearing member may call the other for "variation" margins. These are calculated according to the fluctuations of the market, and a check must be put up within one hour of the call. Clearing members must furnish a certified check. This money is applied against the commodity trades listed on the recapitulation sheet submitted to the Clearing House. It should be noted that variation margins are separate from standing margins.

All margins which a clearing firm receives from customers or deposits as standing margins in a bank, or money paid to the Clearing House as variation margins, are of segregated funds and are separate from funds belonging to the commission house (except for trades for "house accounts" of clearing firms filed on separate reports with the Clearing House).

Execution of Futures Orders

The futures commission merchant's customer dealings in the pits are usually made through independent pit brokers, although a member of a commission firm may, and sometimes does, do some of this trading. Orders are telephoned from the commission-house wire room by phone men, who usually sit opposite the telegraph or teletype operators. Being in constant communication with the Exchange floor, the phone man immediately gives the order to the Exchange-floor phone man, who is near the pit, delaying only for such a contingency as canceling a former order when a reference has to be looked up. If it is a market order or even one with a price limit near the market, the floor phone man may flash it to the pit broker by hand signal. Instantly the pit broker either buys or sells and flashes the price and quantity back to the phone man, who relays it to the wire room. Unless the wire operator is receiving another order, he immediately telegraphs or teletypes the transaction to its destination or to the relay office with which he is in contact. If the pit broker has received the order from the phone man by flash, it is confirmed to him in writing on an order blank. The order is not necessarily flashed, but may be delivered to the broker in writing even when it is "at the market" or at a limit, in which case the broker, after execution, endorses the price on the order blank and returns it to the phone by messenger. The procedure is a matter of choice.

The broker "cards" the pit trade by entering the name or names of all the clearing firms which are furnished him by the broker(s) with whom he has traded, together with quantities and prices. For convenience, the broker customarily has his trading cards printed in red on one side, for sold trades, and blue on the other side, for bought trades. Brokers are required to write the order number on the card under the trade for identification, because prices may be repeated many times during a session of the market. The broker is responsible for his trades as made in the pit until such time as they are accepted by the principal, usually when check slips are exchanged. If for any reason his reported trades fail to be vouched by another clearing firm, the broker must replace the trades and adjust the price to the original pit trade. Immediately after making a trade, the broker or trader must signal the price to the pit reporter for record and dissemination. All members trading in the pits must make all futures offers general, not specifically for acceptance by particular members. An offer to buy or sell is deemed to be for all or any part of the specified quantity and for immediate acceptance by any other member.

Futures Quotations

When there is a change in the price, quotations of trades made or, in an inactive market, bids to buy or offers to sell upon signal from a participating member are recorded by the pit reporter and are immediately stamped by time clock. A permanent book record is kept by the Quotation Department. Without delay, quotations are disseminated throughout the ticker system, so that all prices become known far and wide and may be acted upon in the many uses to which they are put. Continuous quotations may be given to persons only upon approval of the Exchange, but they may go to members or non-members. Many private wire systems carry quotations, and at intervals the radio quotes the market over a number of broadcasting stations.

Trading in grain futures conducted on the Chicago Board of Trade accounts for probably 85% of the annual total for all markets, and the Kansas City and Minneapolis markets, about equally divided, make up most of the balance. Rapid communication between these futures-trading centers permits a quick dispatch of orders whenever there is a sharp change in price in any one of them; thus, trading operations tend to keep markets moving in unison. While from one season to another one market may gain or lose a great many cents per bushel on the others, for shorter periods their price relationships do not vary greatly. Spreaders, who buy in one market and sell in another, are constantly on the alert, watching for even fraction-of-a-cent changes in differences in their endeavor to secure trading advantages. Upon wider changes in differences between markets, merchants change hedges to the market that, in their opinion, offers the greater advantage for the purchase or sale of their cash grain. The changing differences also put the repective markets in proper price position with respect to supply and demand related to the grain available in each area.

The Relation of Other Futures Markets to Chicago

Because Kansas wheat partly fills the demand in more densely populated areas in the eastern United States, and because some wheat grown in Illinois is of the same hard winter type, the Kansas City price seldom is as high as that of Chicago. However, a short market supply of hard winter wheat in the Kansas City area and a large supply of soft red in the Chicago area alters this normal condition. Wheat in Minneapolis may sell at a price either under or over the Chicago market price. The discount under Chicago may even equal the cost of shipping the grain to Chicago; on the other hand, the price may exceed the Chicago price by a considerable amount. Minneapolis represents the northwest and spring-grown varieties of wheat, not produced adjacent to Chicago but for which there may be a strong demand, so that a relatively high price is a means of curtailing demand. Also, because spring wheat shipped via the Great Lakes route from Duluth to the Buffalo area has cheaper transportation to the more densely populated East, relatively higher prices may be paid for spring wheat to offset higher transportation costs on competitive classes shipped from elsewhere.

The interchange of business, regulated by spread differences between different futures markets, aids in the distribution of wheat crops. A market that is relatively cheap compared with other futures-trading centers allows payment of a higher freight rate to consuming destinations, thus providing a larger area for the sale of grain or products. At the same time, grain can be hedged in the market near its origin or in Chicago and may possibly be delivered in consummation of the futures sale. The fluctuations of inter-market spread differences do not necessarily affect the general level of grain prices for the nation;

rather, they adjust demand in relation to supply between areas. When relative scarcities of grain exist in the areas served by the Kansas City or the Minneapolis futures markets, a strong relationship exists in either of these markets relative to Chicago. This relative strength conserves grain for use in each local area or for the necessities of those in other areas who are willing to pay a premium to buy it. When surpluses are large relative to the Chicago area, a weakened spread difference increases merchandising outlets.

In the course of its existence the Chicago Board of Trade has seen the grain trade grow from a local-area service by each grain exchange to a broad national system of service guiding production and marketing opportunities through competitive pricing, made possible by futures trading.

CHAPTER III

Cash Grain and Futures

SCOPE

The grain trade is the marketing system for grain and its products from farmer to consumer. The business we are primarily discussing is the portion that includes the commercial trade after the farmer has sold his grain to the time it leaves the possession of the last wholesaler. Throughout this transitional period, one merchant or another always controls the grain in some form. During this time there are the responsibilities of ownership and storage while the grain is held awaiting sale to a consumer. There are many hazards attendant on ownership, some of which can be transferred and others that must be retained. This is common to merchandising businesses in general; some merchants have less risk of price change than others, but price change is a very large factor in the grain trade. This risk can be transferred from the grain merchandiser to others through the system of futures trading; though this does not eliminate all the risk of price change, it does guard against major adverse fluctuations.

The fact that grain is handled in large volume by grain merchants reduces the unit cost of storage and transportation, but the volume emphasizes the need for protection against loss from market changes. For merchants, as distinguished from brokers and commission merchants, there is no "customary" markup in price when grain ownership passes from one merchant to another within the trade. As prices change, merchants either buy or sell according to their judgment; some merchants are buying at the same time others in the same phase of the business are selling. While grain follows a general pattern of physical movement from the time it leaves the farm until the consumer buys it, there is no time pattern of purchase or sale by merchants handling the grain other than absorbing the heavy harvest selling of farmers and having the grain ready when consumers want it. Prices, however, may be and frequently are higher at harvest than during a later period. Flour buyers or foreign importers may buy heavily at any time of the year, receiving the wheat or its product soon after its purchase or purchasing it for a much later period shipment. Feed manufacturers may buy for immediate needs or defer buying of grain or meal until their requirements are urgent; and at other times they buy ahead for shipment to them at periods scattered during the whole crop year. In the fats and oils trade edibles and inedibles derived from grain are sold in varying amounts at all seasons of the year. Stocks of grain or products derived from the grain harvest are held by the grain and allied trades during the year awaiting the call of the consumer. Sometimes consumer demand is urgent and such purchases are made long before the crops are grown; yet contracts are made with grain-trade merchants at the going price commensurate with the time of shipment to the buyer's destination. In such trades the grain-trade merchant, as in all his trading operations, protects his market position against major price changes by the use of futures contracts.

It is a trade practice to make contracts of sale of grain or products ahead of their purchase just as readily as sales might be made from stocks on hand. It is also customary to buy grain for immediate movement into storage or to be put into store at a later date without a definite plan as to its eventual merchandising. Merchants are willing to buy and carry stocks of grain regardless of their opinion as to the course of the market level; they are willing to make all types of purchase or sales contracts, regardless of possible price change, because of the use to which they put the futures contracts. Purchases of cash grain are offset by simultaneous sales of futures contracts; similarly, sales of cash grain are offset by purchases of futures.

This results in a balanced market position at all times. The grain contracts may represent grain in various physical locations and differ materially from the offsetting futures contracts, but one contract is protection against the other from major fluctuations in price, no matter which way the price of that particular kind of grain moves.

Even though there is a general price pattern, different classes and grades of each grain, and grain of the same class and grade in different locations, move somewhat independently of each other. Despite these intra-changing prices, grain-trade merchants religiously use futures contracts to reduce their risk from changing prices of the grain they own. Grain owned may be held in storage in a section of the country entirely too remote to fulfil the futures contract of sale; or if it is in the right location, it may be of unsuitable grade, even though it is of a suitable classification. Also, if a sale of grain has been made and an offsetting purchase of futures contracted, the class and grade of grain that will likely be received in the futures market may not be suitable to fill the sale of grain. These various futures sales against purchases or futures purchases against grain sales are made primarily for the purpose of shifting, as much as possible, the risk of changing prices. They are known as *hedges*. Hedges are usually in the form of futures contracts, counterbalancing grain purchases or sales.

Firms are likely to have many open or unshipped grain contracts of both purchase and sale. Even though they may not match each other in quality or in time of fulfilment, the purchases and sales offset each other in a market position and leave a net excess of either purchases or sales to be hedged in futures. If there is not too much variance in the terms of open grain contracts, firms customarily enter into only one futures contract as a hedge. However, if the terms of the various grain contracts are quite different from each other, it is good business to place offsetting futures contracts in months of delivery approximately equaling the time of shipment of grain contracts and in cities where futures trading is conducted in grading classification and location corresponding to the grain contracts. This gives more individual protection to greatly differing grain contracts. Sound business judgment is necessary in trading in futures as hedges to offset grain contracts or against stocks of grain held in storage. Inasmuch as hedges normally do not completely match grain purchases and sales, there is a choice of futures delivery month and market left to the discretion of the operating firm.

When futures are purchased to protect sales of grain, the futures are retained until such time as suitable grain is bought to fill the exact grain sale previously entered into. Then as the grain is purchased, the futures contract or hedge is sold out; this offsets and cancels out the like previous purchase of futures and leaves the grain merchant with suitable grain to fill his grain sale. If the futures contract had originally been a sale as a hedge against a stock of grain in storage or against a purchase of grain for a later time of shipment, it would be necessary to buy in the futures to remove the hedge at the time a contract for the sale of the grain was made. In hedging there is always a simultaneous sale at the time of a purchase or a purchase at the time of a sale.

Individual Risks

Price-fluctuation risks, while reduced through hedging, still leave the grain merchant with many problems against which he cannot be protected. Grain, or, as it is called in the trade, "cash grain," is one market and futures is another. The price of each changes with changes in supply-and-demand conditions for a particular lot of grain or time of delivery of futures. The combinations of class of grain, grade within the class, location, time of shipment, etc., of cash grain and all the different delivery months in each market for futures are influenced by independent factors, so that risks from price change are constantly present. Therefore, when a grain is said either to advance or to decline in price, there are many crosscurrents within the grain, and hedging in futures does not always give full protection. When cash grain is of the required quality and is in the position called for in the terms of a futures hedge against it, there is a degree of protection from price change, but this may not be a perfect hedge, because the cost of the cash grain may have been higher than the sale of equivalent futures. This leaves a risk of decline in cash grain relative to futures, so that merchandising is relied upon for disposition of the cash grain rather than fulfilment of the futures contract by delivery of the cash grain. If the cash grain was purchased cheaply enough in comparison to the sale price of the future and there was enough margin to pay storage, insurance, and interest charges to the time of futures delivery, it could be considered a perfect hedge. This can be done by those grain firms that are located at futures-market centers and have the necessary facilities for delivery. Most of the grain that is hedged in futures is not in such a favorable position, so that not all price risks can be eliminated by hedging in futures.

Cash Basis

Merchandising risks are assumed with the knowledge that cash grain and futures prices do not always move in unison and that there are fluctuating differences between their prices. In this relationship grain firms establish their prices rather than in so many dollars and cents per bushel. The term used to designate this is "cash basis." When cash grain is traded at a lower cost than the futures price it is said to be at a discount; if it is traded higher than the futures it is at a premium. The terms "discount" and "premium," i.e., the cash basis, must be stated in connection with location of the grain and a time for shipment or delivery. If a trade involves grain located a distance from the futures market, the discount or premium stated is for that location and gives no consideration to the cost of shipping the grain to the city in which the futures market is located. The terms specify a certain cash basis for quality, time, and location of the trade as is. If grain is purchased at a discount and later sold at a premium, a profit results; if grain is bought at a discount and then sold at a smaller discount there is also a profit. Frequently grain is sold before it is purchased. Therefore, when it is sold at a discount and later bought at a greater discount a profit results. When grain is traded at premiums for cash grain over the futures the same principles apply.

The grain merchant constantly looks for chances to make trades on a profitable cash basis, but at all times keeps his cash grain hedged by making offsetting purchases or sales of futures. In this trading there is little interest in the price of grain. It is in the changing relationship of cash grain to futures that possibilities of profits lie.

Hedges

There are times when merchants may be without hedge protection against price changes. Such periods occur when cash-grain purchases are made at a flat price, as is customary when buying grain from a country grain-elevator operator or his representative. Or the merchant may have to keep his futures contract for a while after he has sold his cash grain to a distributor who, like the country elevator, handles smaller quantities and works on a more or less fixed margin of profit and at a flat or outright price. Other flat-price sales occur when grain is sold to foreign buyers or when grain products are sold. These risk periods are brief during a market session but more prolonged awaiting the opening of the next futures market session.

When a converter of cereals who hedges in futures sells products, he will, with minimum delay, buy futures as an offset. Cash grain may not yet have been bought for the processing operation, but price protection is largely supplied through the purchase of futures. Since the price of the raw cereals, like futures, almost always moves much faster and over a wider range than the cash basis, protection against major losses is obtained by purchasing futures. When this risk of major price change is eliminated, more time may be taken in carefully selecting the cash grain desirable for conversion into the product of sale.

The risk of hedge lifting is greater in export sales, because quantities are larger and the time usually longer before the futures can be bought after the foreign buyer has accepted the offer of cash grain. This risk, however, is usually confined to firms familiar with such hazards and specializing in export sales. Exporters usually have to wait until the opening of the futures market on the next business day to buy their hedges when they sell grain based on the closing price on the day of offering. Even though this delay is somewhat prolonged, it is essential to good grain trading to enter into these futures contracts. It is impractical for the exporter to rely upon his ability or good fortune to find someone willing to sell him the exact lot of cash grain at an outright or flat price to suit his export commitment. The exporter keeps the purchase of futures until such time as he buys the exact lot of grain which he is required to ship on his export sale.

There are many exceptions in hedging practices, especially among processors who carry a large constant inventory needed for wide dissemination of their products: the inventory of grain is continually renewed as grain is converted into products. Hedging activities of such processors are more likely to be purchase of futures in anticipation of a price advance before acquiring raw products needed to operate their manufacturing plants. Over a long period of time as prices readjust themselves to former levels inventory losses offset profits, but frequent or infrequent price adjustments of product prices tend to modify the profit or loss balances of their inventory. Many large processors, however, notably flour millers and those who carry a large stock of unprocessed material for a length of time, adhere closely to a hedging policy. It is likely that when these processors buy futures they are lifting hedges that had been carried against a stock of unprocessed grain. At times, however, product sales are made before the cash grain has been purchased, so that futures are used as interim price protection. Judgment of hedging allowances is required in estimating losses of grain in cleaning, etc., prior to processing and in carrying some unsold converted products that will follow prices of competitive products rather than the prices of grain. An example of this is the amount of millfeeds that remain unsold after the flour portion of wheat is sold.

When Cash Grain Is Bought

Grain merchants, such as terminal elevator operators, processors, and at times exporters, customarily accumulate stocks of grain in small amounts. As they make many purchases of grain, they make many corresponding sales of futures. Sometimes they anticipate the purchase of cash grain and place hedges beforehand, usually selling futures at the close of the market. As overnight bids from the close of the futures market until its opening the next day are based on the closing price, it is reasoned that there is less risk involved by selling futures at the close of the market than by waiting until the market opens to compete in hedge selling with others who have also bought grain overnight. Judgment of volume of their country purchases guides such actions and is normally practiced at harvest time.

There is no way in which those who accumulate large amounts of grain with anticipated later sale at a small margin of profit could operate year after year except by employing futures as hedges. When such a firm's judgment at times would prevent them from buying in fear of a market decline, their opportunity of accumulating grain during the harvest run would be lost, and they would be burdened with the expense of unused grain elevators. Sales of grain to be shipped from country elevators to terminal markets or processors are often made months ahead of harvest. This may be because it seems like the correct time for a producer to sell, and the offering is readily accepted by the buyer even though he, too, thinks that prices are high. The buyer, however, is interested only in the cash basis on which his trading judgment operates, and not in the outright price. As a rule there is uniformity in the seasonal trend of the cash basis. Harvest-run purchases can usually be sold at a higher cash basis later in the season. For this reason, well ahead of the new season's grain movement buyers start stocking up on grain to fill their elevators or to run their processing plants. During other times of the crop year the tendency is for rural interests to sell closer to the time they intend to ship the grain to larger buyers.

When Cash Grain Is Sold

Frequently foreign buyers and domestic cereal-product buyers contract many months ahead of shipment. Often these purchases are made for scattered times of shipments. Firms making these sales sometimes find this demand coming at times when they have no stock or when, because of the forward price structure, it would be unprofitable to sell from their stock; yet it may be a competitive necessity to enter into these trades, so that in order to protect themselves they buy futures as a hedge. This establishes their risk in the cash basis with which they will have to contend until such time as they can buy the cash grain to be used in fulfilment of sales. The time from date of sale until they buy the cash grain may extend through several futures delivery months. Prevailing conditions may necessitate delaying purchase of the cash grain until close to the time for making shipment or delivery on the deferred sale. This is the case when there are inverse carrying charges.

Inverse Carrying Charges

Inverse carrying charges exist when earlier futures are selling higher than the deferred futures-delivery months. Complete reliance on futures by those who have sold cash grain ahead is necessary in such cases. (For example, in October a merchant sells barley to an exporter for shipment next May at $1.28, which is 3 cents over the May future. At the time of this sale the October future is $1.40 [Winnipeg barley], the December $1.32 and the May $1.25.) Were it not for futures protection, the seller would have to make an outright speculative sale and would have no means of protecting himself until the time of fulfilling his sale was relatively close at hand. The premise is that cash grain could not be put into storage for later application on a sale based on progressively lower deferred futures prices. Spot grain, which is for immediate delivery, is related to the price of the near-by futures month (in this case the spot grain would be priced close to the October future selling at $1.40), so that when inverse carrying charges exist in futures markets, spot grain cannot be hedged and carried in storage without penalty, when compared with deferred positions. The element of risk to firms making sales far ahead of the shipping date when inverse carrying charges exist is less if the futures bought as a hedge mature at approximately the same time as the cash grain must be shipped. (In this case it is the Winnipeg May barley future that is purchased.) Then when the cash grain is bought on a day close to its need, it will be based on the current future. Opportunities may arise, however, for profitable covering of the cash grain sooner if inverse carrying charges are reduced. In this use of futures as protection against sale of grain or product for deferred shipment, the risk is established only in the cash basis. Cash grain and futures prices approximate each other at some time during the maturing month of each futures. Some classes and grades of grain may continue at premiums, but one or more of the deliverable grades will be attracted to the futures, or the futures price will advance to that of cash grain, so that deliveries can be made to satisfy futures buyers' wants. Taking risks in the cash basis is the grain man's business; he therefore uses futures to reduce other hazards.

Competition

The structure of the market, both cash and futures, reflects conditions controlled by natural or artificial laws over which grain-trade personnel has no control. Reasons for the market's acting as it does are complex. Those who participate in the different phases of the business are likely to confine their efforts to one, or possibly several, but not to all branches. Some firms have many ramifications, but they, with the many who specialize within smaller or local confines, must trade so as to conform with ever-changing conditions. Many firms and individuals comprise the marketing system, amongst them those who own and operate physical properties which give them an advantage in the areas of their operations. While individual opportunities of doing business are enhanced in areas in which physical properties are privately operated, there are usually in these services (except at country elevators) duplications which cause competition. Some locations have considerable semi-public or public elevator service and little, if any, private elevator capacity; that gives equal opportunities to all grain merchants. Transportation service is mutually available without special rate advantages. Other special services performed by brokers, commission merchants and forwarding agents are widespread. Probably the greatest service to grain merchants is the large participation by speculators in futures in handling risks transferred to them by merchants.

Competition throughout the grain trade is very keen, and trading by members of each branch is extensive. Little business is conducted without the knowledge of competitors, because the search for small price advantages causes buyers and sellers to canvass sufficiently to test the market, and that activity at the same time alerts rivals for the business. Grain merchandising is carried on at a small margin of profit; this does not mean that large profits may not be secured, but if trades result in such, the profits are not often as large as fluctuations in futures during the same period. Fixed charges are assessed by firms that operate handling or storage facilities when they handle grain for others; but in securing business for themselves, even though they use these facilities, they do not assess themselves the same charges. Absorption of these charges in buying and selling is necessary to meet the competition of others. Firms not operaing these kinds of facilities are at a disadvantage in having to pay the charges to others; and they therefore find it difficult to compete.

At times operators find that they can maintain more secrecy dealing in large quantities when they sell to the futures market rather than make cash sales. In order to do this, it is necessary to engage in large futures trading and then to move the grain into futures-delivery position or to deliver on futures grain that is already in delivery position but that had not previously been considered desirable to deliver. When these operations are being conducted, it may be noticed that there is either extensive spreading of futures (buying one month and selling another in the same market) or outright selling of futures (as a spread against another market where purchases are simultaneously made); there is, however, nothing at the outset but conjecture on the part of others to confirm the reason for this trading. This operation usually involves changing hedges from one future to another and increasing the amount of deliverable hedges on grain that is or will be available for delivery, thus making supplies plentiful for delivery, whereas they had previously been scarce. When the operation is understood by the trade in general, it is likely to change the course of market action, especially as to spread differences between futures. Inasmuch as futures contracts are in reality the same as cash contracts but made pursuant to the rules of an exchange for delivery in the future, the diversion of cash grain to futures previously in a strong position is likely to hasten selling by others who had not thought large deliveries likely.

Surprises of this kind may result from trading by those with keen judgment, or may be the logical result of failure of generally anticipated cash-grain demand to develop. Putting hedges into a potentially tight futures-delivery month to protect unsold cash stocks, with deliveries on futures contracts following, is made possible because the futures demand will absorb the cash-grain supply. Logically, chances to make direct cash-grain sales are not as feasible as selling futures in comparable volume, because cash-grain offerings would soon arouse other sellers or the buyers would soon look elsewhere for cheaper prices. Also, buyers of the cash grain may choose the tight futures in which to hedge, thus creating immediate competition in the operation. As the same time, selling of the cash grain would forecast possible futures deliveries and cause liquidation so that the original seller could not dispose of the quantity he desired. Because futures-market prices are the reflection of actual conditions from the composite trading of all interested factions, they adjust markets to the supply-and-demand level as conditions change.

Use of Futures

The fact that many people of diverse interests trade in futures markets makes it possible for producers to find ready buyers for their grain. A large share of this grain is hedged and, when in proper position and when it is desirable to do so, is delivered on futures contracts. Hedgers do not have to seek individual buyers for their grain stocks; there is a meeting of minds through trading activities by which futures contracts aid in the equitable distribution of grain. Futures contracts consume no grain. They are an aid in creating a reservoir for later needs. They protect owners of existing stocks against major price changes. They supply the wants of those who have purchased. They also register prices for various times of delivery, according to the forces of supply and demand for each delivery time. The grain merchant may or may not correctly analyze the potential price for any given time; it is not within his province to do so. The futures-market price is acceptable to buyers and sellers, and it changes when conditions warrant changes. By the use of futures in hedging, the risk of making purchases and sales at wrong prices, except for the cash basis, is removed from the business of handling cash grain. The opportunity of using futures for hedging is open to everyone; there is no limitation confining it to those who operate elevators, export, process, etc. Anyone may transfer a price risk to the futures market.

Firms located at futures-market delivery points may largely

confine their risks to quality of grain. This risk is practically inescapable, because the grain that comes to market is an average of the season's crop, and not all of it is suitable for delivery on futures contracts against hedges. Obviously, when cash-grain premiums exist, the merchandising type of businessman must take the chance of a decline in the cash basis of what grain he owns. He may, however, buy only sparingly if he is fearful of a cash-basis decline. At such times, naturally, there is a demand for grain or premiums would not exist; therefore there are opportunities to sell, but it is not necessary to carry more grain than is likely to be merchandised quickly.

Firms removed from futures-delivery points have to take greater risks than those located near the delivery market. If they are located on the line of shipment to a futures market, prices of cash grain tend to reflect the freight differential to the hedging market. A cash basis at a premium is a reflection of the demand, and resale might easily be effected.

Firms situated in out-of-position locations from which there would be backhaul transportation to the hedging location must view the cash basis in connection with futures still differently. When demand is considered good, premiums over the freight rate from hedging centers to these out-of-position cities permit competition from the futures terminal. Then both locations having stocks of grain (the terminal and the out-of-position point) share the demand for shipment to farther-distant areas. When the out-of-position market premium is less than the cash basis in the hedging market plus the freight, it gives merchandising advantage to the out-of-position market.

Futures Carrying Charges

When cash-basis discounts prevail, firms located along the line of transit to futures markets can pay part or all of the freight to the futures market for selling to terminal handlers for delivery purposes. At such times, however, the structure of the futures market may permit the transfer of hedges from a maturing futures month to a later delivery, so that the stock of grain could be retained in storage in its original position. Such a futures-market structure is a carrying-charge market—i.e., the near-by future is at a discount under the next of maturity. Cash-grain discounts prevailing in areas out of position for delivery on futures prevent futures terminal markets from competing with them, as prices do not permit payment of freight from the futures market to destinations farther away. These discounts usually prevail when carrying charges exist in the hedging market.

Equalization of Areas

Hedges are normally placed in futures markets on grain in out-of-position areas so remote that the freight rate would make it practically prohibitive to ship to the hedging center for delivery. This hedging is admittedly at a greater risk, because the hedge is affected by the conditions in the futures market and the cash grain is affected by the conditions in its own area. For example, cash grain located in Texas or at the Atlantic seaboard and hedged in Chicago futures is in areas that border on or are in export positions that rely upon foreign sales to syphon off surplus grain not needed domestically within the area. Even though out-of-position areas may be at extreme distances east, west or southwest of Chicago, the price of surplus grain in various locations tends to equalize through its disposition by export sales to common foreign destinations. Grain from each location brings its suitable price in the foreign market according to respective ocean-freight charges and the demand for each class of grain.

Supply-and-demand conditions govern cash bases for different classes of grain and also for each location, as they do the general level of grain prices. They also are reflected in either carrying charges or inverse carrying charges in futures markets. Differences between futures markets in different cities are governed by supply-and-demand conditions, and they are also related to the cost of shipping grain towards consuming areas and the different classes and grades of grain deliverable upon each contract. In conducting a grain business, the operator must survey the entire market for all phases of the grain in which he is trading and its relation to other grains, and finally choose those risks he is willing to accept in his own business.

There is a logical reason why the various phases of the grain trade adhere strictly to hedging in futures contracts in operating their businesses, for prices revolve around one price in each area. Such a central pricing system, with all prices related to it according to individual conditions, makes it easier to keep track of prices throughout the country. Reliance on the central quotations upon which grain prices within areas are based, and the fact that the different areas move more or less in unison, result in uniformity and regularity in price changes; and because of such a system, it is the considered opinion of authorities that fluctuations in prices are lessened.

Because all phases of the grain trade use the system of futures trading in their transactions, it is a conveyance of price from the time farmers sell their crops until consumers buy the products.

CHAPTER IV

World Production and Trade of Principal Grains

World Grain Résumé

Each commodity connected with the grain trade has its special place in the economy of the trade. In North America a larger percentage of the grain production goes for the feeding of livestock and poultry than for direct human consumption. In the United States we have a great deal of land and a prosperous people, which make it possible for us to produce the most desired foods. Livestock products are notorious for the low level and the variability of their per-acre production: pork and milk, the highest, yield less than a third as much food as wheat, while beef cattle and sheep, the lowest, yield only about one twenty-fifth (.04) as much. Intensification of production is not only a question of the amount of food produced per acre; it is also a question of the amount of labor required in production. On this basis, field crops are far in the lead for food production. Vegetables and livestock products require about ten times as much labor for a given amount of food as do the field crops. Farmers by means of prices have adjusted the world's agriculture to make the best possible use of the land and their labor, considering the conditions under which they operate.

The food supply is adjusted to the population by changes in the amount carried from one season to the next, by changes in exports and by the amount used in industry and fed to livestock. This system is fiexible enough to permit a decrease of about 50% to 60% in crop production in the United States without the threat of starvation. Europe could probably stand a decrease of about 20% to 30% on the basis of their current imports, and Asia cannot stand any decrease in crop production.

India's 200,000,000 cattle are not a food reserve, because the Hindus, who form the overwhelming proportion of the population, do not eat meat and for religious reasons will not kill the cattle, which are frequently permitted free range over the countryside, where they eat and tramp down the crops. India has, however, a good system of transportation, so that if there is a drought or a short crop in one part of the country, food is shipped from a surplus area or may be imported. China has such poor transportation facilities that food cannot be brought from the surplus areas to drought or flood regions—as many of the people as are able must move to the areas of surplus food, but all cannot migrate. The drought areas are usually in the central and northern parts of China, far from the coast, where imported food offers no solution because little can get to these famine-stricken areas.

In the United States we feed a high percentage of our corn, oats and barley, and even a moderate percentage of the wheat and rye, to livestock. Accordingly our livestock serves as a huge food reserve against poor crops. We have a high standard of living, with 25% of the diet represented by expensive, highly prized, highly nutritious foods—meat, milk and eggs. By this measurement Asia has a low standard of living, for only 3% of the diet of Asia's millions is animal food. Europe occupies an intermediate position, with 17% of her diet consisting of animal products. Livestock condenses about seven pounds of dry matter in the form of grain and other feed to about one pound of dry matter in the form of meat, milk and eggs. It is obvious that where food is scarce not much grain is fed to livestock. If the supply of plant food is sharply curtailed, the animals are slaughtered, adding to the food supply in two ways: first, as meat from the animals and, second, as grain or potatoes (especially in Europe) that otherwise would have been livestock feed. Livestock, of course, refine large quantities of coarse, bulky, inedible crops into food fit for man.[1]

---

[1] Cornell University, *Starvation Truths, Half-Truths, Untruths,* 1946.

In the cereal crops of the world, wheat (surpassed only by rice) comprises roughly 7,000,000,000 bushels out of some 29,000,000,000 bushels of principal grains. While cereals are the most important crops grown in the world, there are more than 8,000,000,000 bushels of potatoes and in addition many large crops such as sugar, fruits, etc. There are many self-sufficient areas; in fact, much of the world is so, but many countries are lacking in adequate diet, according to our standards. However, they do not import in quantity. The areas of food surplus are in the minority. A few highly industrialized countries produce only a small part of their food supply and are largely dependent on the surplus-trading countries for much of their food requirements. Europe makes up most of this group. There are also many nations that in normal years produce in the aggregate about as much food as they consume, but they may also be both large importers and large exporters of food products. For example, the United States and Brazil are two of the largest exporters and importers of food products, and through their world trade in food products they are able to maintain a higher standard of living than would otherwise be possible.[2]

Normally in international trade a country deficient in food must be able to export other commodities in exchange for food. Only about 6% of the world's food production moves in intercontinental trade. Wheat is by far the largest grain in such trade—more than double the average for food. Canada can be counted on for large amounts of wheat yearly, because it is a big producer and has a small population. The same is true of Argentina and Australia, although they contribute less because of smaller crops.[3] Normally, the United States exports a fair share and, in the years following World War II, exported as much as all other countries combined. Wheat of Russian origin shipped from Black Sea ports has always been of an uncertain quantity, varying considerably from year to year.

---

[2] U.S.D.A. Miscellaneous Publication No. 705, Oct., 1949.
[3] Cornell University, *op. cit.*

Danube Basin wheat (and formerly known as such) that passed through the Dardenelles is now included with the Russian Black Sea grain, although it is also shipped overland to other European countries. India, some years back an exporter, has switched to the import column. There is considerable intra-continental trade in wheat and flour: Eastern Europe ships to Western European countries; the United States exports importantly to Mexico, Latin American and Caribbean countries, with Canada as a competitor, while Argentina is the chief supplier of Brazil.

Wheat

The United States raises many varieties of wheat, embracing about all the classes grown throughout the world; that provides wheat and flour for export that is suitable to the needs of all importing nations. Probably only Russia has as much variety in growing conditions as the United States and is able to produce all the classes of wheat. Other countries, because of their location, smaller growing areas or smaller variations in weather, raise more uniform types of wheat, but those that export have large surpluses of the various kinds of wheat available for international trade. This provides importers with a choice of areas from which to fill requirements.

Canada, with its large supply of spring-grown varieties and its small home use, has ample amounts of wheats with sufficient protein to add strength to blends of weaker wheats grown in the large, deficit-production countries. Argentina furnishes wheat less hard than the United States hard winter class, but it provides volume for the importers. Australia exports a soft wheat that competes with United States soft red and white wheats. These three exporting countries normally sell their surpluses to other nations each year and, with the United States and other countries, compete in the sale of like kinds of wheat. Price is the motivating force that moves wheat and governs the amount that each country puts into world trade.

Probably the reason why it is difficult for the United

States to maintain a steady large volume of wheat exports is that its competitors rely upon grain exports for revenue to offset imports. United States wheat sales are of less importance to its international trade than to that of other countries because of the large volume of exports of all its products; yet the volume of wheat shipments is quite important to its wheat production. Of total world wheat and flour shipments of between half a billion and one billion bushels annually, the United States' share over several decades has been from a trifling few million bushels (and even a net amount imported in the drought years of the 1930's) to over 500,000,000 bushels. Its peak and the world's peak came in the immediate post-World-War-II years.

Wheat is harvested somewhere in the world every month of the year. Beginning in the Southern Hemisphere in November while harvesting is still going on in Manchuria, the harvest commences in South Africa; in December it begins in northern Argentina and works south, and is under way in Australia. In January the harvest reaches New Zealand and Chile. During February and March wheat is harvested in the southern part of the Northern Hemisphere—in Egypt and India—and in April harvesting begins in Mexico, Asia Minor and elsewhere and gradually works farther north. The first wheat is harvested in Texas in the latter part of May, at which time the harvest has also reached north to Japan and China. June is a big month in the United States in the southwestern plains states, with a movement north into our largest-producing state, Kansas. During this same month the harvest is progressing in Italy, which is the second-largest producer in Europe, outranked only by Russia, though in some years France has a larger wheat crop than Italy's. July sees the completion of United States winter-wheat harvest in the region of Illinois, Nebraska, etc., except in Montana, third-largest wheat state, which harvests winter wheat into the fall months at the same time they are sowing for the next year's crop and completing the spring-wheat harvest. In July the spring-wheat harvest starts in the

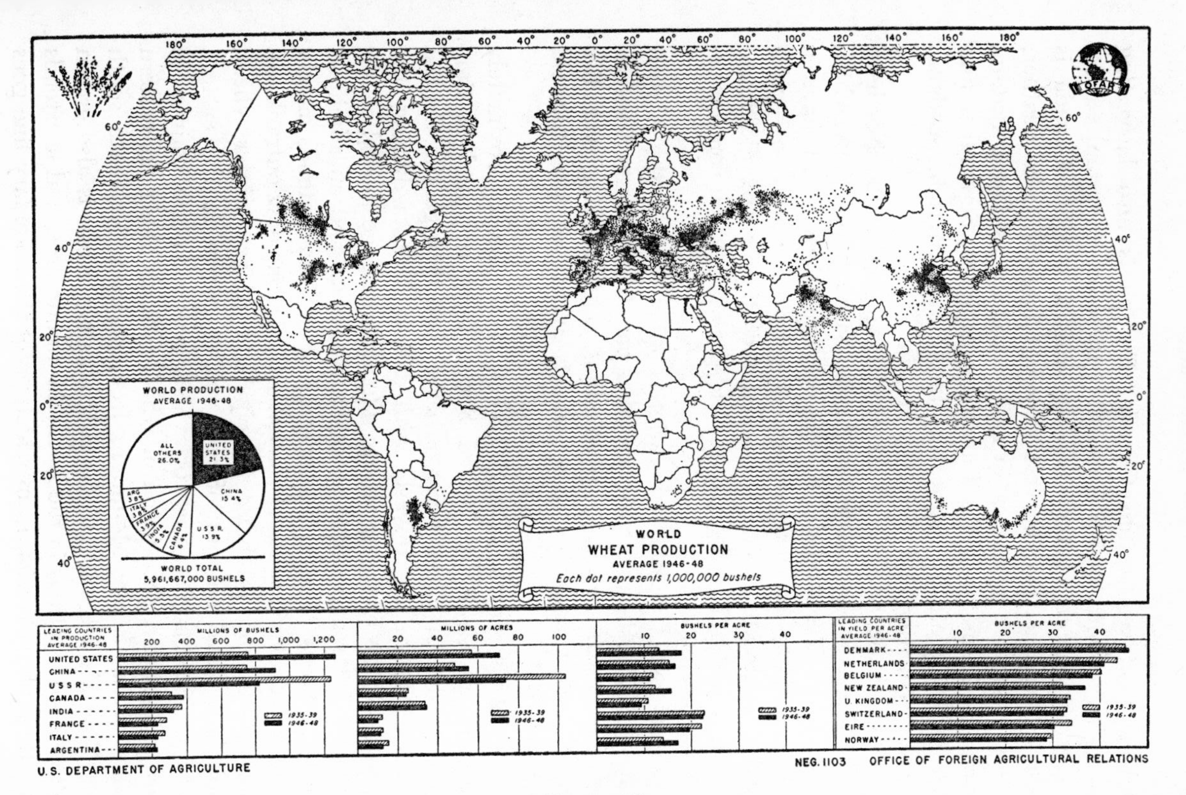
OFAR
WORLD PRODUCTION
AVERAGE 1946-48
ALL OTHERS 26.0%
UNITED STATES 21.3%
CHINA 15.4%
U.S.S.R. 13.9%
CANADA 6.4%
INDIA 5.5%
FRANCE 3.9%
ITALY 3.8%
ARG. 3.8%
WORLD TOTAL
5,961,667,000 BUSHELS
WORLD
WHEAT PRODUCTION
AVERAGE 1946-48
Each dot represents 1,000,000 bushels
LEADING COUNTRIES IN PRODUCTION AVERAGE 1946-48
UNITED STATES
CHINA
U.S.S.R.
CANADA
INDIA
FRANCE
ITALY
ARGENTINA
MILLIONS OF BUSHELS
MILLIONS OF ACRES
BUSHELS PER ACRE
1935-39
1946-48
LEADING COUNTRIES IN YIELD PER ACRE AVERAGE 1946-48
DENMARK
NETHERLANDS
BELGIUM
NEW ZEALAND
U. KINGDOM
SWITZERLAND
EIRE
NORWAY
U.S. DEPARTMENT OF AGRICULTURE
NEG. 1103
OFFICE OF FOREIGN AGRICULTURAL RELATIONS

FIGURE 2

Dakotas and works into Canada. Europe is also harvesting during this month, which is probably the most important wheat-harvesting month of the year. In August western Canada is very active, but their harvest may last into the cold weather; and the harvest continues in such countries as Great Britain, Poland and Russia on the European continent. September and October complete the harvest cycle with activities in Scotland, Sweden, Norway and northern Russia.

Most of the world's wheat crop is grown in the Northern Hemisphere, readily available to the large populations which consume it. Economic and political conditions often have a strong bearing upon acreages, but growing conditions—principally temperatures and the amount of timely precipitation—are likely to regulate the size of yield per acre, which controls resulting production.

There are hundreds of varieties of wheat in the United States and Russia, and many in other countries. Constant breeding for disease-resistant, upstanding, high-yielding varieties brings into prominence new wheats which replace the old varieties.

Wheat is grown about 1,500,000 of the approximately 5,000,000 farms in the United States. Over a period of time the extension of wheat acreage has moved through the Central States into the Northwest, with North Dakota having the largest acreage of spring wheat; then the acreage moved southward until it reached into northwestern Texas and an adjoining portion of New Mexico. The wheat belt in Texas extends mainly to a short distance south of Fort Worth. Kansas now outranks all other states and produces principally hard red winter wheat, though a small amount of soft red is grown in the eastern portion. The largest class of wheat grown in the country is hard red winter, production of which extends along the eastern slopes of the Rocky Mountains from northern Nebraska south into New Mexico and the Texas Panhandle. Some is also grown in scattered locations in the Rocky Mountain area, and it extends east through Nebraska, from which point the boundary line goes southwestward, including most of Kansas, and cuts diagonally through the middle of Oklahoma into Texas. The soft-red-winter area is east of these lines, starting in north-central Texas and includes eastern Oklahoma, part of eastern Kansas, Missouri, the southern and central parts of Illinois, and goes northeast into southern Michigan and east to the Atlantic Ocean. The hard-red-spring area, second in production volume, lies in the Dakotas, Minnesota and eastern and northern Montana; also within this area durum wheat is grown, in eastern North Dakota and adjoining parts of South Dakota and Minnesota as well as Montana. In addition to its spring wheat, Montana sometimes has about half its acreage in hard red winter wheat. White wheat of the sub-class soft is grown in and east of Michigan; and both soft and hard white and some red grow in the Pacific Coast area, which raises both winter and spring western varieties, having the advantage of sowing spring wheat if the fall plantings have not weathered the winter season. The different classes of wheat do best within the described areas, but there are many sizable sections which are also adaptable to more than one class: Illinois grows some hard red winter, in some years a large share, but of a lower protein content than the hard red winter grown in the southwestern states. Climate has considerable influence on the development of the different classes, the soft wheats favoring what might be called a sub-humid climate that is not conducive to the production of wheat of hard-kernel texture.

Winter wheats are sown in the fall usually after the Hessian-fly-free dates after the adult flies have died. Wheat plants lie dormant during the winter and in the spring grow rapidly until harvest. Spring wheat is sown about as early as the ground is workable in the spring, and provided there is sufficient moisture, the plant grows and develops continuously.

Diseases of many kinds are likely to damage or destroy fields of wheat, sometimes in whole areas, and, together with drought and flood, add to the hazards of wheat-farming. There is danger of damage from different kinds of rust, but the most destructive of all crop diseases is black stem rust, of which there are more than 200 varieties, each composed of several strains. Each "race" is specific in that it will attack only certain varieties of grain, though existing races sometimes combine by hybridization to produce entirely new ones which may infect crop varieties that are considered resistant. The plant breeders must continually fight against this so long as the common variety and two other varieties of barberry plants exist. In northern states some rust spores winter on wild grasses; these spores must pass through the hybridization stage on the barberry, however, before they can infect grain crops. In Mexico and southern Texas the infectious stage winters in growing wheatfields, where the green crop can be found throughout the year, so that without the presence of barberries rust can still break out when weather conditions favor the movement of rust spores from the South. A barberry-eradication program has been in progress for more than 30 years, and 84% of the total area in eighteen affected states is now on maintenance, but it is still a long-range program with much to be accomplished.

Precipitation in Colorado east of the mountains, where the hard-red-winter acreage begins, averages about 15 inches annually, and the amount increases eastward. The western third of Kansas, roughly west of the 100th meridian, where Dodge City is located, receives under 20 inches, the middle division of the state more than 26 inches and the east about 35 inches. In Nebraska averages are not as heavy as in Kansas, while Oklahoma and Texas have about the same amounts as Kansas for equal longitudes. The annual 40-inch zone which starts in southeast Kansas extends south of a line running northeastward through the middle of Missouri, Illinois, Indiana and Ohio. The annual amount of precipitation in the spring-wheat area is even less than in Kansas, with Montana receiving 15 inches and North Dakota up to 20 in the central and eastern sections and western Minnesota running up to 25 inches, with a greater amount in the southeastern grain area of Minnesota.

Michigan's average is from 30 to 35 inches. The Pacific Northwest receives heavy rainfall; it has about 20 inches near the Montana boundary, precipitation reaches 80 inches or more near the west coast. Farther south, in California, amounts vary considerably, but that state leads the nation in extent of irrigated land, with a total of more than 6,500,000 acres under irrigation. Most of the irrigated land in the nation is in seventeen western states located west and south of eastern North Dakota, in addition to Arkansas, Louisiana and Florida. The latter states have fewer than 1½ million irrigated acres. The plains states in which grain is grown have only about 4,500,000 acres out of some 25,000,000 irrigated acres in the 17 western states.[4]

Wheat is the country's leading cash grain crop, with production tending to be concentrated in surplus areas. Because its consumption is widespread, the price to the producer must stand the full freight deduction from farm to destination. Grain products move in transit on the railroads at freight rates very close to those of the grain itself, unlike feed grains that have been converted into livestock, which cost less to ship to market than the cost to ship the amount of grain it has taken to feed the animals. For this reason wheat prices tend to vary more between different areas of wheat production than those of feed grains. But there are compensating conditions in wheat, because different classes of wheat are used locally for various purposes and the several export areas are located near the areas of surplus production, so that exports attract surpluses transported over comparatively short-haul routes. In general, however, the farm wheat price must be adjusted to bear all the charges necessary to move the grain to large consuming areas. It is not uncommon for some wheat or its products to be carried pretty well across the country. Bread is always in demand, so that when wheat is needed for this purpose the wheat must be found wherever it is available, and the prices of wheat and flour must be adjusted to bear the cost of the freight to carry the grain from farm to

[4] United States Census, 1950.

mill. This does not infer that the farm price of wheat will be depressed, for often the baker has to pay an increased price for flour without advancing the price of his bread.

The system of grading wheat and other grains under the authority of the United States Grain Standards Act is supervised by the Secretary of Agriculture. The Commodity Exchange Act requires that futures conform to these standards or to other standards officially promulgated for any commodity. Futures markets exercise the right of designating by rule what grades may be delivered on contracts during the month of delivery; exchanges may or may not confine this to one class of wheat, and they permit the seller of futures to deliver at his option any of the designated classes and permissible grades within each class. Limitations are imposed on sellers of minimum quantities of each grade delivered so that they may conform approximately to railroad shipping requirements. The exchanges may change these rules from time to time, but not during the life of trading in a delivery future. If changes are made, they are initiated at the start of trading in a new delivery month or by designation of a "new" contract and retention of the former one as an "old" contract.

Kansas City, a winter-wheat futures market, has two contracts—the active one being for delivery of hard and the other hard and soft red winter wheat. Minneapolis permits deliveries of only hard red spring wheat, and Chicago both winter wheat of hard and soft red classes and hard red spring. The exchanges may, and do, designate limits as to sub-classes of grains and numerical grades deliverable. Exchanges probably determine the quality of a commodity deliverable according to the accessibility of grain grown near the market or its normal flow in commercial channels toward that market.

The commercial value of each class of grain continually changes, as does the value of the different grades within classes of the same grain. Nevertheless, futures contracts are based on one or more grades and classes, with other grades of these classes deliverable at fixed differentials above or below the contract price. Some current market prices differ from fixed-grade differentials, and for that reason some classes and grades are not considered delivery probabilities and are likely to sell relatively higher than a delivery basis; but one or more of the deliverable grades will be attracted to delivery during the expiring month. The futures-delivery requirements, therefore, do not take away the flexibility of cash-grain quality bases; and each grade will, without interference of futures markets, command its premium over the futures and its relation to other grades according to relative demand. Provided there is storage space for futures-delivery purposes, no grade is likely to sell below its deliverable differential (cost of carrying considered) for any length of time.

The apparent reason for the Chicago market's permitting deliveries of both winter and spring wheat is its location; both hard- and soft-red-winter classes are grown locally and normally move to the terminal at harvest time. Southwestern-grown wheat deliverable on Kansas City futures is of these same classes, even though the wheat may be of other varieties and may contain different milling qualities, principally protein. The largest wheat-production area is west of Chicago, and inasmuch as the heavier-consuming section of the country is east of it, much wheat or flour passes through Chicago or equivalent freight-rate points. The quantity varies yearly according to the size of crops in different locations. Spring wheat grown in the Dakotas and adjoining northwestern states, like winter wheat in the Southwest, finds a favorable outlet for its flour product in the more heavily populated eastern states. Considerable spring wheat moves out of Duluth by way of the Great Lakes to Buffalo to provide the large flour mills of that city with sufficient wheat to carry on grinding operations. Spring wheat also moves by rail to the East and, when shipped to New York, for example, has favorable freight rates providing for stopping for storage in Chicago (and elsewhere). If that kind of wheat is brought to Chicago for delivery on futures it is necessary that the price-spread difference between Minneapolis and Chicago be wide enough to equal the costs of shipment to Chicago. While spring-wheat flour is always available in Chicago for bakery and family use, it sells at a relative premium over Chicago wheat futures most of the time. Sellers who deliver wheat on Minneapolis futures have the option of delivering at either Minneapolis or Duluth elevators and can ship from some country origins at the same or little freight difference to either city. While rail freight to Chicago may be the same from Duluth as from Minneapolis, wheat can be shipped from Duluth to Buffalo by lake boat for one freight, whereas if the wheat were shipped to Chicago via lake and again loaded on a steamer and shipped to Buffalo, freight would have to be paid for two lake trips. If lake-received wheat is reshipped out of Chicago by rail to Buffalo, it usually has a higher combined rate than the all-rail rate from Duluth to Buffalo. For these reasons, while Chicago Board of Trade rules permit deliveries of spring wheat on futures, such tenders are infrequent.

The relationship of Chicago futures-market prices, while at fluctuating differences compared with both Kansas City and Minneapolis, is limited, because the same classes of wheat are deliverable in Chicago as in each of the other markets. However, each market has the privilege of establishing rules governing whichever class, sub-class, and grade of wheat it believes proper, and the other two markets permit grades of delivery which Chicago does not. Therefore, this grade factor and the time element of getting delivery in one market and shipping the wheat to Chicago in time for delivery during the same month has a bearing on spread differences between Kansas City or Minneapolis and Chicago. It is most unusual that discounts for either of these markets under Chicago exceed shipping differences, and if they do at all it occurs only near the maturity dates of contracts. Many arrangements may be made to obtain satisfactory delivery wheat in Chicago, and the party who takes delivery when inter-market spreads are wider than shipping costs will be in an uneconomic position, because cash-grain-selling competition will be cheaper from the other market. Unless a firm has storage facilities in Chicago and shipping facilities near the originating market, the wheat is usually sold to a Chicago elevator firm which can put it into store and deliver it more readily than a firm having to engage the services of others.

No standing statement of contract conditions for delivery on futures contracts can be made, because they are subject to change at the discretion of each exchange. Undoubtedly there will always be exchange rules permitting delivery by warehouse receipt for grain in elevators located in a city designated by the contract, although not necessarily in the city where trading is conducted. The required location, etc., of these elevators may be subject to change as well as the presently accepted styles of delivery. For a number of years Chicago contracts have permitted delivery of grain in railway boxcars on tracks, provided that the grain meets grading and other requirements and that delivery is made only during the last three business days of the delivery month. Not all exchanges permit track deliveries on futures contracts, and conditions differ in other respects. Chicago requires that live-transit railroad billing be furnished to the shipper when the grain is loaded out of the elevator, and the elevator must protect the shipper on rail freight rates to certain destinations and abide by other conditions in connection with shipment. Other exchanges have different billing requirements. The Chicago exchange permits buyers and sellers of futures to liquidate their futures positions by exchange of futures against cash during the last seven business days of a delivery month which is after the expiration of trading, provided they have made a bona fide cash trade of the commodity in any location and of any quality. Buyers, however, may demand regular delivery according to contract and sellers must comply.

The Commodity Exchange Act requires that, at least one and not more than ten business days prior to delivery day, the party making delivery shall furnish the party obligated to take delivery with a written notice. Grain exchanges have set the requirements on grain at one business day, but some other commodity exchanges require longer notice. For grain this gives the seller ("the short") until one business day prior to the last business day of the month to tender a delivery notice. Delivery of the warehouse receipt shall be made for payment the day following, or if the grain is in cars, the delivery price is not payable until the cars are unloaded, unless the buyer ("the long") elects otherwise under prescribed conditions. On the final-notice day in Chicago, particulars may be omitted from the delivery notice, but this does not relieve the short of his responsibility to complete delivery requirements on the last business day.

Warehouse receipts covering grain in deliverable position are negotiable and customarily have the highest collateral value against bank loans, especially when the borrower follows the practice of hedging in futures. There are safeguards protecting the owner of warehouse receipts against impairment of the quality of the grain to which he holds title; these are embodied in the regulations of the United States Warehouse Act covering Federal-licensed warehouses and in Chicago Board of Trade regulations covering warehouses licensed by Illinois. Grain elevators located in Chicago must operate under one or the other of these licenses in order to be "regular" for delivery of grain on futures contracts. There is a system of recording ownership of warehouse receipts provided in this requirement for safeguarding the condition of grain so that the owner may be contacted and given the opportunity either of selling the grain at the current market price or of receiving the grade called for in the warehouse receipt, provided it is shipped out of the elevator. Warehousemen must be bonded as required by the exchange as to both amount and conditions. This for buyers is a safeguard of the quality on grain taken on delivery of futures contracts.

Corn

Corn, the principal grain produced in the United States for feed, is raised in many other countries for the same purpose and in some countries mainly for human food. It ranks first in grain production in the United States and third in world grain crops: current world production is around 5,750,000,000 bushels, and in the United States over three billion bushels. Corn is often used as a yardstick in measuring feed grains in relation to prices of livestock, with other grains bearing proportionate feeding values. The largest use of corn in the United States is for feeding hogs, which consume about 40% of all its grains consumed as feed. Production of corn has expanded consistently with growth of population, though we have used less corn and other grains to feed horses and mules as their numbers have decreased, and also less corn per head of livestock and poultry as high-protein feeds have been more generally used. But the need for larger corn crops seems always to be present. Hybrid seed has cut the number of acres required to grow even larger corn crops, but the land has found immediate use in the production of other crops, mostly for feed.

Around the turn of the century Argentina replaced the United States as the largest international corn-shipper. At times the United States has been called upon to supply significant amounts of import countries' needs, but usually domestic uses have required all the production. Most other exporters are countries lying in the Danube Basin, principally Roumania, with other areas—the Union of South Africa, French Indo-china, Russia (in small amounts) and the Asiatic area—also exporting. The United Kingdom, as in wheat, is the largest importer of corn, at times taking almost as much as all other European import countries combined. Aside from Europe and Canada, other countries of the world import very little corn.

Barley, which also is imported by the United Kingdom in larger amounts than by any other deficit country, is interchangeable with corn in feeding and may replace corn when it has a price advantage. Barley also moves in international trade for malting and food purposes.

The corn-growth belts in both the Northern and the Southern hemispheres are much narrower than those of wheat because of the need for frost-free weather; therefore, the world harvest is not as continuous as that of wheat. Nevertheless, export nations gather corn crops far enough apart so that there is rather a steady flow in international trade. Production methods in the United States have advanced because of better seed and a greater use of machinery all the way from plowing through shipment to market. Many other countries continue to produce and handle their corn the same as they did many years ago. Hybrid seed, widely used in the United States, must be continuously produced, just as it must be suitable in several respects to the area in which it is planted. Agriculturally backward nations lack this production advantage.

The United States commercial-corn-producing area, "the Corn Belt," lies south of a line extending from southwestern Nebraska toward the northeastern part of that state into eastern South Dakota and southern Minnesota, thence southeasterly through northern Wisconsin and southern Michigan and ending in eastern Ohio. It covers the entire states of Iowa, Illinois, and Indiana and about the western two thirds of Ohio. From southwestern Nebraska the southern boundary is the northern and northeastern parts of Kansas, about the northern half of Missouri, and also northwestern Kentucky. There is another commercial area in southeastern Pennsylvania extending across the boundary into adjoining states.

If we follow the annual precipitation of the Corn Belt from west to east, we find that it is from 20 to 25 inches in the west and that it increases to 35 inches in eastern Iowa, rising from this amount up to 40 inches through the middle of Illinois to the eastern end of the belt in Ohio. The heavy-acreage areas

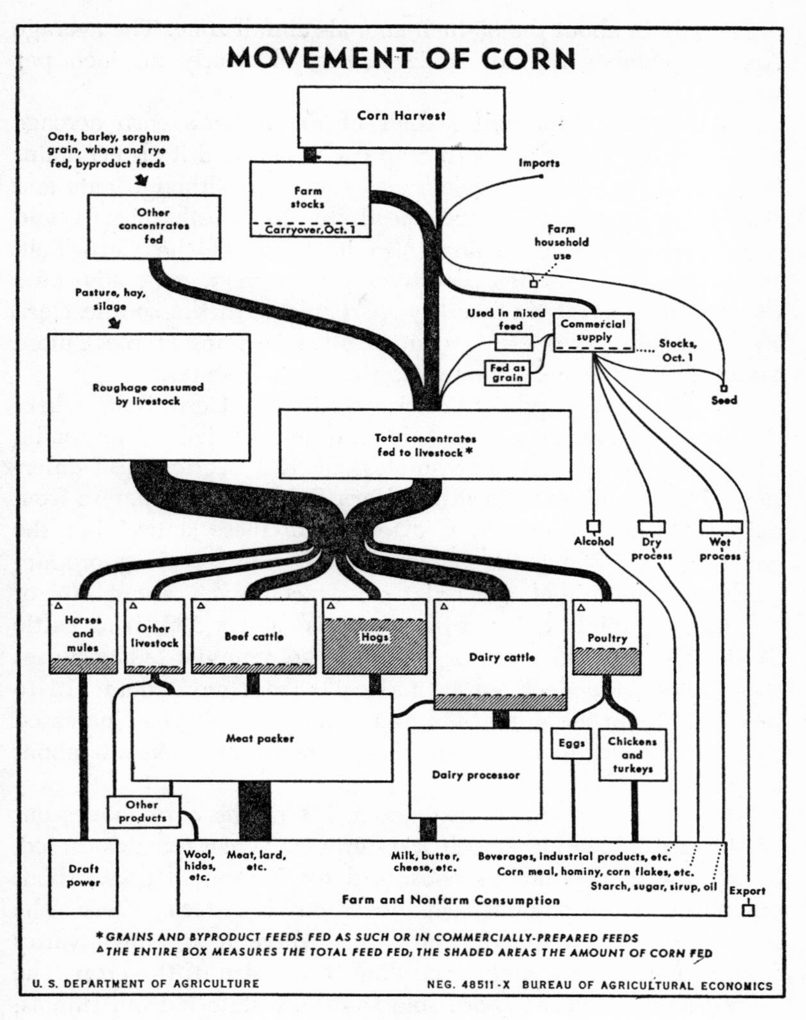
MOVEMENT OF CORN
Corn Harvest
Oats, barley, sorghum grain, wheat and rye fed, byproduct feeds
Farm stocks
Carryover, Oct. 1
Imports
Other concentrates fed
Farm household use
Pasture, hay, silage
Used in mixed feed
Commercial supply
Stocks, Oct. 1
Fed as grain
Roughage consumed by livestock
Seed
Total concentrates fed to livestock *
Alcohol
Dry process
Wet process
Horses and mules
Other livestock
Beef cattle
Hogs
Dairy cattle
Poultry
Meat packer
Eggs
Chickens and turkeys
Dairy processor
Other products
Draft power
Wool, hides, etc.
Meat, lard, etc.
Milk, butter, cheese, etc.
Beverages, industrial products, etc.
Corn meal, hominy, corn flakes, etc.
Starch, sugar, sirup, oil
Export
Farm and Nonfarm Consumption
* GRAINS AND BYPRODUCT FEEDS FED AS SUCH OR IN COMMERCIALLY-PREPARED FEEDS
△ THE ENTIRE BOX MEASURES THE TOTAL FEED FED; THE SHADED AREAS THE AMOUNT OF CORN FED
U. S. DEPARTMENT OF AGRICULTURE
NEG. 48511-X BUREAU OF AGRICULTURAL ECONOMICS

FIGURE 3

are mostly in about the 35-inch-annual-rainfall zone. The average April–September rainfall is 22 inches, or nearly an inch per week.[5]

Within the Corn Belt is half of the nation's corn acreage and three fourths of the corn crop each year, and it also contains large acreages of oats, barley, and soybeans, although oats and barley acreages are located mostly in the northern part and some heavy-yielding sections also lie north of the Corn Belt. In addition to the Belt, corn is grown very generally over the eastern part of the country, particularly in the southeastern states; some corn is also grown in other sections of the United States, but only small amounts in the western states.

The large hog population is within the Corn Belt, where the heavy production makes feed grains available. Fattening cattle for market as a more or less distinct argricultural enterprise is also concentrated in the Corn Belt. This is separate from dairying, which, however, is extensive in these states.[6] For the entire United States the percentage of grains and by-product feeds combined that are fed to hogs comprises about 40% of the feeding total: dairy cattle consume about 18%, beef cattle 8% to 11%, sheep 1% more or less, and the amounts fed to horses and mules have declined in a decade from more than 11% to less than 3%, in the same time that poultry feeding has increased from under 22% to more than 26%; other uses make up about 3%.[7]

It is generally stated that about 15% of the corn moves out of the county within which it is grown. What remains is fed, except for small amounts consumed for household uses. About one third of the amount that moves out is fed elsewhere. The amount of corn shipped from farms where it is grown varies from year to year, mainly according to the size of the crop. The largest amount of cash corn sold from any state is from Illinois; this corn supplies the Chicago market with most of the

[5] Report of the Kansas Board of Agriculture, June, 1948.
[6] U.S.D.A., *Agricultural Statistics,* 1949.
[7] U.S.D.A., *Farm Cost Situation,* Oct., 1951.

100,000,000 to 150,000,000 bushels it receives annually and with corn for direct shipment to other places. During 1952, one of the big recent years, Chicago received 127,000,000 bushels of corn, of which 40,500,000 were shipped in by barges, 4,500,000 by trucks, and the balance, 82,000,000 bushels, by railroads. In 1955 receipts of corn in Chicago were 97,000,000 bushels and of all grains, 198,000,000 bushels. Iowa, although the biggest grain-producing state, uses so much of its corn and other feed-grain crops in raising livestock that it has comparatively little for sale to feed manufacturers and processors or for industry. Firms in these businesses located in Iowa itself seek supplies of grain elsewhere.

Because of its volume of trade, the Chicago corn-futures market is the representative pricing center, and other futures markets are of less importance. The other markets reflect prices in their sections, but they usually lack sufficient volume of trade to permit adequate hedging operations or the changing of hedges from one market to another, or to support a quantity of inter-market spreading. In some seasons of large crops in the western part of the Corn Belt, merchants find markets all the way to the Atlantic seaboard and at the same time fill demands coming from Pacific States areas. In such years Illinois shippers rely mostly on outlets to points that they may reach because of cheaper water-transportation and railroad-billing advantages. At times, eastern Corn Belt surpluses supply a great share of the Atlantic seaboard and New England trade.

Chicago futures-delivery conditions for corn are the same as for wheat and the other grains, as are elevator storage and shipping requirements. Deliverable classes and grades are changed occasionally, with number-three corn considered an acceptable grade at a discount.

Oats

Oats, possibly considered to be in disfavor some years back as the number of horses declined while the use of farm machinery increased, have made a strong comeback. A decline in the quality of oats spurred efforts that have resulted both in improved varieties and larger acreages, and these have found favor in livestock production through different methods of feeding. Oats seeded in the spring should be put into the ground early, as sowing after the optimum date decreases both yield and bushel-weight. Principal growing areas are in the corn and spring-wheat belts, where the climate is cool and moist; there are also fall-sown oats in the South and Southwest, but they are of relatively small quantities. Oats fit in well into a rotation of crops, and are also a nurse crop, because they require little land preparation or direct soil fertilization.[8] World production is about 4,250,000,000 bushels, with North America, Europe, and Russia accounting for nearly 4,000,000,000 bushels of the total.

International trade in oats is usually unimportant, and the United States' share is small; in fact, on balance, they often are importers of oats originating in Canada.

Most oats are consumed on the farms where they are grown, and of the fair share that are sold by farmers, only a small amount (relative to the size of the crop) moves through commercial channels to terminal markets. Chicago's stock of oats is accumulated from the growing area in its vicinity at harvest time, but it also receives oats from the northwestern surplus states frequently throughout the season. The Northwest ships oats west, south, and east, so that their prices, represented by the Minneapolis futures market, in comparison with Chicago futures prices are important as guides to hedging and in spreading operations. Canadian oats at times supply the feed trade in the New England States and elsewhere in the United States with important percentages for the requirements of these areas, and during some years Canada ships oats to Chicago and other western Great Lakes ports.

The classes of oats deliverable on Chicago futures consist

---

[8] *Grow Disease-Resistant Oats,* U.S.D.A. Farmers' Bulletin No. 1941, Aug., 1949.

of those grown near by, which are mostly white, a class that also comes from the Northwest and from Canada. The numerical grades and differentials at which they are deliverable on futures may be changed from time to time; infrequently the Federal grade standards are also altered.

Barley

Barley is more important in the grain trade of the United States than the size of the crop would indicate, because a good share of it moves to market. It is vital to the malting trade for use in brewing and distilling industries, and it finds further use in commercial sale as feed. The world crop is approximately 2,750,000,000 bushels, more than a third of which is raised in Asia and a somewhat less amount in Europe. The United States produces about a tenth (or more) of the world's crop. Normally world trade exceeds 100,000,000 bushels annually (but has been larger in postwar years, when corn shipments have been small), and the United States contributes varying amounts up to over one fourth; on the other hand, while the United States is exporting to other countries, it may at the same time be importing from Canada.

Improvement in seed and great care in threshing barley are stressed in order that high-quality, undamaged kernels will be available for malting. In the malting process barley has to germinate, and it is unfit for this purpose if more than 10% of the kernels are skinned or broken. Even though only a few varieties of the great number grown are used for malting, that trade requires a large share of the amount of barley that comes to market. If through improper handling any barley becomes unfit for malting, it becomes a feed grain and falls within a materially lower price range. Organized efforts to improve seed, growing, and handling conditions are showing results; following success in cotton, where one variety has been grown in a community, efforts are being made in malting barley. Barley is planted largely in the spring, and the most important growing region is east of the Missouri River in North and

South Dakota and the adjourning section of Minnesota, but acreage of lesser concentration covers much of the western section of the Midwest and extends into the Pacific Northwest. Winter barley grows as far north as Pennsylvania in the east, extending somewhat south and then westward toward Oklahoma and central Texas. California is a large barley producer, planting its acreage in fall or winter.

Several attempts to trade in barley futures in Chicago and Minneapolis have been unsuccessful—possibly because of the great difference between the prices for malting barley and feed barley and the fact that the latter may be secured from barley during its cleaning prior to and during the steeping operations in connection with the malting process. Winnipeg, Canada, has a successful futures market.

Rye

In the United States the harvested acreage of rye for use as grain is currently only a little larger than it was during Civil War years. For a few years after World War I the United States acreage expanded so that one year it produced a 100,000,000-bushel crop, and at that time exported a substantial amount. Soon, however, it was about the same as domestic requirements. Historically the United States has been both an importer and an exporter, and at times received rye from Canada and later shipped the same rye to Europe because its prices changed compared with Canada's.

The principal production of rye is from acreage sown in the Northwestern states of North Dakota, South Dakota, and Minnesota and from smaller acreages scattered throughout Nebraska and south through Kansas and Oklahoma. Scattered acreages also extend from the main area east through Wisconsin and Michigan and southeastward to the Middle Atlantic States, and there is some rye acreage on the West Coast. The rye crop consists mostly of winter varieties; the plant is very hardy and able to weather the cold northern climates of the United

States and Canada and, in fact, also the winters of Europe and Russia, which are the world's principal producing regions.

In the United States only somewhat over half of the planted acreage of rye is cut for grain, of which a fair share is fed to livestock, depending largely on the size of the crop, and the balance is used for distilling and for food. As a food, rye flour is mixed with wheat flour—there are divisions all along the line. World production runs up to 1,750,000,000 bushels, but both European and Asiatic Russia are credited with close to 1,000,000,000 bushels of this amount and other European countries with 750,000,000 bushels, Poland and Germany raising more than half of the European total. Elsewhere in the world, quantity production is unimportant, as it is in North America. Rye is primarily considered a bread grain along with wheat. The world importers are European countries, but they get only very small amounts compared to their consumption; they import from scattered countries—Russia, the United States, Canada, Argentina, etc.

The United States' rye supply-and-demand position usually presents a problem. Therefore, the futures trading price serves the purpose of registering production and consumption relations and at the same time serves to protect the commercial handlers. The Federal grade standards are of one classification—rye—irrespective of variety. Grades include those with the special notation "plump," which is recognized in delivery differentials at premiums over the contract grade on the Chicago future. Minneapolis, closer to the main production area, also has a futures market and, as in wheat, has different delivery differentials and grades from Chicago's. When importations from Canada are made for definite commercial necessities, the rye is likely to move by vessels on the Great Lakes to eastern lake ports such as Buffalo. But if imports are attracted by favorable price relationship pending resale to industries or other consumers, the rye most always is shipped to Chicago, where it can be hedged and delivered on futures contracts. Imports may be the result of overproduction in Canada, whose total consumption is small, or it may be the need to add to domestic production of the United States. At one time our requirements attracted rye from Poland.

Grain Sorghums

The official grain standards of the United States include grain sorghums, of which the principal sub-classes are milo and kafir. Their main production lies within a triangular area with the eastern and western borders of Texas as base and the Canadian border as apex. Amounts are grown outside of this area but not in impressive quantity. The first crop of the season matures in southern Texas, while at the same time toward the Panhandle of that state farmers are still planting. The latter section contains the heavy acreage both for the state and for the nation. Kansas is next to Texas in importance, producing heavily in the southwestern counties. Oklahoma ranks third, concentrating its acreage where it adjoins the Texas and Kansas producing areas. In these semi-arid farming districts sorghums are used as a substitute for corn because of their high yield and drought-resistant qualities. These crops are to the Great Plains what corn is to the Corn Belt and are generally recognized as the basis of a permanent diversified agriculture.[9]

Reference to the existence of grain sorghums is found in the ancient history of Egypt. They have inherited their drought-resistance from the tropical climes in which they originated; however, it remained for the plant breeders in the United States to develop (in recent years) dwarf varieties that lend themselves exceptionally well to mechanical handling. The plants have the ability to remain alive in dry periods, even though growth stops, and quickly renew growth when moisture is provided. The composition of the grain is very much the same as corn; the

---

[9] *A Graphic Summary of Farm Crops,* U.S.D.A. Miscellaneous Publication No. 512, Feb., 1943.

feeding value is said to be about equal to that of corn, and industrial uses are about the same.

There are two futures markets for grain sorghums: one in Kansas City, which represents delivery on contract in elevators located in that city, and the other with trading conducted in Chicago but delivery made in warehouses located in Fort Worth, Texas, on a price basis of freight paid to Galveston, Texas. The warehouseman is obligated to furnish the shipper railroad freight billing that will permit—in addition to the Galveston basis as the destination—either the Memphis, Tennessee, gateway or California, with an adjustment of freight equal to the amount it would cost to ship to Galveston. This futures contract differs from others covering grain traded in Chicago, because the others require that the grain must be delivered only in Chicago, whereas grain sorghums are not delivered in Chicago at all.

There are a number of other futures contracts similar to the Chicago grain-sorghums market in which products are traded in one city but delivered elsewhere. Winnipeg, Canada, has Fort William and/or Port Arthur as its only delivery points; this makes grain accessible for loading on Great Lakes steamers as well as accessible for railroad shipment. Cotton is notable for its several delivery points along the Atlantic seaboard and the Gulf of Mexico: it may be delivered at any delivery point at the seller's option. Other futures traded in Chicago having a number of delivery points are crude soybean oil and soybean meal.

Lard

Lard-trading has been associated with Chicago Board of Trade activities for many years, as is quite fitting for a product of the hog, which has a basic connection with grains. The relationship of the price of hogs—which consume so large a share of feed grains, millfeeds, meal production, etc.—to the prices of these commodities is important to grain trading. Actually, lard prices fluctuate independently of hog prices, even though in former years there was a close connection between the two. The change occurred during the years of rapid expansion of soybean production in the 1940's, since which time soybean oil has been important in the fats-and-oils trade. This competition has made it necessary for lard to break away from its historical price connection with hog prices and to follow the trend of fats and oils. During the same period advancement in detergent manufacture has also had a bearing on animal-fats prices.

Chicago lard-futures contracts are for delivery only in Chicago. The lard may be made elsewhere or at first stored as loose lard and inspected when it is put into deliverable position. The quality standards of the Chicago lard contract specifying prime steam- or dry-rendered lard in tierces or drums is generally accepted as a quality basis throughout the world. The contract provides that lard delivered on and after December 1 shall include only lard made on and after the previous first day of October. Thus, futures-delivery lard cannot be more then fourteen months old, and only during October and November can lard be delivered that is over one year old. This is a significant difference from other Chicago futures contracts.

Soybeans

This ancient oriental crop, brought to the United States and developed commercially, has become very important in the agricultural economy of the country. In themselves, soybeans have little use on the farm, but returning to the farm as meal after the oil has been removed through processing, soybean meal saves great quantities of grain in the feeding of livestock and poultry. Soybeans have become so firmly established in the nation's economy that, despite rapid expansion in crop production, they have practically all been consumed during each current year, and until 1955 it was necessary to curtail processing-plant operations each year because of lack of sufficient soybeans in the months preceding the new harvest. There is more soybean meal produced than any of the other high-protein feed supplements. The quantity of oil produced has surpassed other vegetable oils and is second in edible fats and oils, exceeded only by lard.

Soybean production in the United States leads all other countries; China (twenty-two provinces) and Manchuria are the only other important producers. Small amounts are grown in Korea, Japan, other Pacific islands, Russia, Canada, etc. In recent years United States surpassed Manchuria in amounts of soybeans exported and these two, except for small contributions from other countries, make up the whole total entering international trade. As with other foods in international trade, Europe is the chief buyer of soybeans, including their products, but Japan and Formosa also take important amounts.

In earlier years the crops in United States were grown largely for grazing, for hay, and for fertilizer when the crop was plowed under green to enrich the soil; but with higher prices even after crop expansion, these uses reached a peak and then diminished. The acreage planted for bean production continued to grow as the demand for the processed products increased. It has been one of the most striking agricultural developments in this country. Soil conditions favorable to corn are normally well suited to soybeans; and soybeans are especially well adapted to the central and southern parts of the Corn Belt and the northern half of the Cotton Belt. Illinois has led all other states in production; and Minnesota, Iowa, and Indiana have followed, and the production area spreads in all directions except west of these states. Other principal areas of growth follow south along the Mississippi River and in the East around Virginia and North Carolina.

In investigations of soybean adaptation, it has been convenient to divide the country into nine zones, the southernmost along the Gulf Coast, and the northernmost in the latitude of North Dakota. The average depth of these zones is somewhat less than 150 miles. Department of Agriculture scientists have found that varieties can be grouped according to their adaptation to these regions, and that relatively few do equally well in more than one zone. The rather narrow limits of the zones are probably determined more by the photoperiodic requirements of the varieties than by any other factors; they point up the fact that small differences in environment may mean significant differences in the crop. Good farming practice is to rotate soybean production with other crops.[10]

In accumulating soybeans, a processor is likely to get a mixture of varieties grown in a locality, and thus secures an average turnout of products; but as oil is more valuable per pound than meal is, it is important to buy selectively when possible. Soybean seed ranges in protein value depending on its variety and environment, and the protein itself shows a wide range in percentage of important amino acids.[11] The oil content is most specifically a varietal characteristic, and the iodine number, important in paints, varnish, etc., when it is high, is influenced equally by variety and climate.[12]

The crude oil and the meal recovered in the processing of soybeans may be further divided into end products, but this conversion is as far as most mills go. The two products go off in different directions of sales competition. The crude oil has to compete with the long list of domestic and foreign fats and oils of edible and inedible character, and to that extent these other commodities are influences on the price of the soybeans from which the oil is derived. Soybean meal, the remainder after the oil has been extracted, is used mostly for feed; its chief competitor is cottonseed meal, but other oil seeds as well as mill products, animal proteins, and manufactured proteins available to the feed trade are also competitive. All the high-protein feeds compete with grain prices, even though the use of meal is generally accepted, and all feed prices have

---

[10] U.S.D.A., *The Yearbook in Agriculture,* 1943–1947 (1947).

[11] *Soybeans—Culture and Varieties,* U.S.D.A. Farmers' Bulletin No. 1520, 1949.

[12] U.S.D.A., *Northern Research Laboratory,* Peoria, Ill., May 15, 1945.

to be guided by meat prices as well as by general national income and other price-adjusting factors.

The custom of the trade to price both crude soybean oil and meal (not soybeans) on the basis of the Decatur, Illinois, price was adopted in futures contracts for trading in Chicago, as had previously been done by Memphis for meal and by New York for crude oil. Chicago futures contracts are not identical with the contracts of these other cities, but the differences are not of major price importance.

Soybeans for future delivery must be stored in one of the Chicago warehouses "regular" for delivery of grain on a Chicago contract, and sellers have the same option as in grain of "delivery in cars on track" during the last three business days of the delivery month. Deliverable grades include those of only the yellow class. A premium is paid for number-one grade above the contract grade of number two, and there are differential discounts under the contract price for number three according to the percentage of moisture content stated in the warehouse receipt.

Crude Soybean Oil

In Chicago the crude-soybean-oil contract is based on standards specified by the Chicago Board of Trade, because there are none promulgated by the United States Government. Because of the diversification of delivery points and some conditions inherent in the storage of crude soybean oil, it is incumbent upon the warehouseman to furnish a warehouse receipt for crude soybean oil which does not specify the type of oil but instead specifies that when the oil is shipped out of the warehouse it is to be of one of four types and of standards required by the exchange contract. Delivery points are spread over several states; this makes it necessary to adjust the price with Decatur, Illinois, when delivery is tendered on the futures contract. When the freight rate differs from the delivery point to New York as compared with the freight rate from Decatur,

Illinois, to New York, the seller must pay to or collect from the buyer enough money to equalize the Decatur–New York freight rate. Delivery is by warehouse receipt issued by one of the warehousemen who is regular for delivery and who is bonded according to exchange requirements; one exception is that oil may be delivered on a demand certificate on the second and third day after pit trading has ceased. On demand-certificate delivery, the owner of the oil may have it loaded into a tank car during the current month if he desires, but in any event he is obligated to take the oil out of the warehouse within ten days of the date of the demand certificate. There are a number of details of crude-soybean-oil deliveries differing from grain deliveries, because of the nature of the commodity. When a demand-certificate delivery is made on contract, the seller must make the same freight adjustment as on a warehouse-receipt delivery, but the type of oil is named in the demand certificate and no storage is collected by the warehouseman.

Soybean Meal

The soybean-meal futures contract is different from all others, because operators of soybean-processing plants, which are the shippers of the soybean meal (except for occasional storage and shipment by warehousemen), do not necessarily carry a warehouse stock of meal. Therefore, the exchange contract does not make warehousing of meal a requirement for regularity of delivery.

The delivery of meal against a "short" futures position is accomplished and title transferred by means of a document called "a soybean-meal shipping certificate" issued by the processor or nonprocessing shipper approved as regular by the Exchange. Although the soybean-meal shipping certificate differs from a warehouse receipt, the owner has the privilege of carrying the certificate as long as he wishes, subject to a daily premium charge, and of shipping meal when desired.

After the owner of the certificate gives shipping orders, the issuer of the certificate is allowed five days in which to load the meal in bulk into boxcars, but this time may be extended (though the premium charge stops) if there is an accumulation of shipping orders on hand in excess of two thirds of the processor's production capacity. However, the processor cannot delay shipment more than twenty days beyond the date of receipt of shipping orders, nor can he at any time have certificates outstanding in excess of the amount he can ship within twenty days. The meal must be shipped on a daily schedule of two thirds of the processor's production capacity; this permits the processors to ship the meal as it is processed or from stocks on hand and at the same time leaves the balance of their facilities available for shipment on their cash contracts.

The price basis of soybean meal is "free on board cars, Decatur, Illinois," regardless of the delivery point. The processor prepays the freight from the delivery point to the destination of the car as ordered by the buyer, charging the buyer the full rate from Decatur to the destination. There is no official grade inspection of the meal at the point of shipment; but if the owner and the processor do not agree on the quality of the meal at the destination, exchange regulations provide for a procedure of sampling and analysis and a means of settlement.

The soybean products—oil and meal—and the prices of their derivatives are constantly attracted to competitive-product prices, and in the adjustment of supply and demand they fluctuate in price patterns different from that of soybeans themselves. For this reason, in order to reduce price risk, each of the principal products, oil and meal, may be hedged separately. Futures markets afford the opportunity of lifting hedges out of soybeans at a time one of the products is sold commercially and the other remains in the possession of the processor. Sale of futures as a hedge against the other product, and, if desired, with delivery following, completes liquidation of the original holding. Even if neither the oil nor the meal has been sold commercially, the processor has the opportunity of placing hedges in both of the products rather than in soybeans if the combined futures price is relatively higher than that of soybeans. Or he has the opportunity to hedge only one of the products in futures in a quantity equal to the product from the amount of soybeans owned and to keep the balance equal to the amount of the other product hedged in soybeans. The same hedging privilege is available to users of products in protecting oil or meal acquired in commercial channels or in buying futures to fill or in anticipating their needs. Oil or meal may be interchangeable with other products used in a business, so that futures trading may be a means of quick divestment of one or, by use of hedging, may protect the price until a buyer is found and at the same time the substitute acquired.

CHAPTER V

Growing, Marketing and Merchandising

Farming Hazards

Successful grain farming, like most agricultural pursuits, is a difficult undertaking wherein the farmer combats with his own ability and the natural resources of his land all the weather, insect, and plant-disease hazards and the risks of changing values which often lie outside of his control. While all these hazards make the final results of farming operations uncertain, the farmer has such aids as mechanical devices, irrigation, and fertilization to help him resist the adverse forces of nature; he also experiences normal years when nature's forces are favorable for his crops. In the conduct of grain-farming operations, some activity, such as planting, cultivating, or harvesting, is usually being carried on in different parts of the United States during every month except, normally, December and January.

Of all the hazards which the grain farmer faces, perhaps the most disastrous is drought. The occurrence of droughts in the Great Plains states and parts of western Canada has probably not been more frequent or extended in recent decades than in many periods of the past; but as a result of the increase of settlers in this semi-arid region of the West and the extension of the farming areas in which the crops are grown to be sold for cash, the effects of droughts are becoming an increasing concern to the whole nation.

Farmland in semi-arid sections is not as desirable as the land throughout the Mississippi Valley, but the prices of this land are lower, and aside from the problem of water, it contains good soil so that crops should grow in abundance. A dry autumn gives the wheat plant a poor start, and unless moisture conditions during the growing season are very favorable the poor start may reduce the final yield.

Frost endangers winter wheat from late seeding time to spring; and spring wheat is susceptible to it during practically the entire growing season—especially early fall frosts, when the crop matures late in the season. Winter wheat has the hazard of alternate freezing and thawing during winter months, when the soil may heave upward and break the roots, thus damaging the plants. In the case of corn, both ears and stalk may be damaged by frost usually occurring in September or early October, when the plant is in the last stages of growth. Frost coming just before maturity checks the last run of sap to the kernels; hence, the cob is left wet from stagnated sap. The kernels of such ears are likely to show some rot after being stored for a period in the crib, or if left where air circulates, the kernels may shrink from evaporation and loosen on the cob. Late planting or a cool summer increases the likelihood of frost damage owing to potentially later maturity.

Other hazards to wheat are the green bug, or aphis, at times found in Texas, Oklahoma, Kansas, Nebraska, and Missouri. The Hessian fly, which destroys or damages winter wheat, is found from Maryland to western Kansas. An infested plant is likely to fall between heading and the time for harvest. The chinch bug, an old enemy of the farmer, destroying corn, small grains, broom corn, and most grasses, is found chiefly from central Ohio westward to central Colorado. It kills the plant by sucking the sap. The grasshopper, which destroys all grains and grasses, is found practically everywhere in the temperate zone in one season or another. It eats the leaves and sometimes the kernels of small grains. Drought is favorable to hopper damage, since absence of moisture and food in dry weather drives them to grain crops.

Then there are certain plant diseases which affect grains. Orange leaf, or red rust, is commonly found in practically all parts of North America where oats and wheat are raised. The disease is checked by dry, hot weather. Black stem rust, the most destructive of all crop diseases, ruptures the stem, halts the upward flow of sap, and reduces the size of the kernel. Cool, dry weather is needed to check its development.

The farmer's experience, training, and judgment in the planting and care of his crops do much to ward off or minimize the natural hazards of farming. Irrigation, crop rotation, fertilization, and better tillage and harvesting equipment are also important in successful farming.[1]

Fertilizers

The use of fertilizers in the production of crops is expanding, and because of them, shortage of food is a long way off. Plants obtain nitrogen and carbon dioxide from the air, but they must get minerals almost exclusively from the soil; as each succeeding crop is removed from the land, the supply of these essential nutrients becomes less. The subject of fertilizers is a scientific one and there seem to be different opinions as to the right course to follow in replacing them. The quality of milk reflects differences in feeding and soil management, and eggs may be decidedly different in composition because of soil or feeding conditions. The same holds true of meat, bread, vegetables, and fruit.

As the population grows, the United States will need to expand crop production, but the amount of new land that can be put into cultivation in this country is less than the proportionate rise in food requirements. The yearly removal of plant nutrients from soils by cropping alone is more than the amount that is being returned. Additional heavy losses occur each year through leaching and erosion. Thus, we come to the realization that most of the additional production will have to come from an increased production per acre—from gaining higher yields per acre.[2]

The United States has increased its annual fertilizer con-

---

[1] Grain Exchange Institute, Inc., *Grain and Its Marketing,* revised ed., 1947–51.

[2] U.S.D.A., Yearbook, *Nutrient-Element Balance,* 1943–47.

sumption since 1880, when 1,150,000 tons were used, to more than 22,000,000 tons at the present time. There have also been changes in the composition of fertilizer—in the increase of plant-food content. More than half of the fertilizer manufactured is used in twelve states toward the southeastern part of the country. Only small percentages are used in the large grain-growing Great Plains states, but the amount is increasing. Some European countries use many times the per-acre amount of fertilizer used in this country. As additional fertilizer becomes available it will be possible to increase grain production materally on the same acreage.

About three fourths of the cultivated land in humid regions in the United States needs lime, without which more than half the agricultural crops now produced would start to decline. Not only would harvests drop, but control of soil erosion would become increasingly difficult. In 1911 it was estimated that under 175,000 tons of ground limestone were used; in 1947 consumption reached a peak of 29,250,000 tons and it was estimated that much more should be used on arable and pasture lands. It is known that cattle will remain on limed fields in preference to others.[3] Agricultural limestone provides the backbone for any successful system of soil management on many farms; lime is not only a soil-sweetener but also a source of plant foods—calcium and magnesium—necessary in all stages of crop growth from germination to harvest. Lime in the soil increases the efficiency of the nitrogen, phosphorus, and potash supplied by mixed fertilizers.[4]

Advancement in Farming Methods

Soil-conservation measures are necessary for saving and rebuilding soil. These may embrace terracing, drainage or irrigation ditches, contour strips, and ponds or other structures or

[3] U.S.D.A., *The Yearbook in Agriculture,* 1943–47 (1947).

[4] *Fertilizer Review,* July, Aug., 1948.

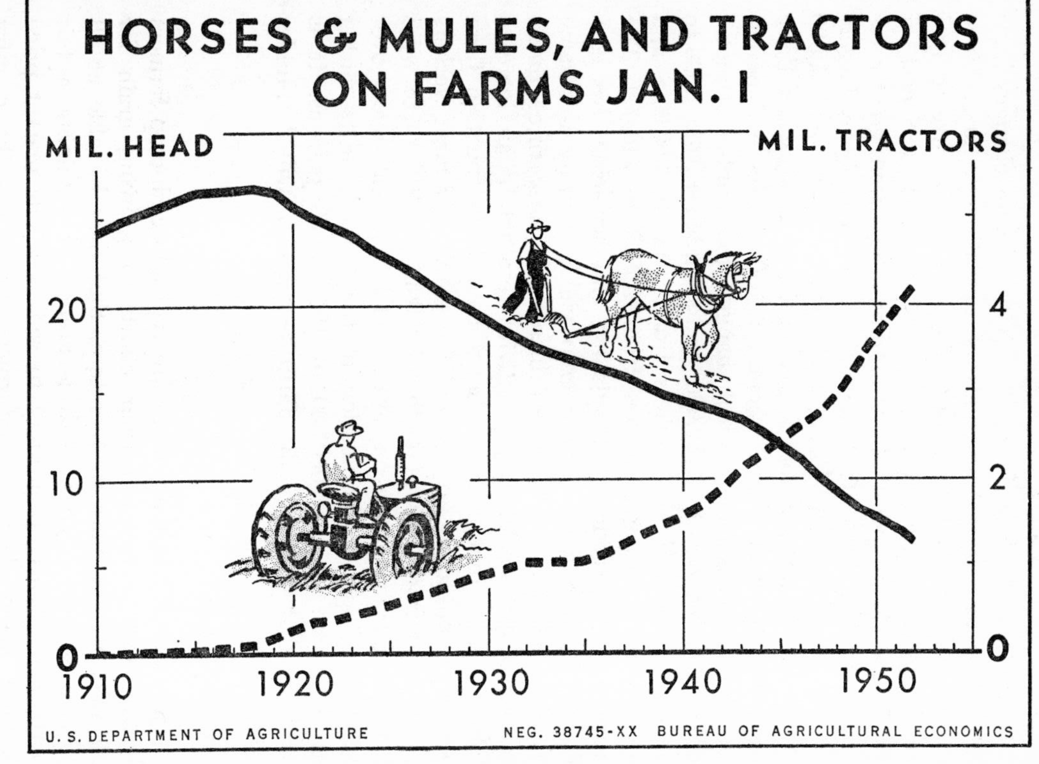
HORSES & MULES, AND TRACTORS
ON FARMS JAN. 1
MIL. HEAD
MIL. TRACTORS
20
10
0
4
2
0
1910
1920
1930
1940
1950
U. S. DEPARTMENT OF AGRICULTURE
NEG. 38745-XX BUREAU OF AGRICULTURAL ECONOMICS

FIGURE 4

operations, including conservation cropping, pasture, or woodland practices.

In addition to these farming activities, many changes have contributed to different methods of operating a farm. Since the years from 1866 to about 1893, when the oxcart and the stagecoach were replaced by the railroad, the cost of conveyance to the point of consumption has been greatly reduced. On the farm itself animal power has been largely replaced by machines. From 1910, when there were 1,000 tractors and 24,000,000 horses and mules, to 1955, when there were 4,750,000 tractors and about 4,500,000 horses and mules, there have also been mechanical changes: the number of motor trucks rose from zero to 2,750,000; grain combines from 1,000 to 960,000; mechanical corn-pickers from none to 660,000; and farms having milking machines from 10,000 to 740,000. The greater use of insecticides, fungicides, and herbicides has contributed significantly to higher crop yields. During this same time farm output per man-hour increased nearly three times. This rapid rate of labor productivity resulted in an increase in output even though fewer hours have been spent in farm work. Farm output is up 85%, but the number of farm workers has declined from 13,555,000 to 8,190,000. In 1910 there were 32,000,000 persons living on farms, and in 1955 not many over 22,000,000. The total population of the United States during this time rose from 96,000,000 to 166,000,000 persons. It is estimated that by 1975 the farm population will be under 20,000,000.

Sale of Crops

Many farmers in grain areas are typically cash-crop farmers devoting their acres and their efforts to growing grain for cash sale. It is important, therefore, that they be able at all times to sell their grain with assurance of obtaining a fair market price. This opportunity to sell at a fair market price has been made available to farmers throughout the country by the grain trade with its complex organization and equipment

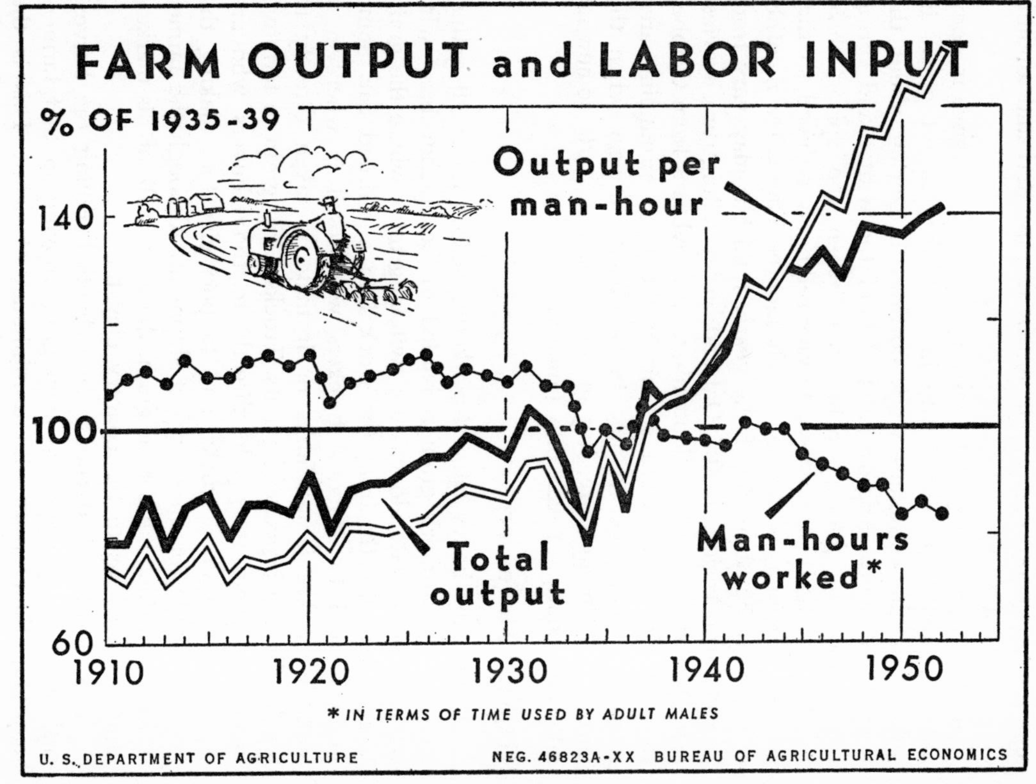
FARM OUTPUT and LABOR INPUT
% OF 1935-39
140
100
60
1910
1920
1930
1940
1950
Output per man-hour
Total output
Man-hours worked*
* IN TERMS OF TIME USED BY ADULT MALES
U. S. DEPARTMENT OF AGRICULTURE
NEG. 46823A-XX BUREAU OF AGRICULTURAL ECONOMICS

FIGURE 5

for measuring quantity and quality, for storing, for financing, and for merchandising the movement of any kind and amount of grain at any time.

From the time the winter-wheat crop starts to move in commercial quantity in Texas late in May, the harvest grows in volume as the combines work northward. During about the next three months approximately 50% of the winter and spring crops are sold. During September, when the spring-wheat harvest is largely completed, farmer selling is reduced so that smaller percentages are sold each month. Thereafter monthly selling may be about 5% of the yearly total but may vary from 3% to 8% or occasionally 10%. Oat and barley selling runs heaviest from July through about September, and soybeans from October through November. Corn selling in the large producing area starts in rather good volume in October in a year when the corn is low in moisture, but in other years it starts somewhat later and continues well into January.

Harvest Movement

During the heavy harvest-marketing season for small grains, some of the farmer's grain is hauled to "scoop-shovelers," who temporarily operate alongside a switching track where the grain is shoveled directly from the truck into a railroad car. Some grain is sold to itinerant truckers who resell it wherever a suitable market is available, or it may be taken directly to local mills and processing plants. Trucks carry grain to terminal elevators, where it is sold directly to those buyers who are equipped to unload trucks, and to port elevators making the grain available for direct export shipment. Although the farmer has these various outlets for grain, the great bulk of his marketable surplus goes to the country elevator.

The elevators and country merchants handling the harvest rush must be equipped to keep grain moving so that farmers may ship their crops with a minimum of delay. This is the first step in grain marketing, and country elevators dot the entire Grain Belt. There are more elevators in denser areas of cultivation or where larger percentages of crops are marketed than where crops tend to be fed on the farms. Some country elevators are busy almost all year and others just at one season, and their activity varies according to the number of different grains produced in their district. Primarily, the country elevator's function is not to store grain (except that considerable elevator space has been constructed for this purpose since the government price-support program has been in operation) but, when there are large crops, to hold the grain until a place can be found for it in the large centers of accumulation—at terminals or at large mills and processing plants. As soon as farmers haul their grain to country elevators it is loaded out to various destinations, so that there may be a continuous movement through the elevators, enabling the farmers, if they wish, to send large portions of their grain into commercial channels. Some of the early movement of wheat goes right to the ports and is loaded on steamers that sail for foreign destinations, mostly in Europe. Other wheat goes to flour mills, some to terminal elevators, and some is retained in country elevators.

Congestion in handling grain occurs when the movement is at its height, with long lines of trucks waiting to unload at the country elevators. In some years wheat may be piled on the ground at the elevators, but more often if this is necessary it is done on the farms. The amount of grain piled on the ground may be quite extensive in those areas where normal rainfall is light. Terminal elevators become congested as thousands of freight cars arrive from points of origin in the country. This slows up the movement all the way back to the farms, because boxcars are not returned to loading sites to enable the country elevators to keep a steady stream of grain moving.

In northern inland ports such as Chicago and Duluth, steamers may take grain out of large elevators and carry it by the Great Lakes route to Buffalo and other eastern ports; that helps relieve rapidly filling terminal elevators. This, however, is not always possible, because it is necessary that the price structure be attractive for merchants in the Midwest to send their grain to another market—the price of the grain has to be higher in the East than in the West. In some years the eastern price for soft red winter wheat is not high enough over Chicago to compensate for the cost of shipment; or it is actually lower than the western price at harvest time. Such conditions are not always natural but may come about through conditions created by support and export programs of the Government. Duluth, as compared with Chicago, is less affected by an adverse eastern price structure, because spring wheat which moves from the northwestern farms to Duluth is not grown in the East and the eastern mills require this kind of wheat in the normal course of their business.

Long before the wheat-harvest movement reaches its peak, oats start to move. This crop movement tends to be heavy in Illinois about the middle of July and works northward with the harvest, reaching into the northwestern states and taxing their facilities in August and September. Barley, with concentrated production in the Northwest, moves heavily in that area at about the same time as oats. Then, just when the harvest movement is slackening in the Northwest, the soybeans start to move; in September and October Illinois, the biggest-producing state, sends large quantities to market. These soybeans do not move to terminal markets in the largest volume but instead go to the processing plants located close to the major producing area. The Illinois soybean marketings continue in heavy volume through November, while at the same time other states are also harvesting and marketing soybeans.

Soybean and corn country shipping schedules overlap, but corn country movement comes after the other grains. Usually cold weather is required to dry corn sufficiently for harvest, shelling, and shipment to market; but both soybean and corn harvests may vary in time from year to year according to the weather during the growing season and at harvest. By the time the corn movement has started in the Corn Belt some elevators in the wheat area of the Southwest, where only a single crop is grown, are already shut down for the season. Elsewhere as the season progresses and some of the grain is shipped out of terminals for export and as grain is consumed by the mills, there is more room for additional flow of grain from interior elevators. This movement does not approach the proportions of the harvest run, but it clears up the congestion that had been blocking country elevators, so that gradually ground storage is eliminated and the season's grain crop is all under cover, protected from the winter weather.

Country Elevators

Country elevators located where several crops are grown have a turnover throughout the year, although operations are slack during some periods. These elevators endeavor to carry some grain on storage for others if they are licensed to do so, and own and maintain a stock of grain for sale to feeders in their area.

First and foremost, a country grain-elevator operator is a businessman. The value of a country station is not only its physical structures of elevator, office, corn cribs, etc., but also the available markets. When you buy such an elevator you buy the territory, including both outlets and the opportunity to service farmers; such a business may have taken years to develop, and its value lies in the opportunities of this service. In addition to handling grain, the operator may carry staples such as coal, feeds, salt, fenceposts, bale wire, etc., for sale to farmers who bring in loads of grain and take back such articles as they require.

The elevator man must know his markets at all times and keep in touch with prices at which he can sell in order to pay competitive prices for the incoming grain. If there is a choice of more than one market to which a country elevator operator can ship and sell his grain, it is necessary for him to have contacts in several directions, although often one cash-grain commission merchant keeps him informed on outlets to several markets. This gives the elevator man advantages in buying, for he can pay to producers prices in accordance with the best outlet and attract more grain to his elevator. By adjusting his price with changes in the futures market, the country man can buy from farmers at the current market and still protect his margin of profit and operating expenses. The operator knows the terminal price as well as local mill and other outlet prices, but must make allowances for market changes. This may be done by following futures prices, which are broadcast by radio at regular and frequent intervals. As the trucks unload at the elevator, the quality of the grain must be checked to determine the premium or discount for the grade; although the quality runs quite uniform on some grains, on others each truckload is sampled and tests of the grain are run for grade analysis.

There are dealers who buy grain from country elevators for the purpose of merchandising it to buyers in terminals, to exporters, or to processors and do not make a strict practice of hedging in futures. They may give shipping orders in any direction to which grain originating at such an elevator on the particular railroad line can be shipped. Also, these dealers follow a practice of selling before they buy, and when they cover their short sales, they buy from country elevator operators with some disregard for current terminal and processor buying prices. These dealers, in acting as intermediaries between country elevator operators and other buyers, merchandise a large quantity of grain and use the futures market for hedging only when they wish to speculate on the cash basis or in an emergency when they wish to protect themselves pending country-elevator purchases, or to hedge pending a sale of long-position country purchases.

During the heavy rush of the harvest movement there is likely less opportunity for the country man to be as discriminating in buying and selling as at other seasons of the year. At such a time the terminal price of cash grain relative to futures is usually lower than the cash basis later in the season; the farm price, too, permits the local country-elevator grain man to work on a larger margin between farm and terminal prices.

The farmer and the elevator operator are, however, assured that so far as transportation and terminal facilities permit, there is always a market for grain offered for sale. Even while elevators are blocked by congestion, it is possible for the country elevator operator to make sales to terminals in the "to arrive" market or to hedge grain in futures until it can be physically moved to market. There is never too much grain to be absorbed by the futures market. The price which the futures market registers acts to adjust the level at which farmers' and country elevator operators' trades are made. This premise is very broad, because futures buyers' prices are not based on the price which shipments from country elevators in one area will bring, nor are they based on the price for immediate disposal of the grain from the terminal markets. They include all the outlets available within this and foreign countries to which grain may be shipped in the near future and they include the potential demand.

Sales to Terminals

If grain has not been sold ahead for forward shipment on a "to arrive" contract, it is often sold at the time it is ready to leave the country location or even while the car is in transit to its destination. Otherwise, sale is made on consignment after a sample has been taken and the grade is officially determined upon arrival at its destination, when a buyer is solicited in the spot market.

It is usual that a higher cash basis is obtained on consignment sale as compared with a "to arrive" sale, but the country shipper in thus delaying sale retains the risk of flat price changes longer unless he has the grain hedged. At times the cash-grain commission merchant is instructed to buy in a hedge when he sells a car of grain on consignment, or the country shipper may give such futures orders immediately upon telegraph or telephone notice of sale.

Grain is paid for promptly when it is shipped to market. The country shipper receives payment for about 80% of the value of his grain upon presenting to his buyer or his commission merchant a draft with the bill of lading attached, and the balance is paid after the car is weighed at the time of unloading. Some shippers mail the bill of lading to their agents and await complete returns after the car is unloaded before requiring payment for the grain.

In pricing a sale of country-elevator grain the shipper may choose a "track country station" price which includes only the value of the grain loaded out of the country elevator into the car, with the grade and the quantity still to be determined at the destination. Meanwhile the sale price is on the basic grade—usually number two—with the final grade settlement being made at the terminal-market discount for a lower grade upon arrival, unless it is arranged otherwise. Another basis may be "track destination" price—when the railroad freight to the destination is included in the price—otherwise, there is little difference from the former. "Consignment" differs as the agent's commission is included in the price as well as the freight to the destination. All these terms, however, net the shipper the same price—fluctuations considered—and are little more than different cutoff points for charges, with prices calculated accordingly.

In negotiation of all sales the shipper has the opportunity of ascertaining the cash basis and then of informing his commission merchant of his desired selling price and awaiting a market change before the sale is made. When he instructs the commission merchant to obtain a certain flat price, and the combination of the cash basis and the futures quotation equals this price, the buyer "spots the board" and purchases the grain without necessarily making a futures trade. The buyer then hedges the grain at his own convenience.

If the seller should instruct to "exchange" futures with the buyer, it may be arranged, but this is not customarily the practice on a single car of grain. In the exchange of futures, which is termed an "office trade" and is made outside the trading pit, the seller of the cash grain "takes" or buys the future and the buyer of the grain "gives" or sells the future "in exchange for cash." These futures trades henceforth are handled the same as others, are cleared through the clearing house and are just as valid and binding as all pit transactions. The shipper may have different reasons for exchanging futures on a cash trade; if he had previously hedged the grain at the time it was bought from farmers, by an exchange of futures when he sells the grain he removes the hedge. If it is a "to arrive" sale for deferred shipment, he stays "long" the futures acquired through the exchange and, having established the cash basis, retains the futures until later when he buys the farmers' grain to fill his cash sale, at which time he sells out his long hedge.

Terminal or Processor Buying and Hedging

If the terminal buyer who purchases the grain from the country elevator operator is a merchant and buys the grain at a flat price and hedges it in futures, or if he buys the grain on a cash basis and exchanges futures, he is most likely to maintain a hedge against the grain until he sells it in his merchandising operations. If the buyer is a processor who carries an inventory of more or less constant size representing goods in the course of distribution, often in scattered locations for convenience of sale, he may not hedge at all. If his inventory is of variable size similar to a flour mill's business, the buyer most likely hedges all purchases and sales, keeping the net hedge and inventory or short sales position in balance.

Most buyers bid for the grain which they wish to buy strictly on the cash basis and closely follow fluctuations in the futures market, even though their actual purchases may be at a flat price and they may or may not hedge after making purchases. If they customarily hedge, their overnight purchases may offset their overnight merchandising sales, thus voiding the necessity of hedging. Large organizations may buy cash grain and sell products at a number of locations through several offices but handle their hedges from a central office, so that, as purchases and sales are reported, they trade in futures for hedging in the net of their inventory or sales position—their long or short position.

The merchant who buys cash grain and hedges it may retain the grain in his terminal elevator for a considerable length of time, even for many months. Prior to merchandising sale, the grain may be shipped to another location for more advantageous sale, but still the hedge is retained. When the futures-delivery month in which the grain is hedged becomes current, it becomes necessary to change the hedge to another delivery month. This futures-trading operation is executed at the merchant's judgment a part at a time in a simultaneous purchase of the short position and sale of a later-maturing futures delivery, thus transferring or changing the hedge. The merchant, if operating an elevator "regular" for delivery in a futures market, may, however, deliver the grain on the futures market against his short futures contract, provided his grain is of deliverable quality. If delivery is made, the merchant becomes the custodian of the grain for which there is a warehouse receipt outstanding in possession of a new owner. Ownership of the grain may change several times through direct sale of the warehouse receipt or by further futures deliveries. Meanwhile, the regular elevator operator has the grain available for immediate loading out of the elevator upon presentation of the warehouse receipt.

Storing and Selling Terminal Grain

Following the course of grain movement in the grain trade we find that a farmer's grain, which was harvested and marketed in truckload lots, has been shipped in carloads from the country elevator with other farmers' grain to the terminal market, where large amounts have been accumulated by different kinds of buyers and possibly held in storage awaiting sale as various interests require it. It may then go to exporters, who take very large amounts at one time, or to processors, who buy according to selective grading factors in moderate-sized lots, or to the distributors, who may buy it in as small a quantity as one carload at a time and make further disposition in the retail trade. Futures contracts have been used throughout to protect all these businessmen against price fluctuations, for it is their purpose to merchandise with the least risk of price change. When larger lots are sold, futures usually accompany the cash grain in exchange so that the new buyer has the grain hedged; or the futures trade that is turned over to the buyer of the cash grain may offset a long-position hedge previously acquired pending purchase of the cash grain. The exchange of futures is termed "a give-up against cash" and is always opposite to the cash, i.e., a futures purchase against a cash sale or a futures sale against a cash purchase.

A merchant operating in a terminal has different avenues through which he may make purchases: railroad boxcar purchases are the most commonly used method; many elevators are equipped with truck dumps so that they buy from truckers; in some markets there is extensive use made of barges operating on the inland waterways; and for merchants located on the Great Lakes boat purchases may be the chief method of buying. Care must be taken in each method of purchasing because of different structures of freight rates pertaining to inbound and outbound traffic movement. An initially profitable purchase might result in a loss when the grain is sold unless favorable billing is applied to the outbound shipment. It is permissible to switch inbound railroad billing by applying it to different grain on an outbound movement from an elevator, providing it is applied on the same kind of grain. In so doing the merchant can sell grain more cheaply in order to meet competition.

Most of the domestic grain for markets at the head of the lakes, Chicago, Milwaukee, Duluth, etc., is of inland origin, but Buffalo and other eastern lake ports unload much of their grain receipts from lake boats and ship it out again by railroad, trucks, or barges for transportation on the barge canals. Some grain may be moved out of lake ports farther east on small boats through canals, Lake Ontario, and rivers to eastern Canadian ocean ports. When a grain firm makes a purchase, it calculates the through freight rate from the origin to the ultimate destination of the grain and chooses the cheapest route of transportation so that competition cannot buy at the same origin and undersell at the same destination by using cheaper methods of transportation.

Terminal merchants, like country elevator operators, must buy their grain on the basis of the quality of the year's production as it comes from the farms. It is their task to handle the grain so that it can be brought to a commercial grade and stored without deterioration in quality, and be shipped to buyers to conform to their needs, so far as the original quality permits. A latitude within grades permits blending, so that after cleaning, drying, etc., a rather uniform quality may be obtained. In some markets wheat is stored separately according to small percentage differences in protein content or even according to variety, which affects its milling value. In other markets protein is not a factor in storage, but there may be a fine distinction between classes, such as wheat grown in parts of Illinois that resembles both hard or soft red; it may even be graded "mixed." Test weight per measured bushel is important in the value of all grains. Heavy test grain commands premiums, and low test grain is adequately discounted. Clipping or other methods to increase test weight, when grain is handled in elevators, conditions it so that the best sale price may be received. Moisture content in grain, especially in corn, which runs higher in moisture content than other grains at harvest, affects its storage qualifications, so that it must be adjusted according to atmospheric temperatures at certain times of the year. Usually cribbed corn dries sufficiently after the winter so that it comes to market at a low enough percentage of moisture content to avoid spoilage in the elevator from this cause. Often, however, the percentage of damaged corn kernels is higher during spring and summer following the months that the corn has been kept in the cribs in the country. The terminal buyer is tolerant of damaged grain because he can discount it on purchases and segregate it in storage. Highly damaged grain has special outlets, largely as a cheaper type of feed. When terminal grain is merchandised, it is common for the quality to be straight commercial grade that can be stored or shipped again without danger of spoilage, it is therefore the task of the terminal elevator operator to accept grain as it comes from country locations, condition it while it is in the elevators, and sell it in a form that qualifies for ready use in consumptive channels.

The merchant elevator operator keeps his stock of grain stored so that it may be shipped immediately to satisfy buyers' desires. But if he sells grain for a deferred shipping period, he may not have the grain on hand and may delay its purchase until close to the time when he is required to make shipment; meanwhile, he is protected against major price changes by purchase of futures as a hedge. The cash-basis risk cannot be protected until the actual cash-grain purchase is made. The quality risk is one with which he is familiar, and like the cash-basis risk, it is part of the merchandising business.

When there are inverse carrying charges in futures it is important to the merchandiser whose storage is not a futures-market delivery point to limit his stock of grain to a quantity that is readily salable. The reason for not overstocking is obvious: unsold cash grain with a hedge against it will necessitate purchase of the higher-priced near-by futures month and a sale of a later-maturing futures at a lower price when the hedge has to be changed, thus increasing the original cost of the cash grain over the new hedging month. The merchant who can deliver his grain on futures contracts does not have to change his hedge to a later month but can consummate his futures sale by delivery, in which case his loss is limited to any premium he may have originally paid for the cash grain.

Hedged grain held in or outside a delivery point can be retained with only small price risk (except for cash basis) when carrying charges prevail in futures markets. The carrying charge between futures months may be wide enough to equal the cost of charges for interest, insurance, and either operating an evelator or paying storage to others, or it may cover only part of these costs. To the extent that carrying charges fail to cover the costs of carrying grain, they add to the merchant's risk as he continues to retain ownership of his grain, and to this extent it adds to the owner's cash basis cost. The breadth of carrying charges determines whether or not a merchant will ship grain out of a delivery point to a more advantageous place for better merchandising possibilities. The same reasoning prevails among prospective buyers in contemplating purchases from terminal merchants. Buyers tend to make purchases and carry larger stocks of grain when carrying charges exist and to defer purchases and reduce stocks when there are inverse carrying charges.

Buying Grain From Terminals

Grain moving out of terminal markets is ultimately used for food, feed, or export and, in minor amounts, for industrial purposes. Grain needed for food is processed; therefore it is purchased on qualifications desirable for conversion to the end product. Such buyers seek the grain they need even at great distances from their processing plant and negotiate for its purchase, but they must be aware of the possible limitations of the sale of their product in areas where others may buy grain to better advantage and undersell their product. Large flour-milling companies may have several mills capable of supplying the demand for the same kind of flour in different areas, and they buy their wheat for each mill with this in mind. Singly operated mills may have to curtail their operations if they cannot compete for certain business because of inability to buy grain favorable to meet a competitive product selling outside their local area. Corn-processing buyers are located mostly within the Corn Belt and can buy and distribute their products without great distadvantage. They can use most of the general country-run grain but usually want only natural-dried corn. Feed-handlers seek their grain in the cheapest market for commercial-grade grain, and it must be reasonably dry so that it will not spoil in transit or after it is mixed in a feed-manufacturing process. Oats for edible purposes must be of good test weight and of good general quality. There are various feeding outlets for the lower grades of oats according to the relative prices at which they are available. Barley is appraised according to its malting or feeding value; malting barley is purchased by specialists in that trade and may originate thousands of miles from its use. Rye goes mostly to the domestic milling and distilling trades. There are outlets for all grains, even though they may be greatly damaged by weather or by deterioration in storage. Elevator dust and cleanings obtained prior to and during grain processing are also sold in the feed market, finding outlets for special types of feed. Very little grain is wasted.

Export Grain

The exporter is limited in his dealings to the grain which is priced competitively with comparable types in other export countries. If one country's price level is too high compared with others it is eliminated from the export field; this may last for part of a season, for an entire season, or even for several consecutive seasons. This is one of the largest factors in determining acreages in potentially surplus-producing countries. Economic conditions within a country may determine whether or not it can afford to raise grain for sale in competition with other exporting countries.

Exports usually leave the country through ports that are favorably located to the area in which the surplus is raised. In the United States the largest wheat-export ports are located on the Gulf of Mexico. The wheat is of the hard-red-winter class and is grown in Texas, Oklahoma, Kansas, and to some extent Illinois, but when a higher cash basis is paid it permits the payment of more freight and draws wheat from greater distances. Other important wheat-export ports lie along the Atlantic seaboard; wheat exported from them is normally of the soft-red-winter class originating in larger-producing eastern states, with some originating close to the ports; when higher freight is paid the origin is Illinois. Hard red spring wheat grown in northwest states moves via the Great Lakes to Atlantic ports and sometimes to Canadian St. Lawrence ports for export, as well as by rail to Atlantic ports. The other major export area is the Pacific Northwest for wheat grown west of the Rocky Mountains.

Corn exports may be handled through Gulf or Atlantic ports. When the United States is selling corn for export, these areas compete for business that varies between the outlets as the interior price of corn fluctuates in the different areas and becomes favorable for movement in either direction. A thin line of demarcation may determine movement in one direction or another because of freight rates. Corn originating in the Corn Belt may move either south or east. While the East has an advantage because ocean freight rates to European destinations are lower from Atlantic ports than from Gulf ports, there are advantageous rail and river rates from some points of origin that give the Gulf ports the preference. St. Lawrence River ports also handle United States export corn when it moves down the lakes and through the canals and rivers; also, corn may move across the lakes to Georgian Bay ports and then by rail to the same Canadian ports. The Georgian Bay route is often used for corn destined for United States domestic consumption when it ultimately moves to the New England states via rail from Georgian Bay ports.

Barley is exported from both Atlantic and Pacific ports. Rye is exported from Atlantic ports, and oats, likewise, are exported mostly from Atlantic ports.

Export firms have various ways of securing their grain. Some are equipped with country elevators, elevators in subterminals in the interior of the country, and large elevators at terminals. These firms buy grain right from the farmers and sell it to the foreign buyer, stopping it at different points in transit for accumulation, blending, drying, cleaning, etc. Other exporters buy grain from merchants and have it shipped to the ports for concentration prior to loading on ocean vessels. Still another method which exporters employ is to buy from domestic firms who load the grain onto ocean steamers as ordered by the exporter; these firms, known as "fobbers," do not make sales abroad. Considerable grain is bought by exporters, paid for when it is loaded on Great Lakes steamers—basis cost, insurance, and freight. This grain is transferred through elevators located at Georgian Bay ports or at Buffalo and other eastern lake ports and is shipped by raidroad to the seaboard. Or the grain may be transferred to canal barges at Buffalo, etc., and be sent to Albany or New York, or it may be transferred to smaller lake boats for shipment to St. Lawrence River ports such as Montreal. Small vessels may go direct from western lake ports to Montreal, or even to a foreign destination. Each offering which an exporter makes for sale abroad has to be figured separately for even slight advantage. There is nothing haphazard in tne various movements for export either within the country or on the ocean voyage. The ports which the exporter plans on using when the grain leaves the country may vary from day to day as sales are made and as advantages move one way or another. When United States prices are competitive for export, the constant variation of routes by which the grain moves from interior locations to different ports syphons off surpluses arising in various markets as they are priced lower than other markets, thus keeping an equal price balance.

Export grain may be sold far in advance of the time of shipment, often in anticipation of surpluses in excess of domestic requirements. The general price level of the nation's crop for the time of export clearance is known from the futures-market price in combination with the estimated cash basis for the grain in the location in which the grain originates. Other considerations are freight to the port of exit and ocean freight, plus all the necessary handling and service charges. When these are combined in pricing an export sale, the actual purchase of the futures (later converted into cash grain) and other commitments result in buying power that offsets some of the pressure on prices from surplus production. Such sales may continue in volume while prices are competitive, so that when harvest time actually arrives there is a large outlet for the grain as it comes from the fields. This helps to reduce congestion at harvest time, because the outgo keeps elevators free to accept grain coming from the fields above the storable amount to the extent that ocean-going ships load out former sales.

Exporters are entirely dependent upon their own resourcefulness. There is no percentage of the sale price or set fee that an exporter might calculate he is entitled to receive as profit for his services in finding buyers; but rather, the exporter is held down largely by competition to a margin of profit which he may secure by properly judging the trend in the cash basis. The one from whom the exporter buys the grain can, and freely does, sell to all domestic and export buyers available when he is ready to put his grain on the market. The exporter has no edge on other buyers, for there is but one price for domestic and export traders alike. It is true that sustained export business aids in supporting values both in futures and in cash markets, and to that extent it is a measure of protection to the exporter if he should go "long" the cash basis in anticipation of making foreign sales. One exporter has little advantage over another at the ports, because there are few private elevators at these locations; with some exceptions port facilities are equal for all firms.

As export trade continues during the season, exporters anticipate forward business and carry a stock of cash grain from which to make sales; and they make sales ahead of purchases, which they cover either promptly or at their convenience. A necessary practice, especially in the Canadian wheat-export business, is the shipping of grain down the lakes, prior to the freezing of harbors, rivers, and parts of the Great Lakes themselves, for use in export shipment during the winter and early spring months. United States grain is also moved in this manner in smaller amounts for export. The practice as applied to United States grain is mostly for the domestic trade. This combination method of transportation and storage is known as "winter storage." The grain is held in boats at eastern lake ports and not unloaded until it is needed to fill an export sale or until there is space available in an elevator. Winter-storage grain is held mostly in the East, but some may be held in Chicago or other Lake Michigan ports after shipment from Lake Superior ports; this latter is for domestic uses. Some steamers are held at the loading port in order to add to the storage capacity of the elevators and to secure a lower rate than is charged by the elevators. There are a great many steamers used in this business, because many that carry iron ore during the navigation season become available for winter storage of grain.

CHAPTER VI

Transportation

Trucks

Transportation of grain starts as it leaves the harvesting machines in the fields, except for corn, which is usually not shelled from the cobs as it is picked and therefore has one more handling than other grains. Grains that are stored on the farms are hauled to bins or cribs, from where they must again be transported when marketed.

Trucks are the first means of transportation, carrying grain to country elevators, near-by mills, and processing plants, to other farms for feeding purposes, and also to more distant places to persons engaged in these kinds of businesses. A transient trucker will haul a load of grain or other merchandise in one direction and pick up grain for the return trip. Some truckers are engaged almost wholly in transporting grain between different country elevators, being hired by dealers or self-employed, and some truck grain from either farms or country elevators to terminal or port elevators for export. Long-distance grain trucking has expanded rapidly in recent years, and there are as many combinations in trucking grain as there are possible profits. Truckers set their own rates or receive as compensation the price difference between purchase of the grain and its sale. In May, 1956, the I.C.C. set aside a pattern of "floors" established in 1934 in order to permit western railroads to make rates competitive with those of trucks to move feed grains from Nebraska, Kansas, etc., to the livestock-producing regions of Texas, Oklahoma, etc. Truckers may work in conjunction with corn-shellers, taking corn at the direction of a local grain firm to an elevator operated by a different firm; this is the practice along the Illinois River, where corn is unloaded into river elevators and transferred to barges for transportation to terminals. Trucks are also employed in moving grain from terminal elevators and processing plants to consuming areas. While the cost of trucking grain is often less than transportation by other methods, it carries with it none of the special privileges enjoyed by grain moving to or from market by railroad or water transportation, such as storage in transit and reconsigning to other destinations on a "through" rate. Grain moving to Chicago, for example, by barge or by lake steamer is entitled to the reshipping or proportional rate to New York and other eastern destinations, the same as for grain moved to Chicago by railroad. Because of this, trucked grain is subject to a price discount in order to overcome the loss of these proportional rates.

Because of the importance of transportation it behooves firms engaged in grain merchandising to pay close attention to this phase of their business. Before purchasing or constructing a plant, a firm should examine the location to assure favorable rates for movement of its grain and products. Consideration should be given to installation of such facilities as truck dumps or barge-unloading facilities, etc., in order to be in a position to buy from many areas at favorable rates and to reach many markets in selling its goods. Improper choice of location may permanently deprive them of business opportunities; they may lose the advantage of favorable railroad billing or methods of transportation enjoyed by competitors, and that (if impossible to overcome) would cost them considerable money. Some elevators in Chicago have all possible transportation facilities for use of trucks, railroads, barges and other vessels. Others have most of these, while some can handle only railroad cars. Elevators located elsewhere may have several features, but (with minor exceptions) all have track connections for railroad movement, which is the principal method of transporting grain.

Railroads

Grain moves to market initially by trucks to country elevators, from where it is loaded out in carload lots for shipment to terminals or processing plants. This method of transportation puts the grain into channels that entitle it to favorable railroad rates and the privileges that go with them. The day when the grain is first loaded into boxcars and the bill of lading issued is the *date of origin*, from which freight rates and billing privileges follow. The *date of the manifest* or other shipping document applying to grain loaded on barges destined for Chicago elevators determines the date of the rail billing, which will follow when the grain is shipped out by cars. Rail rates for "ex-lake" grain unloaded from steamers takes effect as of the date that shipments are tendered to the railroad for transportation from the lake port.

Freight-Traffic Territories.—The United States is divided into a number of railroad-freight territories. Chicago is in the Illinois Freight Association Territory, embracing Illinois and some points outside the state, and within this area originates most of the grain that supplies the Chicago market. The Trans-Mississippi River Territory and the Northwest Territory lying to the west also furnish some grain. Grain is shipped from Chicago principally to the East, chiefly to the Trunkline Association Territory, embracing Middle Atlantic points, and to the New England as well as to the Southeastern Territory, which lies in general south of the Ohio River. The intermediate Central Territory, extending east from the Illinois-Indiana line to western New York, is not very important as destination for Chicago-market grain, because in it are produced the same kinds of grains and, being closer, it has lower freight rates to the East.

Gateways Rates.—Grain moves through "gateways"—principal freight centers or junction points—at which freight is interchanged between various railroad lines. The principal movement of grain is from west to east and south. Some of the more important gateways are Chicago, Kansas City, Omaha, Sioux City, Minneapolis and St. Louis. These gateways are "rate-break points," by which is meant a point on which rates are made.

There are different kinds of rates. One with which the grain man is familiar is the "through rate," from point of origin to destination. It may be either a "joint" rate, from an origin on one carrier with forwarding via one or more to a destination on another carrier, or a "combination" rate, so designated because it reflects combinations of separate factors. Another, the "proportional" rate, or "reshipping" rate as it is sometimes called, is specificially published for use only as a factor in determining a combination through rate and may be proportional on the origin end, or the destination end, or both.

There have been two underlying factors in establishing rates on grain: first, an effort to adjust freight rates to enable producers to reach as many markets as possible, and, second, establishment of freight rates from and through various markets to enable the markets and the various carriers to compete fairly with one another.

Chicago elevators receive grain by trucks, barges, lake boats, and railroad cars, and the grain may also leave the city by any of these methods. Only the railroads give transit privileges or proportional rates on outbound movement; the others give the same rates no matter how the grain has arrived. Truck-received grain has no privileges on outbound rates. If it moves out by barge or lake vessel it is at no disadvantage, but if it moves out by rail it must pay the local rate—the highest chargeable by the railroads—to its destination or to a rate-break point. Ex-lake grain destined east of Chicago to the Central Territory takes "Northwest" basis, which to some locations is higher than many other rates; or if it moves to Ohio River crossings it carries the Northwest proportional to the river and destination proportional beyond. The rate of ex-barge grain moving into territory generally east and south of Chicago is determined from the origin of barge-loading, i.e., Illinois reshipping rate, Trans-Mississippi, or Northwest basis. Ex-barge grain takes either the local rate to Ohio River crossings and the destination proportional beyond, or the proportional to the river and local beyond, whichever is cheaper.

To some extent railroad-rate applications are constantly changing. Since the rate structure is quite complex and there are exceptions to general applications, nothing may be taken for granted. Different interests apply for favorable rates by petition to the Interstate Commerce Commission, which is empowered by Congress and charged with the duty of regulating interstate rates. The broad application of the rate-break principle has been in effect for a number of years.

Chicago is a rate-break point. For example, rates are made from western points to Chicago and from Chicago to eastern points. Rates on grain originating west of and moving through the Minneapolis gateway, break at Minneapolis and again at Chicago or Peoria, and take the same rates to Chicago and Peoria and also the same rates from Chicago and Peoria to eastern destinations, thus making the same through rate from origin to destination via either Chicago or Peoria. Grain moving through the Kansas City gateway and some other Missouri River crossings via St. Louis, Peoria, or Chicago, although at different rates to each of these rate-break points and at different rates from each to New York, have the same through rate from origin to destination. While rates from Chicago applicable on grain originating in Northwest, Trans-Mississippi or Illinois Freight Association territories may differ to the same destinations in the Central Territory east of the Illinois-Indiana boundary, they equalize east of Buffalo in the Trunkline Assocation Territory. Illinois grain to the Central Territory moves out of Chicago mostly on transit balances.

Regulations for billing on grain delivered on Chicago futures require that when the grain is shipped out of the elevator the billing must be "live billing" and must carry the proportional or reshipping rate to the eastern Trunkline Territory. Rates to other destinations are supplied to the shipper from billing that the elevator operator has on hand. When grain is shipped from an elevator, billing need not be applied against the same lot of grain as received, but it must be the same kind of grain. To be "live," billing on the out shipment must bear a date not earlier than one year from the date of the shipment from Chicago, unless the billing has been renewed under tariff provisions, in which case it is good for an additional year.

Although distance is the most important factor in establishing rates, other things enter in. Proportional rates from Duluth are the same as from Minneapolis to Chicago, even though the distance from Duluth to Chicago via Minneapolis is approximately 150 miles longer than from Minneapolis. Here the competition of lake rates to Chicago affects rail rates. Minneapolis futures contracts provide that delivery may also be made at Duluth. The rates from Minneapolis to St. Louis and to Kansas City are equal, though the distances are not; but while the rate from Duluth to St. Louis is the same as from Minneapolis, it is higher to Kansas City.

The Great Lakes

Lake-boat rates are not fixed but are free to fluctuate, and no tariffs are published by the operating companies. Rates vary moderately, and sometimes considerably, over short periods of time, and they vary greatly over longer periods as the demand for movement of ore, coal, and other commodities competes with that of grain. The separate ex-lake rail rates on domestic and export grain from Lake Erie ports published by eastern railroads are used by the grain man, in combination with lake-boat rates, in competition with all rail rates in the movement of grain from western lake ports to inland or seaboard destinations. Duluth on Lake Superior may be counted upon quite regularly to ship grain via the lakes to Buffalo to supply flour mills with wheat for milling. When spring-wheat prices are in line for export, this is usually, but not always, the cheapest route if combined with ex-lake ("at-and-east") rates.

Feed grains also move out of Duluth to both Canadian and United States lake ports for distribution or export. Lake vessels carry grain less regularly from Lake Michigan ports than from Duluth but a large volume is moved from these ports in most seasons. Lake grain arriving at eastern lake ports may be elevated, and in addition to rail movement may be transferred through elevators to trucks for local or distant distribution or to barges for shipment via canal to Albany or further down the Hudson River to New York. Lake grain shipments originating at western ports after leaving Lake Erie move direct through the Welland Canal, Lake Ontario, and the St. Lawrence River to Canadian ports for export, or the grain may be transshipped at Buffalo or Port Colborne via smaller vessels to the same destinations. This is one of the routes for Canadian grain when loaded at Fort William or Port Arthur, Ontario, at the head of Lake Superior. Another water route is to Georgian Bay ports or Lake Huron ports from both Canadian and United States lake ports. American grain, moving thus, may be for export via Montreal or other ports or for distribution in eastern Canada or within the New England States. United States grain moving back into this country or re-exported from Canadian ports passes through Canada duty-free, just as Canadian grain moving through the United States and re-exported is duty-free, and is held in bond while it is in transit or in storage, even though it may be milled into flour in the United States.

Inland Waterways

The inland waterway traffic on rivers is quite extensive and includes all grains, probably the largest in volume being corn trucked from farm locations many miles on either side of the Illinois River and transferred through river elevators into barges for shipment to Chicago. Similar shipments, usually from points of origin closer to St. Louis, are barged to that city or down the Mississippi River to New Orleans and intermediate river ports. Points south of St. Louis use the river mostly for southbound traffic. The upper Mississippi and Missouri rivers barge grain to various ports, including Chicago; some also moves (rarely) from Kansas City to Chicago by this route. There is an inland waterway route along the Gulf of Mexico to Galveston and Houston, Texas, connected with the north-south route, and also a route to Mobile, Alabama. Grain loaded in Chicago makes these trips.

Barge rates are considerably lower than rail rates, and grain attracted from Illinois farms to Chicago sells in the Chicago market cheaper than grain from sources at similar distances that use railroad transportation. In practice, farmers located for many miles on both sides of the Illinois River receive a higher price for corn trucked to river elevators and barged to Chicago than buyers could pay them for corn to be moved to Chicago via country elevators and by rail movement to Chicago; yet the delivered Chicago price of barge corn is several cents lower than rail corn shipped from similar distances. When barge-received corn is sold for shipment out of Chicago after elevator interests have calculated a fair profit, its price is approximately equal to the incoming price of rail corn in the spot market. It is mostly barge-received corn that is delivered on futures contracts. Chicago local-industry buyers are handicapped in using barge-received corn because they have to pay the elevator operator a profit and the railroads a crosstown switching charge; also, outbound billing does not meet all product-destination requirements. If grain is reshipped out of Chicago to destinations east of the Illinois-Indiana line, the proportional (reshipping) rate applies, as it does to all-rail grain originating in the same territory. This barge-grain billing carries transit privileges that allow its profitable use after grain is shipped out of Chicago to these eastern destinations and stopped off "in transit" for storage or processing en route, even at some Illinois locations.

In order to meet barge competition to Chicago, some of the railroads have published lower intrastate rates on corn from near-by points. The price paid for corn with intrastate billing is usually lower in Chicago, as it does not enjoy full rail advantages when leaving the city but in the Chicago market receives higher prices than trucked corn. Grain elevators take the opportunity of shipping some grain, especially corn, by lake in order to use the "corn intrastate rate" billing and trucked-in grain, which carries no billing; otherwise they would be penalized when the grain is shipped out. Some Illinois lines have published special rates on corn to Chicago for destinations east of the Illinois-Indiana state line; these rates are proportional on the Chicago end and apply only when the shipment moves from Chicago.

"Illinois Proportional"

A very important method of buying Chicago grain, one by which a large percentage is purchased, is by rail on Illinois proportional billing. The term "Illinois proportional" is generally used in the trade to include all inbound billing which protects the proportional rate to New York. Specifically, the term "Illinois proportional" or "Illinois specific" applies only in connection with billing from origins in Illinois, Indiana, and west-bank Mississippi River points in Iowa and Missouri from which joint rates to New York are in effect, and represents the proportion of the through rate which accrues to the carrier from its point of origin to Chicago.

When grain is sold to Chicago on this basis and the local rate is higher or lower than the Illinois proportional or specific, the shipper must pay the railroad the local rate and collect from the elevator operator, if the local rate is higher, or pay him, if it is lower than specific. This difference between the local and the Illinois proportional or specific is held in a suspense account by the operator of the transit elevator and is recovered from or paid to the railroad, as the case may be, when billing is applied against outbound shipments. In other words, the elevator operator will lose the money represented by the difference paid to the country shipper unless he makes proper application of his transit billing on outbound shipments; also, he cannot get reshipping rates unless he brings the inbound local rate up to the required minimum. Incoming and outgoing railroads make the proper adjustment of these rates between themselves. If the grain should be shipped by lake there would be no refund, and the amount paid to the country shipper would be lost. The use of Illinois proportional makes grain transited at Chicago competitive with through rates on direct shipments from similar origins to points east of Buffalo and Pittsburgh.

Transit-Balance Rates

Although proportional rates have been established from most of the larger markets, the through rate with transit privileges has been retained at numerous markets where it has not been practical to establish proportional rates. When transit and routing privileges are given at an intermediate point even though not in a direct line from origin to destination, and the combination of the rates would be higher, the "transit balance" is the difference between the through rate from origin to destination and the rate paid to the transit point. Grain shipped out of Kansas City to the Southeast (via Ohio River crossings) transited at Chicago pays a transit balance from Chicago very much less than the proportional rate in order to equalize the through rate from Kansas City direct or via St. Louis to the Southeast. Minneapolis grain transited at Chicago pays a transit balance from Chicago to St. Louis that is less than the local rate in order to equal the through proportional rate from Minneapolis to St. Louis. Illinois grain may transit at Chicago and work to Central Territory on transit balances.

Tariffs

All schedules of railroad rates are contained in "tariffs" published by the railroads. Interstate rates are filed with the Interstate Commerce Commission and intrastate rates with various state commissions. Copies of tariffs are furnished to shippers and interested bodies, such as boards of trade who have traffic departments. The Chicago Exchange has thousands of tariffs on file and advises members of rates and prepares and handles cases before commissions and other bodies. The railroads publish tariffs covering charges in addition to rates; these cover switching between different railroad lines, reconsigning, installation of grain doors, demurrage, etc. Switching of cars arriving in Chicago is free to the unloading elevator, but when grain loaded out of an elevator is destined for a different one within the switching district, there is a charge based on the number of railroad lines over which it moves some of which may be recovered on the outbound movement. Free time is permitted in which to order the arriving cars after the grain has been inspected and the sample delivered to the consignee, after which reconsigning and demurrage charges are assessed.

Loading Cars

When cars are loaded they must conform to requirements of loading to proper weights. The general basis is to marked capacity (except that oats must be 80% of marked capacity), subject to exceptions that the actual weight governs when the car is fully loaded, or when the grain is to within 24 inches of the roof or up to the grain line, when such a line appears in the car. If the grain does not reach the required minimum, freight is paid on the basis of the marked capacity of the car (except under the conditions mentioned above), unless a larger car is furnished than was ordered. When a carrier, for carrier convenience, furnishes a larger car than ordered, the minimum weight applicable to the car ordered governs the freight rate. Railroads pay claims for loss of grain in transit when liability is established, but in most cases a uniform shrinkage of one eighth of one per cent is deducted from the amount of the loss before making payment. Railroads also pay claims for other authorized purposes.

Freight Bills

It is necessary that paid freight bills be registered with the official bureau within a required time in order that they may be used to obtain reshipping or proportional rates or transit balances on outbound billing; otherwise, the local rate is applied. It is the duty of the traffic manager in each firm to sort inbound bills properly according to their respective values to some ultimate destination beyond the terminal. The grain trader in making sales is constantly guided by information from his traffic department concerning rates to destinations and the billing on hand.

Milling in Transit

When grain is stopped for milling in transit, the outbound-product rate is calculated from the origin point of the grain, which to certain territories is higher than the rate for the whole grain. A feed manufacturer must allow for shrinkage and cancel billing according to the ingredients of the mixed feeds shipped, except in cases where the unit rule is used, which permits surrender at one point of a freight bill covering one of the ingredients for the entire carload, and the next time a freight bill for a different ingredient.

Grain Movements

At times methods of transportation are temporarily employed that, although not generally affecting the country's system of grain movement, cause shipments to be routed so as to take advantage of these facilities and in so doing grain-area values are adjusted by competitive pricing. Wheat has moved by way of sea routes or intercoastal shipping from Pacific Northwest ports to southeastern U.S. ports and even to the North Atlantic ports for further shipment into the interior—a matter of price differential permitting the use of vessels in this service. Wheat frequently moves overland from the Pacific Northwest to the eastern part of the country, and more often from intermountain territory. It moves quite regularly from these areas into the Southwest. Barley, largely because of its malting quality, regularly moves from the West Coast towards the East. Corn is not grown in any quantity in the Mountain States or West Coast area, but seasonally moves west from the Corn Belt to the feed trade along the Pacific. Grain sorghums likewise move from the Southwest to the western trade area.

Imports

Imported grain enters the United States along all of its borders. Rye and barley have come from Europe into Atlantic ports and then into the interior via rail and the Great Lakes. Argentine corn and oats have come all the way to the Central States in quantity via the St. Lawrence River and the Great Lakes, then by rail to various destinations, and also up the Mississippi River by barge and then by rail. They have also gone to Pacific ports. Argentine wheat has been shipped to Atlantic ports and held in bond for re-export, but the high duty has worked against importations of overseas wheat for consumption. Argentine flaxseed is very familiar to United States crushers. Canadian wheat, limited to small quantities, is imported for food consumption yearly. Feed wheat, on a different duty than wheat for food consumption, and feed grains are imported when prices are competitive; at times they are imported heavily. Wheat millfeeds from milling-in-bond operations are regularly consumed here. This milling is done mostly close to the Canadian border, and a mill handling the business bonds its warehouse and a unit of the mill to avoid payment of duty and to come within the import regulations on grain products re-exported.

Export

Transportation of grain for export from the United States follows the pattern of domestic routing, but mostly at lower railroad rates. Rates change at certain rate-break points, taking a lower basis from there to export ports. This does not change the rate from origin to rate-break point. At the Atlantic seaboard proportional export rates are related to Baltimore, with higher specific differentials when the destinations are other ports. These differ from domestic proportional rates, which are tied to New York, but domestic proportional rates are also lower to Baltimore. Rates from Kansas City are the same to Galveston as they are to New Orleans. Even though higher from Omaha and Sioux City than they are from Kansas City, the rates from both these cities are equal to Galveston and New Orleans. Grain shipped from more southerly points to Galveston moves on rates according to distance and from transit points on transit balances. New Orleans receives considerable grain via barge and also has favorable rail rates from the southern Corn Belt. St. Louis has a low railroad rate to New Orleans because of river competition.

Most eastern and midwestern export grain goes to Europe. The distance by ocean routes to European ports is greater from Gulf of Mexico ports than from the Atlantic seaboard, and this requires larger steamer-operating expenses because the passage takes longer; therefore the rates are higher. There is no set differential in the ocean-steamer rates, because they are negotiated according to the demand for tonnage.

Each port of export competes with others both in favorable purchase of the grain in the interior and the cheapest route to the port, as well as in ocean-shipping costs. Wheat, differing in class and shipped from different ports, has its relative value in European markets that use wheat from all over the world in flour production. This helps to equalize prices of wheat in different parts of this country. As the surplus wheat in one area is reduced, the price advances so as to eliminate it from the export market, and if there is a shortage, the price rises to attract wheat from other areas for domestic requirements. The same condition prevails within each area of the country. For example, cheaper export offerings of wheat grown near Atlantic ports prevent export sales of wheat from Chicago, but as the price of the more-eastern wheat advances it brings Chicago prices into line for export, provided, however, that like classes of wheat are not available at cheaper delivered European prices for shipment from such ports as Portland or Seattle on the Pacific coast.

Ocean Transportation.—Ocean transportation by steamers carrying grain is in bulk as "full cargo" or as part of a cargo, which is referred to as "a parcel." When there are parcels, the balance of the ship's cargo is general merchandise, or the ship may carry only grain made up of a number of parcels, all of which may be run together if they are the same kind and grade. Ocean liners making regular trips between ports often carry parcels of grain. At times their rates, especially from Atlantic ports, are cheaper than those of other steamers, for, having to sail on a schedule, they will take grain to fill out the cargo. Like other cargo-carriers, ocean steamers issue bills of lading as receipt for the grain. This document is the shipper's proof of shipment, and when it is properly banked with other documents necessary to the terms of a foreign sale the exporter's responsibility ceases.

Freight Rates

Freight rates are quoted in various units. Railroad rates are invariably expressed in cents per 100 pounds. Based on legal weights per bushel of 60 pounds for wheat and soybeans, 56 pounds for corn, rye, and grain sorghums, 48 pounds for barley, and 32 pounds for oats, a rate of one cent per 100 pounds is equivalent in cents per bushel to 0.6 for wheat, etc. Barge-grain rates are quoted per 100 pounds and per ton. Great Lakes boat rates are in cents per bushel but in Canadian funds for Canadian vessels; and it must be noted that oats in Canada are 34 pounds per bushel and in the United States 32 pounds per bushel. Oats rates are less per bushel than other grains because the vessel can carry more. (Lake boat rates for oats may be in terms of wheat-carrying capacity.) Other Canadian grains are the same number of pounds per bushel as American grains. Truck rates are based on cents per bushel with some tolerance for mileage (especially on long distances when a return load is obtainable) and the size of the truck; there are lower rates for oats, as more bushels can be carried than other grains. Ocean-steamer rates are on a long-ton basis of 2,240 pounds of heavy grain (wheat, corn, or rye), and rates may be in the currency of United States or of Great Britain or occasionally in other currency corresponding to the destination, or per 100 pounds in United States money.

Even though transportation rates quoted to the grain merchants vary in size of unit and in currency for different kinds of transportation, the domestic- and export-grain man must convert all the rates to United States money per bushel, on which basis he works. This transportation cost is then added to the per-bushel cost price of the grain in order to arrive at a price at which it may be sold. There is an exception to this calculation when the ocean freight is collected at destination, if it is payable in the same currency as the foreign sale is priced. When there are taxes on freight, which in effect are part of the rate, they must be considered as such.

Other Charges

Railroad accessorial charges may be per car for such as reconsigning and demurrage; the latter is on a basis of daily charges and starts after the expiration of free time for ordering incoming cars to the unloading elevator or to another city. There are also demurrage charges for cars standing at an elevator. The cars must be unloaded or, after being loaded with grain out of an elevator, must be released within a prescribed time. Demurrage charges at an elevator are usually based on a monthly average, with some credit for time saved applying against delays.

There are charges for coopering cars and for grain doors before grain can be shipped. Grain in lake boats is customarily insured for quantity loss in addition to marine risks. A similar quantity risk is insurable during ocean voyages of steamers either to the full extent of loading weights or to within a small percentage.

There are no commissions payable on railroad freight, and on lake steamers the commission is a fraction of a cent per bushel. On ocean vessels there is no commission payable by shippers, but a percentage of the freight may be paid by the owners to the charterers, and a broker collects a fee from the vessel's agent for booking parcel space.

Summary

Those who engage in any phase of the grain trade can never relax their concentration on transportation. Ability to meet competition in the sale of grain or products may depend solely on billing on hand that can apply to the buyer's destination. The location of the elevator permits purchase of grain in areas carrying favorable billing, so as to allow shipment to destinations that exclude competition from elevators located elsewhere. There is a tolerance for penalty billing if quality of grain permits profitable blending that will more than offset the loss of the extra freight paid. Also, grain is bought with billing that permits transit at the elevator location, and the billing may be applied to truck-received and other grain. Grain may be shipped out via truck, barge, or lake or may be consumed locally, and the rail or other inbound billing held until it can be favorably applied against a different grain shipment. Truck- or "lake-rate"-rail-billing grain can be purchased at a discount and sold via lake steamer at prices competitive with local or "even rate" billing, but at times such grain has to be sold cheaper if there is too much on hand. Inasmuch as billing remains "live" for one year after receipt of grain and can be renewed for another year, opportunities for use extend over two crops. Nevertheless, at times grain sales are forced so that billing does not expire, with consequent loss of monetary investment in the billing.

Buyers have to watch the minimum rate "paid in" to their transit point so that penalties do not have to be paid to apply reshipping rates. Also, grain moving over certain railroads carries billing to destinations not provided by other railroads on shipments from the same origin.

The network of transportation that handles grain has a bearing on where crops are produced and co-ordinates distribution with favorable and unfavorable growing conditions, marketing centers, and consuming areas. The constant interchange of ideas between buyers and sellers, aided by brokers and commission merchants seeking the most favorable prices, keeps prices within areas and between areas at differences commensurate with minimum transportation rates.

CHAPTER VII

Storage

Kinds and Places

Grain is stored in many different ways and places, in the bulk or bagged, all the way from the farm to marketing centers, distribution points, and export ports; furthermore, it is stored in farm bins and cribs (of permanent or temporary construction), country elevators, terminal elevators, sub-terminal elevators, vessels, railroad cars, improvised warehouses, and even on the ground. Some of the storage space is privately owned and is used to store only grain owned by the operator. Other storage, privately owned or leased, is available for use for other people's grain and is operated under the terms of the laws of the state in which the elevator is located or under the laws of the Federal Government. Railroads own some elevators and lease them to private firms which operate them as private or public storage; and some elevators are operated by railroads themselves for public storage. City and state bodies have built a considerable number of storage and transfer elevators and operate them for the use of the general public. The Federal Government also owns many storage bins, which are used primarily in carrying out the grain price-support programs.

Practically all the grain that is grown must be stored for a while, much of it for a long time. Even that portion that is used on the farms must be kept under cover until it is fed to livestock or poultry or is used for other purposes. Farmers may keep some of the grain they have raised for seed for the next crop. Some farm uses of grain do not require that the grain be stored, but they are few. Farmers turn livestock into some fields to glean the grain not gathered at harvest; hogs and cattle are turned into fields after the corn is picked to feed on what has fallen to the ground, or fields may be left to be "hogged down." However, percentage-wise, nearly all the grain grown is harvested and put into some kind of storage.

In years when wheat production is large in the Southwest or the Northwest, some grain has to be piled on the ground until elevators can relieve the situation. There is usually no severe deterioration in the quality of this wheat even though it may encounter some rainfall. It is necessary to harvest a crop of small grain when it is ripe, as it would be almost completely lost if left standing, though some would reseed itself for a volunteer crop the next year.

There is not an accurate record of the amount of farm storage, but it is extremely large. Temporary storage often has to be provided to shelter the overflow from the normal granaries. Farm storage is divided into bins for small grains and cribs for corn. Expanded crib space is more easily provided, for ear corn does not have to be weatherproof and storage can be temporary because of the rapid use of corn in farm feeding operations. Permanent corn cribs are of good construction with strong foundations, reasonable protection against rodents, and adequate strength to hold corn and resist stress, and they give certain protection against surface moisture, rain, and snow.

As most farm-stored grain is corn, the greatest need is for cribs, but tight bins must be available for all the other grains. When all grains that leave the farms are put into storage they are held in the same kind of elevators, whether they are corn or other grains. First, the grains are likely to be moved to country elevators, then to sub-terminal or terminal elevators, and finally to mills or export-port elevators. There is much deviation from this pattern. Some grain goes directly from farms to the mills which are scattered over the country in many locations; other grain moves directly from farms to terminal elevators and some even goes to export elevators.

By volume, wheat is the largest crop moving off the farms for storage, and percentage-wise the soybean crop is the greatest.

As off-the-farm movement for these grains is substantial, the need for farm storage to house them is less. Such a big share of oat and barley crops are fed on the farms where they are raised that large farm-storage facilities must be available in heavy-producing areas; but still, by volume, they too occupy considerable other storage space.

Farm Bin Storage

Grain bins on farms vary in size from a capacity of under 100 bushels up to several thousand bushels; in isolated cases, farmers have more than 200,000 bushels of bin storage space. There has been considerable experimental work done to determine the best kind of farm storage bins for farmers to build and the various types of bins that they can buy. Farm granaries are constructed of several materials, but mostly of wood and different kinds of metals.

More than 25 years ago, when grain in a territory was threshed over a period of two to three months, the grain was hauled to market largely by teams and wagons. This required that farmers living more than a few miles from a local shipping point provide considerable storage on their farms. Now, with the combine, it takes only two to three weeks to remove a crop from the fields in a local area. With modern methods, the grain is hauled to the elevator more easily over better roads and for greater distances, but there is still a tendency for farmers living considerable distances from local elevators to store more grain on their farms than those with shorter hauls to the elevator. This is influencing country elevator operators to build additional storage space and to speed up truck-unloading facilities. Waiting in line to unload trucks at elevators is serious, as it can mean a delay in combining operations. The bottleneck at country elevators is often the lack of boxcars in which to transport grain from the elevators. This causes elevators to close temporarily or to limit receipts from farmers, sometimes for a considerable length of time.

To store grain safely on farms, the moisture content of the

grain must be low and insect infestation must be avoided. Ventilated bins safely store grain of higher moisture content than unventilated bins of the same size, but the percentage of moisture in the grain tolerable for safe storage depends upon the part of the country in which the grain is stored. Where temperatures range colder, grain can have a higher moisture content than it can have farther south. A bin of grain of uneven moisture distribution provides an extra storage hazard. The grain has to be watched while in storage and treated for insect control or turned to avoid heating. Bins should be sprayed for insects before filling them with grain. A farmer with an appreciable amount of grain to put into storage needs a mechanical loader.

Farm storage of grain to be marketed for cash may encounter the extra hazard of bad weather when it is loaded into trucks and hauled to market at the time the farmer desires to sell. This may cause him to delay marketing and to miss the opportunity of selling his grain when he considers time or market price favorable. Grain that has already been moved off the farm into public storage can be priced and sold at the same daily bid of the elevator operator as grain just brought from the farm. In some years even well along in the season there are times when congestion from crowded elevators or inadequate railroad-car supply continues, so that the farmer cannot market his grain.

There are many angles to the storage of grain which the farmer has to appraise. For corn, if he intends to feed livestock, he must have sufficient crib space to contain the grain. For other feed grains required on his farm he has to provide enough bin storage. And for his next year's planting he needs space to store and possibly clean and treat the seed. These storage requirements apply to many farms. Beyond these needs there is the calculated cost of building new storage for replacement, or for additional use, or even using existing farm storage instead of sending the grain to elevators for storage and paying their charges.

Farm Storage vs. Elevator Storage

Conclusions based on surveys published in 1950 for Oklahoma and in 1951 for North Dakota, both surplus-wheat-producing regions, favor sending grain to elevators even when the farmers had available farm bin storage. On the average farm in Oklahoma at 100% capacity use, the fixed charges were 4.4 cents per bushel for a whole year for a 2,000-bushel capacity of new bin storage. This quantity of storage is common on farms in that state, and the charge goes on year after year, whether or not the storage is used. Some farmers do not consider fixed charges as expenses, but the charge is there nevertheless, and if not used otherwise, the money could be used to reduce a mortgage. The charges consist of interest, depreciation, insurance and taxes. While the survey found wide variation between farms, the average use of farm storage was 41% of bin capacity. This raised the per-bushel fixed charges for the storage used to 10.8 cents per bushel per year. The average yearly elevator charge amounted to 10.3 cents per bushel, or 0.5 of a cent less than the survey showed for fixed charges on farm storage. Variable expenses were: shrinkage of grain in bins (2.7%), insurance on grain, treating for insect control, turning or conditioning, cost of lower grade because of deterioration, risk of inconvenience at a nominal amount; these total 8.3 cents per bushel. When extra transportation and labor expenses on cash grain, averaging 3.1 cents per bushel, were added, the variable expenses for 100% of storage-capacity use rose to 11.4 cents. This totaled 15.8 cents per bushel for fixed and variable expenses at 100%-storage-capacity use compared to a full year's elevator storage cost of 10.3 cents. At 41% farm average use the farm charges would be 22.2 cents per bushel.

Further, the average length of storage was 172 days, or nearly six months. The survey found that farm costs for this period would be the same as for a full year. Elevator charges were seven cents, a saving of 8.8 cents over 100% farm capacity, or 15.2 cents less than the 41% average use.

For a three-month period, farm costs were two cents per bushel less than for 172 days, amounting to 13.8 and 20.2 cents, respectively, for 100%- and 41%-capacity use. The elevator charge for three months was 4 cents per bushel, a saving of 9.8 cents or 16.2 cents per bushel according to the percentage of capacity use.

As the crop for the year under survey was low in moisture, there was less deterioration in quality while in farm storage than in many years. When an elevator stores grain it assumes the risks in both quality and quantity and charges only for the time the grain is in storage. Most of the country elevators charged country-elevator rate of storage even though farmers had the grain forwarded to terminal elevators, where the rate might have been higher.[1]

Farm storage in North Dakota was found by the following year's survey to be less than in Oklahoma for both fixed and variable expenses, but still decidedly higher than elevator storage. Fixed charges for a year were 3.8 cents per bushel on the basis of 100%-capacity use and 6.9 cents for 57%, the average capacity use, and variable expenses of 7.6 cents per bushel, which does not change with the amount of bin space used, for they are charges connected only with the grain. A full year's elevator cost was 10 cents. Even when costs of owning a farm granary are omitted, it still costs more to store on the farm than in an elevator unless the grain is stored for at least eight months.

The average length of time of farm storage was 163 days, or 5½ months. This cost the farmer for all expenses, fixed and variable, 11.4 cents per bushel at 100%-capacity use and 14.5 cents at 57% of capacity use, against 4.5 cents at the elevator. Two months' storage on the farm cost 9.9 cents or 13 cents, according to the percentage stored, but only 1.7 cents in an elevator.

---

[1] *Where and How Much Cash Grain Storage for Oklahoma Farmers,* U.S.D.A. Farm Credit Administration Bulletin No. 58, May, 1950.

The saving at the average capacity use (57%) for the average length of time (5½ months) was 10 cents per bushel in favor of the elevator or, for two months, 11.3 cents.[2]

Off-farm Storage Capacity

The United States Department of Agriculture made a survey late in 1954 estimating the off-farm commercial type of grain-storage capacity at 2,819,815,000 bushels for the entire country, including both private and public storage and some flat storage, for the storage of wheat, oats, barley, shelled corn, field seeds, dry beans and peas, rice, and other grains. The survey did not include Commodity Credit Corporation storage structures. Bulk capacity totaled 2,586,788,000 bushels and sacked or other storage 233,027,000 bushels. Kansas led all other states in storage with 332,470,000 bushels, followed by Texas with 289,962,000 bushels, Illinois with 224,697,000 bushels, Minnesota with 212,230,000 bushels. Kansas also had the largest amount of bulk storage, 331,430,000 bushels, and Texas was also second at 257,025,000 bushels; Illinois came third with 222,913,000 bushels and Minnesota fourth with 211,686,000 bushels. The largest sacked or other storage for any state was 65,776,000 bushels in California, which state also had bulk storage for 78,328,000 bushels, giving it the fifth-largest combined total. Texas followed California in sacked space with 32,937,000 bushels, then Louisiana with 23,653,000 bushels.

The Commodity Credit Corporation owned or leased emergency storage space amounting to around 984,000,000 bushels in the spring of 1956. Most of this was of small metal-bin construction, and the major portion located in the Corn Belt.

Corn Cribs

Corn differs from other grain crops in that it is nearly always too damp to store in a tight bin when harvested but

[2] *Where and How Much Cash Grain Storage for North Dakota Farmers,* U.S.D.A. Farm Credit Administration Bulletin No. 61, May, 1951.

requires further curing after it has been gathered. The necessary additional curing or drying takes place when the husked ears are stored in a crib. Good judgment is necessary in selecting the time to harvest and crib corn. Corn dries faster in the field than in the crib, and the risk of loss by delay in harvesting may be more than offset by spoilage if damp corn is cribbed. The urge to start harvesting too early is therefore strong.

Under normal conditions in the central part of the Corn Belt, corn has from 18% to 20% moisture in the kernels and about 35% moisture in the cob when harvested in the latter part of October or early in November. Ordinarily corn dries very little in the crib during the winter; under humid winter conditions there may even be a little increase in moisture in the kernels because of movement of moisture from cobs to kernels and snow blown into the crib. Drying takes place as the weather warms up in the spring. By June or July under normal weather conditions the grain is down to 13% moisture content and is dry enough to shell and store in a tight bin. The corn does not stay this dry in a crib in humid weather. To reduce corn from 20% to 13% moisture in the kernels, about eight pounds, or nearly a gallon, of water must be removed from each bushel of corn.

Immature or soft corn generally is not of desirable quality for long-time storage. However, if the quality is good except for excessive moisture, it can be brought to good condition by mechanical drying, or in some cases by use of ventilators. If the corn has more moisture than is safe, some type of interior ventilator should be used, and that will practically divide the cribs into two narrow cribs. By mechanically forced ventilation with either heated or unheated air, ear corn too moist for safe storage in an ordinary crib can be brought to a safe condition. The cost of mechanical drying varies with the amount of moisture that must be removed from the corn, and is influenced also by weather conditions when the drying is done.

To dry corn from 25% to 18% moisture to make it safe for crib storage, the cost of power for drying by forced ventilation with unheated air under favorable weather conditions is about two or three cents per bushel. To this must be added labor, interest, and depreciation, which may bring the cost up to five to seven cents per bushel and—as with power expenses—even more if conditions are not favorable.

Drying with heated air is more reliable, but its cost is likely to be higher. For the amount of drying just specified, including fuel, etc., the cost is likely to be 10 to 12 cents per bushel. With more efficient equipment and if the corn is in a steel bin, the cost may be no more than for drying with unheated air.

Another method is to dry corn with heated air to 13% moisture content, then shell it and store it in a weather-tight bin. For this method, drying can be done somewhat more economically in a drying bin.

Rats and mice sometimes cause heavy losses of cribbed corn, especially when corn is held in the crib for a year or longer. No ordinary construction can completely exclude rats and mice, but their activities can be greatly reduced by the use of concrete or wood floors supported well above the ground.

The practice of delivering corn to the elevator on the ear still prevails in some sections, although most corn is shelled on the farms before loading it on trucks for delivery to the elevator.[3]

The Country Elevator

Country elevators fall into three general classes: independent or privately owned elevators, co-operative elevators, and line elevators. Independent elevators are usually owned and operated by individual grain men. Co-operative elevators may be owned and operated by the associations. Line elevators are simply chains of elevators owned by a grain company, a mill, or other grain processor and are usually located along a railroad system;

[3] *Storage of Ear Corn on the Farm,* U.S.D.A. Farmers' Bulletin No. 2010, Sept., 1949.

managers of these elevators receive instructions from headquarters regarding buying prices and operating practices. The costs of separate services may not vary much between elevators of different types of ownership, but those operated for private use, if available at all, may not be as readily available for storage of farmer-owned grain as others are.

Country elevators dot the entire grain belt. Some are busy fairly regularly throughout the year but others only in the season of heavy crop marketing. Their services vary according to the number of crops produced in the area. Most grain taken into country elevators is shipped to buyers' mills, other processing plants, and semi-terminal or terminal elevators. The country elevator may resell some grain for local use, but primarily the grain received is shipped out to a market for resale.

Sizes of country elevators run from those of a few thousand bushels' capacity to modern houses of more than a million bushels' capacity. A typical elevator is of a 25,000-to-30,000-bushel capacity. They are constructed mostly of wood covered with galvanized sheet iron or of reinforced concrete. This description may be considered elaborate for some country elevators but it covers features of country elevators in general. While there is great variance in equipment, even the large ones follow the more simple method of handling grain rather than being patterned after terminal elevators, many of which have a smaller storage capacity. Large country elevators, of course, are designed to store grain and have large bins for this purpose. For weighing the incoming grain they are more likely to have a hopper scale, and for outgoing grain also a scale of large capacity. They probably have only one elevator leg, but use conveyor belts to move the grain horizontally within the elevator.

Wooden elevators as we know them date back into the last century. Improvements have replaced many outmoded facilities. "Cribbed" elevators are those with walls constructed with the lumber laid flat side down instead of sideways, thus giving strength to prevent bulging and leakage. The planks start with 2-by-8's or 2-by-6's, and as they rise the size used are 2-by-4's. "Studded" or "balloon" elevators have the boards nailed on the outside of the studding and are braced with tie rods through the house. Reinforced-concrete elevators have walls 6 or 8 inches thick; these walls resist both heat and cold and are considered to be better for grain storage than those of wood.

A country elevator may be 80 feet high to the top of the cupola, in which is located the motor for driving the shaft attached to the head pulley and other vital features of an elevator.

As a truck drives to an elevator to unload grain, it may be weighed on a platform scale and weighed again when it is empty after discharging the grain, to ascertain the weight of the grain. Another method is to weigh only the grain after it has been dumped into a hopper scale.

When the loaded truck drives into the elevator driveway, its body is either tipped or the elevator has a platform that tips the whole truck to dump the grain. Some elevators have several truck dumps. The grain falls through a heavy grating in the floor into a hopper scale to the sink or directly into the sink. The best method of inspecting grain for grade is to do so as it leaves the truck by cutting across the stream of grain at regular intervals to obtain an average sample. Samples taken are then thoroughly mixed and reduced to standard size for grade analysis.

The grain falls by gravity into the boot from which it is elevated into the storage bins by means of an elevator leg. An elevator leg is an endless belt running over the head pulley in the cupola of the house and under the boot pulley. Buckets or cups attached to the belt scoop up grain at great speed and, after carrying it up, discharge it over the head pulley into a hopper, from where it is distributed by a spout to the desired storage bin. In modern elevators distributor spouts to bins are close-fitting and provided with collars to keep the dust with the grain, lessening the hazard of explosion from a spark igniting the grain dust. Cupola walls of light construction and with many windows glazed with thin glass reduce resistance to the explosive force of dust, should an explosion occur, and check the spread of explosions to other parts of the building.

In case the grain becomes choked up in the head of the elevator leg, an overflow duct carries the grain down into the boot again. When the power is turned off, a head ratchet prevents the loaded buckets from reversing the belt. Most elevators have lifts to carry men to the cupola for quick access and regular inspection of the working parts in the head of the elevator.

Each elevator has as many storage bins as are considered necessary for the operations; they are of sizes that will hold from probably 500 to 10,000 bushels of grain. There is nothing uniform in the shape or dimensions of bins; some elevators have steel tanks or tanks of other materials, and if they are not connected with the elevator they may be filled by using spiral or other types of conveyors.

When the grain is to be loaded out, the elevator manager selects the desirable grade of grain in a certain bin. The grain is then dropped from the bin through the hopper bottom into the boot of the leg and is again elevated, and the distributor spout drops it into an automatic scale. The scales weigh the grain in draughts of from about 4 to 10 bushels, or maybe considerably more. Though these weights probably will not be official, they may be used for records, and if there is an excessive shortage of grain in transit the railroad might pay a claim on the basis of these weight records. The grain flows into and out of the scales in a very nearly continuous stream and is then spouted to a boxcar on the tracks alongside the elevator. The end of the loading spout is flexible so as to direct the grain to either end of the car. The force of gravity with which the grain falls carries it some distance into the car. If the top of the grain is uneven, it should be leveled off so that there is room for the sampler to probe the trier into the grain at all parts of the car in order to secure an average sample for inspection purposes. Sampling of country-elevator-loaded grain usually is done at the destination of the car. But as the country shipper settles with his buyer on the grade of the grain, it behooves him to load the car so that a correct grain sample may be taken.

A country elevator may be equipped with some machinery for conditioning grain by cleaning, clipping, etc., and some elevators have conveyor belts for moving the grain from one part of the elevator to another. Grain can be turned to keep it cool or in condition or to fumigate it by moving it through the elevator leg from one bin to another. Some elevators have purifiers which also aid in drying or removing odor from grain. The various pieces of equipment in a country elevator, if they are available at all, are used in moderation compared with their installation in terminal elevators.

Drying Grain

More and more country elevators in the Corn Belt are installing driers to reduce the percentage of moisture in shelled corn before shipping it to market for sale. There are many companies manufacturing these driers, but they all work on the general principal of holding the corn within the drier while hot air applied to the corn drives out the moisture. Shelled corn is kept moving from the top to the bottom of the drier, passing baffles as it slowly falls. The final treatment with cold air again brings the corn to atmospheric temperatures before leaving the drier. Care must be taken not to apply too high a degree of heat nor to hold the corn in the presence of the heat too long; if this is done, or if returning it to a bin is not carefully supervised, a considerable amount of broken corn may result which, when screened to separate it from the sound corn, has to be sold at a sacrifice price.

A general calculation used to figure price loss in drying corn considers both the price and the corn containing the excessive moisture, termed 100%. In addition to the reduction of the moisture content to the desired dried percentage, there is also an invisible shrinkage, which increases in proportion to the amount of moisture taken out of the corn. If 23%-moisture corn is dried to 15%, there is a loss of 8% of water and about 2% invisible shrinkage, or a total of 10% less corn than you have paid for. Therefore, the 23%-moisture-content corn has a value of about 90% corn on a 15%-moisture basis. To find the true value of your corn, you start with the purchase price, divide by 90, and multiply by 100, and deduct a further amount for the couple-of-cents-per-bushel cost of fuel and power used in operating the drier. As drying losses differ, the careful operator tests batches of corn for moisture and weighs them both before and after drying in order to watch actual operating results. Some elevator men use commercially prepared tables for this purpose. It is also essential not to dry wet corn to too low a moisture content, in order to avoid cracking the corn in the process.

Terminal Elevators

Almost all grain elevators work on the same general principle as country elevators do. The grain is unloaded from an incoming conveyance—a truck, a car, a barge, or a steamer. The largest types of elevators have special facilities; and a barge or steamer will be unloaded by a marine leg: an endless belt with buckets attached that dip into the grain and carry it upward into the house.

To unload cars after they are "spotted" over the unloading hopper, the grain doors are removed. In most elevators power shovels are used to unload cars; the shoveler enters the car and pulls the shovel attached to a cable to the end of the car, whereupon a clutch automatically engages and by means of the cable scoops the grain toward the door. Men work at each end of the car and, by guiding the shovels, clean out the grain, after which the car is swept clean. Another unloading method is the car dump, in which the car is clamped to the tracks on the platform. A grain-door opener pressed against the door forces the boards inward; then the car is tipped 15 degrees laterally and 40 degrees vertically and rocked back and forth until all the grain has been removed.

Car-puller cables, when used, eliminate the need for switch engines in an elevator, because the car is attached to these moving cables to pull it to the desired position. There are other methods for moving cars in an elevator, but switch engines are needed to move them outside an elevator. Terminal elevators use conveyor belts, mostly 42 inches wide (but up to 60 inches), both over and under the storage bins and to move grain to cleaning or shipping bins. These belts may be reversible, and along their course are trippers that can be moved from one position to another to divert grain into a bin or to another belt moving in a different direction.

Larger elevators have storage bins 100 feet deep and work-houses that rise to a height of 200 feet above the basement and contain the machinery to handle and condition the grain. Large bins are 25 feet in diameter and have the capacity to hold 35,000 bushels of grain. In the spaces between the round bins are interstice bins, which hold smaller amounts of grain and are handy for storing special lots of grain necessarily kept separate from grades carried in large bulk.

In order to speed the operations of an elevator a number of elevator legs are used in these houses; and their belts may have several rows of buckets. The grain is collected in garners above scale hoppers; and grain weighed up prior to loading out of an elevator is held in shipping bins. To blend or mix again to arrive at a desired grade, regulated portions are dropped from bins onto a moving belt or are spouted onto a belt via a mixing hopper. An elevator has a system of signals between related parts so that men can co-ordinate their operations and control the flow of the grain without mishap.

Binning of grain is determined by grading factors—classification, test weight, moisture, protein content, damage, or any factor that might be necessary to keeping quality or be valuable in the merchandising of the grain. The elevator superintendent works closely with the trader for the firm and advises him as to what qualities he can ship from grain on hand and what grade factors are best to watch for when making purchases of grain to be sent to the elevator. Regardless of the incoming grade of a car of grain as determined by the official inspector, the superintendent determines from his own inspection how the grain is to be binned in the elevator. Incoming grain loses its identity when run into a bin with other grain and may be blended again with grain from other bins before it is inspected on out movement. The "out" inspection is made from samples drawn after the grain is loaded into a car or before it enters the shipping bin, or after it leaves the elevator spout upon entering a vessel.

Public-warehouse men may be requested to store grain in their elevators for others on terms of "separate bin" or "identity preserved." If the operator consents to this request, the stored grain is kept separate and the warehouse receipt issued for the grain is marked to that effect and also states the bin number or other identification of its location.

Terminal grain elevators have equipment that would be useful only to houses of their size and in handling great quantities of grain, often of different kinds. The size of storage bins containing a great mass of grain makes necessary means by which quality may be watched without having to remove the grain from a bin, run it on the belts, elevate it, and return it to the storage bin. For this purpose there are bin thermometer systems to check on the temperature of the grain. The thermometers are placed about five feet apart and attached to a cable running down the middle of the bin. Separate contact can be made with each thermometer and readings made in a central office. The temperatures recorded keep the operator informed of the condition of the grain in each portion of the bins, thereby saving the expense of turning the grain on suspicion.

Dust-collecting systems gather the dust from sweepings and various other operations and from machines located throughout an elevator. The dust is carried along by air currents and allowed to settle in a cyclone from which it is gathered. The dust has a market value and is sold into the feed trade.

Terminal elevators differ in the equipment installed to carry out their functions. Driers are used to reduce the amount of moisture in grains for safe storage or shipping quality; oat clippers are used to increase test weight per measured bushel; and bleaching plants are used for sulphuring oats to improve the color. Some elevators have separators, washers, sizing machines, cleaning machines, and magnets placed where the grain is moving to remove tramp iron in order to protect machinery and avoid sparks. Some elevators also have sacking facilities. A large elevator needs sufficient trackage on which to hold cars before they are loaded, on which empties can be coopered, etc., and await loading or, after they are loaded, on which they can be held until the grain is sampled and inspected before being released to the railroad for transportation.

Grain placed in a terminal elevator is usually the property of the operator. They also contract storage space to shippers who hold the grain prior to its sale, or to processors to carry grain in excess of processor's storage facilities. Both types of firms reserve this space prior to or during the harvest movement and normally pay for the use of the storage room for a period of several months whether or not it is used.

When the elevator operator issues a warehouse receipt, the charges are printed thereon and payment is made by the party who ships out the grain. It is a requirement in Chicago, however, that storage charges must be paid up to the eighteenth day of the month previous to its delivery on a futures contract. Any storage accruing after the date to which the storage is paid is allowed by the seller to the buyer on the futures-delivery notice.

Storage rates differ at the various markets but are charged at a daily rate at all of them. Free time of varying duration is given at only some locations, but all ports give free time on export grain.

The charge for elevation in Chicago, including both putting the grain into the elevator and loading it out, is paid by the party who orders it out of the elevator. Terminal markets vary in the amount of the charge and as to who is responsible for it. Some markets divide the elevation charge between incoming and outgoing handling. Eastern Great Lakes elevators collect it from the railroads, which include it in the at-and-east freight rate.

Tariffs are published by each public-elevator operator covering the charges for services which they perform. When grain threatens to go out of condition, they notify the owner, asking for his consent to run the grain to cool it or to treat it for weevil, etc. If consent is not forthcoming, or if handling will not condition the grain, the owner is obliged to issue shipping instructions. The condition of grain in Chicago for which warehouse receipts have been delivered on futures contracts is watched by the warehouseman, but there are Federal and Board of Trade regulations stating the procedure to be followed if this grain should be moved. Meanwhile, the operator must condition the delivery grain at his own expense and after due notice, etc., must load out grain of the grade called for in the warehouse receipt, on the requirements of the regulations.

Barge Elevators

A special kind of grain elevator is one located on the bank of a river handling incoming truck grain to be loaded into barges on the out movement. Some elevators may also load out grain into cars. Since the middle of the 1930's there has been a revival of the former type of Illinois and Michigan Canal grain movement, which started the same year as the Chicago Board of Trade was organized, in 1848. Most of the elevators handling this business are modern, fast-operating, reinforced-concrete houses that have a grain capacity of up to several hundred thousand bushels. They do no conditioning but only transfer the grain from trucks to barges, holding it until there is a sufficient amount on hand to load a barge; or they await the arrival of a sufficient number of barges to load out enough grain to make room for more incoming grain. They do not have many storage bins, as there usually are not many kinds of grain moving out of the farming area at one time; it is mostly corn. The barge transportation rate is low, and in combination with the trucking rates from the farms it is less than the combined truck and rail rates from the same origins to barge destinations. The railroad reshipping-rate privileges from Chicago on ex-barge grain are more favorable than on incoming rail grain from the same origins, because there is no requirement of minimum rate paid in which is necessary to move out rail grain to obtain certain transit privileges. Many barge elevators are operated by terminal elevator firms, but some are independently operated and sell their grain on the open market.

Eastern Lake Elevators

Elevators at ports located at the eastern end of the Great Lakes—principally Buffalo—receive a great share of their grain from lake boats. Some of these elevators have marine towers containing marine legs that can be moved on tracks alongside the elevator to accommodate unloading steamers. All marine legs, however, are not movable. Elevators at these locations can load out trucks, cars, barges, or steamers that move to various eastern destinations.

Export Elevators

Some export-port elevators have loading galleries to supply grain to more than one ocean vessel docked alongside at the same time. One elevator in particular has no railroad facilities because it receives barge grain and ships out via ocean steamers. A different kind of a transfer elevator is a floating elevator in the port of New York. Upon arrival at the port the grain is dumped from cars into lighters which are towed to the ocean steamer. The elevators are brought alongside the ocean vessel, with the lighters on the other side, and the elevator lifts the grain out of one and drops it into the other. These floating elevators are very efficient and often mix grain from several barges or lighters while loading a steamer. Free towing of lighters is provided in the rates of the incoming railroads to any ship's location in the port.

Vessel Storage

"Winter storage" is the practice of loading grain into steamers at the close of navigation on the Great Lakes and storing the grain in them for the winter. This is done on the last trip of the season. The grain stores well, as it is loaded during cold weather and unloaded before the weather warms up in the spring; but the vessel is kept in a position so that the condition of the grain can be watched. The usual terms of payment are a rate covering the freight for the trip of the vessel to its destination and including storage until the following April first. The rate is higher than the seasonal voyage trip, but the excess is considerably less than the storage that would be paid to hold the grain in an elevator. When the vessel arrives at its destination it is moored or anchored in a location accessible to an elevator so that it may be unloaded at the convenience of the owner of the grain. One free tow to an elevator is provided in the contract, and if the owner does not unload the entire cargo at that time he has to pay for extra towing.

Many millions of bushels of grain are held in winter storage annually. Operators of elevators at the western end of the lakes are anxious to reduce their stocks to make room for the winter's accumulation of fresh arrivals from interior locations. The grain shipped down the lakes for this business goes to all the eastern lake ports and, in addition, to Lake Michigan ports, which usually receive grain of Canadian origin. As grain is needed either for export or for domestic consumption, the elevators take the winter-storage grain and the boats are released. There is usually very little to be unloaded from steamers at the end of the contract period.

Some boats are loaded and held at the loading port to provide storage over and above the port's elevator capacity. These boats may sail to an eastern destination in the spring or they may be unloaded where they are.

Emergency Storage

At times under crowded conditions, grain has been stored in "bad order" boxcars at a grain elevator on special agreements with the railroads. Also, there have been all kinds of structures used for temporary storage.

Laws

Laws governing the operation of grain elevators differ in each state. If the grain handled is owned by the elevator operator no license is necessary. In Illinois, the Public Warehouse-Receipt Act regulates and licenses elevators in which grain is stored for compensation, in which elevators the grain of different depositors is stored together or, if the operator consents, the identity of the grain is preserved in separate bins. Warehouses located in cities having not less than 100,000 inhabitants have separate rules for reporting and publishing amounts and grades of grain held in storage. One feature of the law is that in no case shall grain of different grades be mixed together while in storage without the written consent of the depositors affected. A warehouse receipt for all grain deposited must be delivered to the depositor within 15 days following receipt of the grain for storage. Each operator is required to file with the Illinois Commerce Commission a surety bond for the faithful performance of his duties and to post in a conspicuous place his schedule of rates for storage of grain. Grain received in excess of licensed capacity may be forwarded to certain other warehouses, and the redepositing warehouseman is responsible to the original depositor regarding disposition of the grain. Grain going out of condition or grain that is out of condition that cannot be restored may after proper notification and advertising be sold at public auction.

A custom of operators of country elevators in the northwestern states is to issue "storage tickets" to depositors of grain. Though different from warehouse receipts, these tickets carry the same essentials of security of warehousing and choice of time of sale of the grain at the discretion of the depositor.

The United States Warehouse Act may be used to regulate grain stored for interstate or foreign commerce, or grain stored in any place under the exclusive jurisdiction of the United States. The law may be applied to any agricultural product, provided that rules and regulations have been made for the particular product. Many grain elevators throughout the nation are operated under the provisions of this law and are generally referred to as Federal-licensed elevators. When grain is stored on the grade, it must have been inspected by a licensed inspector and weighed by an official weigher. The law provides for the licensing of inspectors to inspect grain stored in a warehouse for which they hold a license, or for grain to be inspected by an inspector licensed under the United States Grain Standards Act.[4]

A warehouseman may not mix lots of different grades of grain stored or received for storage, except when a depositor surrenders receipts covering two or more lots and requests the warehouseman to deliver the amount of grain represented by the canceled receipts in such a manner that they will become one lot. The balance of the grain, if any, resulting from this operation after weighing and inspecting is to be stored with grain of like grade.[5]

The warehouseman must keep stocks of grain in storage by grades, in balance with the grades of grain represented by outstanding receipts, except when the grain has unavoidably

---

[4] U.S.D.A., *Code of Federal Regulations,* Title 7, Chapter 1, Part 102; reprint, Nov., 1947.

[5] U.S. Warehouse Act, *Regulations,* Sec. 102.50.

improved or deteriorated through natural causes. In case the grades of stored grain should get out of balance with grades represented by outstanding receipts, the warehouseman effects proper adjustments.[6] Upon proper presentation of a receipt for any grain, the warehouseman delivers grain of the grade and quantity named in such receipt.[7]

There are some special conditions covering terminal and futures-contract markets. One feature is that where bond requirements of a board of trade exceed the requirements of the United States Warehouse Act, the additional amount shall be required for the protection of the public. The administrator may approve a registrar to register warehouse receipts in terminal or contract markets. Under this provision, all warehouse receipts must be registered and any change in ownership reported to the registrar by the owner. All registered receipts are entitled to protection from stored grain going out of condition. After prescribed notifications, examination of the grain, consultations, etc., between the warehouseman and the chief inspector, or chief sampler in the market, or a specially appointed committee, if it is agreed that the grain should be loaded out the registrar and the administrator are notified. The registrar selects the oldest warehouse receipts as no longer being regular for delivery on futures contracts and notifies the holders or their agents and the president of the contract market of the condition of the grain and the necessity of its being loaded out.

The president of the contract market appoints a committee of five, who meet at once; and after taking into consideration various factors that establish the value of the grade of grain called for by the receipts, the committee determines the fair value of the grain on the basis of the market quotations. This price is paid to the owner of each receipt by the licensed warehouseman. If the price offered is not satisfactory to any owner,

---

[6] *Ibid.,* Sec. 102.51.
[7] *Ibid.,* Sec. 102.48.

a committee appointed by the president procures other offers for the grain, which are immediately reported to the owner. If the owner refuses to accept any such offers, he has the two following business days to order and furnish facilities for loading the grain out of store. During this period the warehouseman is obliged to deliver the grain covered by the warehouse receipts; but not more than three days may elapse after notification by the registrar to the holder of the receipts before satisfactory disposition of the grain is made either by sale or by ordering out and furnishing facilities to load the grain, provided the amount does not exceed 100,000 bushels in any one elevator (the owner has 48 hours additional for each additional 100,000 bushels or fraction thereof). If the owner fails to remove the grain or to make other satisfactory disposition within the prescribed time, it will be held for his account, and any loss in grade sustained shall likewise be for his account.[8]

Exchange Regulations

The Chicago Board of Trade has a regulation—similar to that of the United States Warehouse Act covering grain that may go out of condition—for grain held in Illinois state-licensed elevators regular for delivery on futures contracts. It has regulations whereby, under its Custodian Department, for grain in elevators which are really private warehouses, custodian warehouse receipts are issued to the owner covering his own grain in storage to be used as collateral for a bank loan. The certificates state only the kind of grain, no class or grade of the grain.

A deputy of the Custodian Department is placed in the elevator to keep records of the commodities unloaded into or out of the elevator together with weights and other pertinent data. He seals bins to prevent removal of grain during his absence, sees that the operator carries the proper insurance, and also watches over various operations. Official custodian

---

[8] *Ibid.*, Sec. 102.110.

certificates are issued covering grain in the elevator, but it is required that there be at least 3% grain in the house over the total represented by outstanding custodian certificates. No grain may be removed from a warehouse without surrender to the Custodian Department of the certificate properly endorsed. Grain stored in custodian elevators is not deliverable on futures contracts.

Weighing

Grain weighed into and out of Chicago elevators or within elevators is under the supervision of the Chicago Board of Trade Weighing Department, the services of which are extended to the supervised as well as the private elevators in the Chicago market. The United States Warehouse Act authorizes issuance of licenses to such a weighmaster and his deputies.

The Weighing Department has direct supervision of all equipment used in securing the weight of grain and has scale-testing equipment, including United States standard test weights, for use in the field. All scales are tested and approved before certification of weights. When weighing a car of incoming grain, the deputy weighman examines the car for leaks, noting any leakages on a condition blank, and records the seals protecting the car doors. He examines and balances the scale and sees that the weighing is done without delay. It is the duty of the deputy weighman to prevent waste and to see that each car is thoroughly swept after unloading.

The certificate of weight and/or the weight records issued by the Weighing Department are used (1) in determining the quantity of grain in settlement between the country shipper and the terminal buyer, (2) as evidence of the amount of grain delivered on a futures contract, (3) as the basis of payment of freight to the inbound carrier, (4) in substantiation of claims against a railroad for losses in transit, either to or from Chicago, and (5) as the basis of payment to the outbound carrier.

Another storage agreement is that of the United States Department of Agriculture Commodity Credit Corporation—

the Uniform Grain-Storage Agreement—between the government agency and warehousemen with elevators of all sizes and descriptions located throughout the country. There are many conditions to be met by the warehouseman. Special schedules of rates are applicable to receiving, storing, loading out, insurance, conditioning the grain, etc., probably differing from tariffs filed by the warehouses for their regular service charges. In general, the agreement does not change the operations of an elevator or the state or Federal license conditions under which they operate. From time to time the agreement conditions and rates are altered to meet changing aspects of government programs and costs of storing grain.

CHAPTER VIII

Inspection

Purpose

The advantages of the grading system are many. It provides the required incentive to the farmer to farm well, since he has the assurance that his return will be determined by the quality of his crop. His grading certificate provides him with bank credit immediately. Then grading is the absolute prerequisite of bulk handling. If grain is not graded it cannot be bulked with other grain, but must retain its identity and be sampled frequently for selling purposes. The immense economy of the terminal storage system is only possible after dependable grading. Next, it alone provides the basis upon which organized marketing, future sales, and hedging become possible. This forms the most economic machinery for financing the crop, paying cash to the farmer months before the grain is exported, holding it, transporting it, and getting it to the miller. Finally, it provides the last buyer with a standard article upon which he may depend in the same manner that buyers depend on the trade-mark of goods manufactured by reputable firms. It only becomes a possible international system of certificate final terms when experience shows—as it does—that the grading in the exporting country is entirely dependable.[1]

The United States Grain Standards Act[2]

The United States Grain Standards Act, passed August 11, 1916, provides in part for (1) the establishment of official

[1] S. J. Duly (City of London College), *Grain,* 1928.

[2] Willis B. Combs and Fred G. Smith, *Grain Grading Primer;* U.S.D.A., revised ed., May, 1950. *Handbook of Official Grain Standards of the United States.*

grain standards, (2) the Federal licensing and supervision of the work of grain inspectors, and (3) the entertaining of appeals from the grades assigned by the licensed inspectors. The Secretary of Agriculture is authorized to make investigations and to establish Federal standards for the most common grains. Federal standards are now in effect for wheat, corn, barley, oats, feed oats, mixed feed oats, rye, grain sorghums, flaxseed, soybeans, and mixed grains.

The act provides in part that all grain shipped in interstate or foreign commerce to or from a point at which an inspector licensed under the act is located must be officially inspected and graded if the grain is merchandised by grade. As most of the grain that reaches any important market is moving in interstate or foreign commerce by grade, it is necessary for practical purposes that grain inspectors hold Federal licenses to inspect and grade grain.

Licensed Inspectors

Most of the licensed grain inspectors are employed by state or by trade organizations and are paid salaries by the agencies that employ them. Some licensed inspectors work independently for fixed fees and are paid by those who request their services. No licensed grain inspectors are employed by the Federal Government.

Appeal

The grain-grading activities of all federally licensed grain inspectors are supervised by Federal supervisors of grain inspection employed by the United States Department of Agriculture and stationed at important grain markets. In the first instance, grain is graded by a licensed grain inspector. Any person financially interested in the grade of any lot of grain may appeal from the grade assigned by a licensed inspector to the Secretary of Agriculture through the local grain supervisor. For the purpose of appeal a new sample of the grain is drawn. There is a fee for the appeal service, which, however, is refunded if the inspector's grade is changed. It is necessary to surrender the certificate issued by the licensed inspector, in place of which the supervisor issues an appeal certificate. A review of the supervisor's grade designation may also be called by any interested party; this is called a "board appeal." For this purpose a new sample is not usually drawn, but the findings of the supervisor are reviewed by Boards of Review at Chicago and at Portland, Oregon. Finally, recourse may be had to the Secretary of Agriculture. There is no reason why anyone should suffer loss from an incorrect grading if he exercises his rights under the Grain Standards Act.

Any appeal from the licensed inspector's grade determination must be taken before the grain leaves the place where the appealed inspection was made—before the identity of the grain has been lost and within the reasonable time prescribed. Incoming cars of grain are resealed on the inspection track after the sample for the original inspection is drawn. The appeal sample may be taken before the car is switched to the unloading elevator, or it may be taken later when the car arrives at the elevator, as agreed between buyer's agent and seller. Unusual delays on this procedure are costly to the country shipper, because he is responsible for any deterioration in quality occurring between the original inspection and the final grade. It is of course favorable to the terminal buyer to delay the final inspection as long as possible.

Appeal of grain grade on outgoing cars or vessels may be ordered before the lot is loaded, but it may also be ordered for cars after the licensed inspector's grade is known. Buyers and sellers have the same right of appeal on grain loaded out of elevators after it has been delivered on futures contracts as they do under other circumstances. Appeal is frequently ordered by exporters when grain is loaded at interior inspection points, for it gives them more assurance of securing the required grade at the port of export. At times exporters have no other grain on hand in the seaboard elevator than that which they have bought on grade and had shipped from an interior terminal market, so that Federal appeal is an added protection to meet their export-sale grade requirements. At other times the exporter accumulates grain from country stations in the interior to be mixed in the export elevator at the time of loading on the ocean vessel; then reliance is placed on the export elevator to blend the grain to secure the desired grade—the same service performed by interior terminal elevators when making domestic shipments.

Sampling Methods

When an inspector grades a sample secured from a lot of grain, whether it is in a car, barge, vessel, or an elevator bin, it should be representative of the entire lot of the grain, and the first essential step in grading grain is to obtain a correct and representative sample of the lot. Considering that there are about one million kernels of wheat or 600,000 kernels of oats in a bushel, each kernel in the sample represents a large number of kernels in the lot sampled. The basic instructions issued by the United States Department of Agriculture on this subject provide for a sample not less than approximately two quarts in size.

Carlots, Trucks and Wagons.—In the case of bulk grain in a car, truck, or wagon, or in any other container in which the grain is about the same depth as in a carload, the sample is taken with a double-tube compartment trier 62⅝ inches long by probing flaxseed in seven or more, and other grains in five or more, well distributed places in different parts of the car. At the discretion of the sampler, as many more probings as may be necessary may be taken from the grain in different parts of the lot.

As each probe of the grain is drawn, the grain is emptied upon a canvas for examination. If, after examination of each small pile of grain from the separate compartments of each probing, no material portion of the grain is found to be distinctly inferior to the rest, the grain from the separate probings is combined as an average sample. If grain of distinctly different qualities are found, separate samples are drawn and a "dual" grade certificate is issued showing approximate quantity and grade of each portion. If the time to elapse between the drawing of the sample and the determination of grade is enough to permit changes in the condition of the sample that might affect the grade, a representative portion of at least 1⅛ pints of the grain should be enclosed in an airtight container; at country elevators a pail with a tight cover to hold the entire sample is often used. A device known as a "truck sampler" has been developed for cutting the grain stream as it falls from a truck. Automatic sampling devices for use in grain elevators are also being developed by research.

Bins in Elevators.—In the case of bulk grain in bins and warehouses, where the depth of the grain is so great as not to permit thorough probing with a trier of either standard or special length, or where conditions make it hazardous for a person to enter the bin, grain should be transferred and samples taken from a falling stream of grain pouring into or from the bin. Samples from the falling stream are taken with a device known as a spout sampler, or "pelican," or with any other device that gives equivalent results.

Cargo Grain.—The pelican, used to sample grain being loaded on a boat, barge, or other vessel, samples the stream at regular and frequent intervals to assure a correct and representative sample of the lot. Grain may also be sampled on an elevator belt while it is running to the shipping bin prior to loading on a steamer. When it appears that the cargo lot being sampled is not uniform in quality and condition, because of the presence of a material portion of grain of a different grade, the licensed inspector considers the portions of such lot, parcel, or cargo which are of different grades as separate lots tendered for inspection, and separately inspects, grades, and certificates as to grade such different portions; and each such certificate of grade must bear a statement to the effect that the grain to which it applies has been loaded on board with other grain, the grade, description, and approximate quantity of which is also specified.

Analysis

To reduce the size of a sample containing foreign substances of different specific gravity or size from those of the grain with which they are mixed, and at the same time to obtain a sample as representative as the original, is hardly possible except by mechanical means. A device generally referred to as a "Boerner sampler" divides the sample into smaller portions and still maintains proper proportions for the various factors of the original sample. The grain is placed in a hopper at the top of the machine and then released directly over the center and down the sides of a cone. Around the base of the cone are 36 pockets or openings which cut the grain into 36 streams. Alternate streams unite into one stream, which empties into one receptacle and the other streams empty into a second receptacle. The sample may be reduced as many times as it takes to obtain the final size sample desired. This device is a "must" for inspectors and grain-elevator operators who use grades.

Some of the tests of grain quality that producers and consumers have always considered important are tests for plumpness, soundness, cleanliness, dryness, purity of type, and the general condition of the grain. Plumpness is measured by the weight-per-bushel test, supplemented by sizing tests for some grains. Soundness is indicated by the absence of musty, sour, or commercially objectionable foreign odors and by the proportion of damaged kernels in the grain. Cleanliness is measured by determining the foreign-matter content; dryness by making a moisture test. Purity of type is provided for by classes of the various grains and by limitations for admixtures of other grains or of other classes of the same grain.

"Condition" is a general term and refers to whether the grain is in sound condition or is out of condition because it is musty, sour, or heating. Condition is also indicated by such designations as "smutty," "garlicky," "weevily," "bright," "stained," "tough," or "treated," which describe various conditions in which grain is sometimes found.

In the commercial grading of grain, the lot as a whole is examined at the time of sampling for the condition factors of temperature, odor, infestation of live weevils, and any other noticeable factor not requiring a detailed analysis. When samples are brought to the inspection office, dockage tests, weight-per-bushel tests, and moisture tests are usually made first. Further analysis is made for such grading factors as the careful examination of the sample may have indicated are important. For making further tests, a representative portion of the sample is taken from either the mechanically cleaned grain or from the sample as a whole, as governed by the basis of determination of the standards.

In standard inspection procedure, all determinations based on fractional parts of a sample are made on standard-sized portions cut from the sample by means of the Boerner divider. When the grade of any lot of grain is determined by a narrow margin concerning a single factor, another determination is made on an additional portion, and the grade is based on the average of the two determinations. All percentages except moisture are percentages by weight.

Grading Factors

Grain falls into various classes and sub-classes identified almost entirely by the grader's knowledge of and familiarity with the different kinds of grain that come under his observation. Color, kernel texture, and variety characteristics are helpful indexes in determining class or sub-class of many of the grains.

Grades of grains are defined by specifications of factors limiting each numercial grade. The numerical grade is determined by the lowest grading factor as determined in the analysis. Test weight per Winchester bushel (2,150.42 cubic inches) except for Western Barley is a factor in all grains. Other grading factors are foreign material (in some grains the percentage of cracked grain is combined with the foreign material), damaged kernels with limitation of heat damage included, grains of the same kind but of other classes including colors, percentage of splits in soybeans, and in oats the minimum percentage of sound, cultivated kernels.

If the grain is tough, smutty, garlicky, weevily, treated (the kind of treatment), ergoty, etc., it is graded and designated according to the grade requirements of the standards applicable to such grain if it were not so, and the special grade designation is added to and made part of the grade.

Test Weight per Bushel.—Test weight is an important index of the pounds of flour that may be milled from a bushel of wheat. Millers prefer wheat of high test-weight-per-bushel quality, and premiums are usually paid for such wheat.

To determine the test weight per bushel of any grain, approximately 1⅛ quarts of grain should be used. When this test is made with wheat, rye, or barley the dockage must be removed. With corn, oats, and soybeans, for which there is no dockage provision, and with grain sorghums, the original sample of each of these grains, inclusive of foreign material, is used.

In making the weight-per-bushel test, the one-quart bucket of the testing device is placed beneath a funneled hopper having a capacity of approximately 1⅛ quarts of grain. In the bottom of this hopper should be an opening 1¼ inches in diameter, and the bottom of the hopper must be placed two inches above the top of the bucket. Grain from the hopper is allowed to pour into the bucket until it overflows. Without moving or jarring the heaped bucket, the grain is leveled off with a special smooth, round-edged stick in three zigzag strokes. The scale beam of the test-weight-per-bushel apparatus should never be used to level off the grain, because the constant wearing effect on the beam and bucket will eventually affect their accuracy and because the square-edged beam has a tendency to hollow out the surface of the grain in the bucket, which will cause a lower test-weight-per-bushel reading than does the official method.

Moisture-testing.—Dryness has always been a much-sought-after quality in grain. Any grain that contains moisture in excess of its normal air-dry condition is nearly always unsafe for storage, especially if the grain is stored at a high temperature. The water oven is specified in the official standards as the official tester for determining the percentage of moisture in corn, and the air oven is specified for all of the other grains. In practice, however, the moisture content of any grain may be found by any device and method for ascertaining moisture percentage that will give results equivalent to those obtained by the water- or air-oven tests. Two types of moisture-testers now in use give quicker results than can be obtained by either oven test.

One of the rapid testers is the electric moisture meter used by all Federal grain supervisors and also by a large majority of the licensed grain inspectors throughout the United States. To make a moisture test with this apparatus, not less than 150 grams of small grain or 250 grams of corn are passed between two roller electrodes. The meter measures the electrical resistance of the grain as it passes between these electrodes. Tables are used to convert the electrical resistance into terms of percentage of moisture in the grain.

The other type of rapid tester is the Brown-Duvel moisture-tester. To determine the moisture content of grain, 100 grams of grain are mixed with 150 cubic centimeters of suitable engine oil in a distillaton flask. Heat is then applied and the water is distilled into a graduated cylinder to determine the percentage of moisture in the grain.

Moisture percentage is a factor in the numerical grade of corn, soybeans, and grain sorghums, but wheat, barley, oats, and rye have maximum moisture percentages for all numerical grades. These maximum moisture percentages differ with the various grains and even between some classes of wheat and of barley. If the moisture exceeds a set percentage but is under a certain maximum, the designation "tough" is added to the grade. There are exceptions for flaxseed. Above the maximum moisture percentage any grain is graded "sample grade."

Dockage.—Dockage determination is provided in Federal standards for wheat, rye, barley, flaxseed, and grain sorghums, and is noted as part of the grade designation but does not lower the grade. In wheat, rye, and barley dockage may be defined as the foreign material which can be removed readily by appropriate sieves and cleaning devices and undeveloped, shriveled, and small pieces of grain removed in separating the foreign material which cannot be recovered by rescreening or recleaning. In the case of grain sorghums, dockage consists only of the material that will pass through a prescribed sieve. Some of the dockage material, such as other grains and wild oats, is valuable for feed, but most dockage is worthless. Much of the material, like green weed seeds or finely broken grains or fine dust, contributes toward grain heating or becoming musty unless the grain is exceptionally dry. Machines may be used in determining dockage in place of hand sieves. Dockage, stated in whole percentages, with fractions of one per cent disregarded, is calculated on the basis of the total weight of the grain including the dockage. Dockage differs from foreign material in that it can be readily removed from the grain by appropriate cleaning machinery. When grain is sold the percentage of dockage is deducted from the gross amount of grain and payment is made only for the amount of dockage-free grain.

Damaged Grain.—Damage is divided into types—field and storage damage. In turn, field damage may be subdivided into two kinds—preventable and non-preventable. Frost damage and such fungus damage as scab and cobrot may be considered practically beyond the control of the grower, although much of the damage caused by these fungus diseases may be reduced by crop rotation and seed treatment. On the other hand, grade loss from sprouted and stack-stained, ground-damaged, and weather-damaged kernels and damage resulting from such fungus diseases as smut are more or less preventable.

Storage-damaged grain includes heat-damaged, weevil-damaged, and moldly grain. Damage caused in storage usually is preventable, because it all takes place in storage bins which are under the control of the operator of the storage facilities. Ventilation or artificial drying of high-moisture grain and fumigation are the usual means for preventing damage in storage. Ordinarily more grain is damaged during storage than from all sources of damage to grain in the field.

Official interpretations of damaged kernel in grain when grain is being inspected and graded are conveyed to grain inspectors by means of type samples and by Federal grain-inspection supervisors' review of individual samples containing damaged kernels.

Damage in Wheat.—Some types of damage in wheat are frosted, weevil- or insect-bored, sprouted, blighted and scabby, sick wheat, green kernels, other damaged kernels, and heat-damaged. "Sick wheat" is a term applied to a type of storage damage usually associated with brown, discolored germs, evidence of dead, deteriorated germs and of other damage to the kernel. Bulk samples of sick wheat usually have a dank off-odor. Development of sick wheat is favored by abnormally high temperatures and moisture conditions and is highly unlikely to occur in wheat stored at safe moisture values (below 12%) and at moderate temperatures (below 70 degrees). No cure exists for sick wheat except the obvious preventive of storing the grain from the time of harvest under dry and cool conditions with frequent inspection and turning and possibly drying.

Unfit for Mixing.—Under the provisions of the Federal Food, Drug and Cosmetic Act wheat may be "tagged" or condemned as unfit for mixing with wheat of a higher grade when it is pungently musty or sour, when it contains a high percentage of damaged kernels, with or without heat damage, and when it has deteriorated to the point where it is essentially unsound or contaminated. Wheat is tagged as an adulterant, and the term "unfit for human consumption" as used by the trade may or may not apply.

Hidden Infestation.—Grains that may grade "number one" may actually have infested kernels. If this grain is used in milling, not all the hidden infestation can be removed and some of the different stages of weevils, together with cast skins and excrement, will be ground up in the milling process and the finished flour or meal will contain fragments. There are methods of detecting hidden infestation by the use of dyes which stain the egg plugs and weevil punctures, but because of certain objections these staining methods are ruled out. Other methods are by X ray, or by placing a sample of wheat in a flat-bottomed pan, pouring a pint of 2% solution of ferric nitrate in water over the wheat, thus causing the weevil-damaged kernels to float to the surface, where they can be counted. These two methods are still being researched. The Food and Drug Administration recommend a visual examination of 100 grams of wheat for exit holes.

Damage in Corn and Soybeans.—Corn damage may be blue eye mold, damaged germ, weevil-bored kernels, slight surface mold, silk cut, heat-damaged kernels, or slight discoloration by heat.

Soybean damage may be from frost, which in cross section may be an intense green or a less intense color, immature damage, heat damage, insect-damaged kernels, sprout and other damage, stain, mottle, or slight surface mold.

Classes

There are seven classes of wheat: Class I, hard red spring; Class II, durum; Class III, red durum; Class IV, hard red winter; Class V, soft red winter; Class VI, white; and Class VII, mixed wheat. The official standards provide that wheat of any class, except mixed wheat, may contain not more than 10% of wheat of a different class or classes, either singly or combined. Classes are for the baker and designate consumer use, i.e., bread, pastry, cake, etc. Grades are for the miller and indicate flour yield and storability.

Hard red spring and hard red winter wheats are especially

suited for making bread flour. These two wheats contain a large quantity of strong elastic gluten—an essential element in making a bread that meets public favor in the United States.

Durum wheat is used in making semolina that is especially suited for the manufacture of macaroni, spaghetti, vermicelli and other alimentary pastes. The principal use for red durum wheat is for poultry and stock feed.

Soft-red-winter- and white-wheat flours, both usually low in protein content, are especially suited for making pastry, crackers, biscuits, cakes, and similar products.

Sub-classes of hard red spring wheat are (*a*) dark northern spring, (*b*) northern spring, and (*c*) red spring. Sub-classes of durum wheat are (*a*) hard amber durum, (*b*) amber durum, and (*c*) durum. Red durum wheat has no sub-classes. Hard red winter wheat sub-classes are (*a*) dark hard winter, (*b*) hard winter, and (*c*) yellow hard winter. Soft red winter wheat sub-classes are (*a*) red winter and (*b*) western red. Sub-classes of white wheat are (*a*) hard white, (*b*) soft white, (*c*) white club, and (*d*) western white. Numerical grades of wheat are one through five and "sample grade."

Corn classes are yellow, white, and mixed corn. There are five numerical grades and sample grade.

Barley classes are Barley, Western Barley, and Mixed Barley. Barley sub-classes are (1) malting barley, (2) blue malting barley, and (3) barley. Western Barley of some grades and varieties may be classed as malting barley. There are five numerical grades and "sample grade" for all classes of barley, except that malting barley has only three grades. "White" (malting) or "blue" is determined by the color of the aleurone layers.

The sub-classes of oats standards (except feed or mixed-feed oats) are white oats, red oats, gray oats, black oats, and mixed oats. There is a grade of special red oats, which consists of Columbia oats or other red oats having similar characteristics. Numerical grades of oats are numbers one through four plus "sample-grade oats."

Rye has no sub-classes, but has four numerical grades, plus "sample-grade rye."

Grain sorghums are divided into five classes, with some classes having sub-classes: Class I, white grain sorghums, having sub-classes (*a*) white Kafir, (*b*) white Durra, and (*c*) white grain sorghums; Class II, yellow grain sorghums, with sub-classes (*a*) yellow milo and (*b*) yellow grain sorghums; Class III, red grain sorghums, with subclasses (*a*) red Kafir and (*b*) red grain sorghums; Class IV, brown grain sorghums; and Class V, mixed grain sorghums. There are four numerical grades of grain sorghums and "sample grade."

There is no sub-class of flaxseed, but there are numerical grades one, two, and "sample grade."

Soybean classes are five: yellow, green, brown, black, and mixed. There are four numerical grades, plus "sample grade."

The feed oats and mixed-feed oats standards are each divided into three numerical grades and "sample grade."

Standards for "mixed grain" define it as any mixture of those grains for which standards have been established that does not fall within the requirements of any of the standards for such grains and that does not contain more than 50% foreign material. Wild oats in mixed grain are classed as a grain.

Inspection Service

There are approximately 200 grain-inspection offices and laboratories distributed throughout the country where official sampling and inspection are available. Unofficial samples of grain may also be taken at locations where no inspection laboratory is located, in which case the sample may be forwarded to a laboratory for official analysis and issuance of an inspection certificate covering the submitted sample. This is a service valuable to country dealers in getting a line on correct grading.

The official grain standards do not include protein-content analysis, which is a recognized test for trading in wheat in a number of markets, as it is an important factor in the wheat-milling industry. This analysis is made by trade chemists.

Inspection in Canada

Most of the grain grown in Canada is produced in the western prairie provinces of Manitoba, Saskatchewan, and Alberta. Canadian "statutory grades" are defined in the Canadian Grain Act, but the act also provides that the Western Committee on Grain Standards name and define standards for "commercial grades." The grain-inspection branch of the Board of Grain Commissioners performs the same function as the United States grain-inspection service does.

The Western Committee on Grain Standards meets annually as soon as possible after the first day of August to select and settle standard samples for each statutory grade. The committee also names and defines all such commercial grades of western grain as, in its opinion, it is advisable to establish for the current crop year, and it selects and settles the standard samples representing the minimum of each of such commercial grades. The board establishes specifications for off-grades—all kinds or varieties of grain that cannot be assigned to any statutory or commercial grade unless treated or specially cleaned.

The procedure followed by Canadian inspectors is briefly as follows:

1. Determination of weight per bushel. (The Canadian bushel is the imperial bushel—2,219.36 cubic inches.)
2. Determination of the percentage of dockage (weed seeds and other foreign matter). According to the Canadian Grain Act, all grain except certain feed grains received at terminal elevators must be cleaned to remove all the dockage assessed against it on primary inspection so that when it is shipped from terminal elevators it does not contain any dockage. Inspectors at the terminal elevators carefully examine samples of all shipments to insure that the grain is commercially clean.
3. Examination as to type, variety, color, soundness, and maturity. In some classes of grains one variety is used as the

standard of quality. Thus Marquis is the standard for hard red spring wheat for number-one Manitoba hard and number-one and number-two Manitoba northern. Mindum is the standard for amber durum wheat, and O.A.C. 21 is the standard for barley grading number-one and number-two Canada western, six-row.

4. Determination of the percentage of foreign material other than dockage.
5. Examination as to condition (moisture content) by standard moisture-testing equipment.
6. Comparison with statutory definitions for the different grades.
7. Comparison with the actual standard samples.

Wheat grades sold in the export trade in normal years are numbers one, two, and three Manitoba northern, which are the predominating grades grown. Other grades of red spring wheat are the top grade, number-one Manitoba hard, plus the grades of number-four Manitoba, number-four special, number-five and number-five special, number-six and number-six special, as well as feed wheat. There are grades for garnet wheat, winter wheat, amber durum wheat, red durum wheat, soft white spring wheat, white spring wheat, and mixed wheat.

All grain containing the odor of smut, or having smut balls, etc., is classed as "smutty," and the designation is added to the grade according to the grade requirements of such grain. "Tough" or "damp" classes are added as grade designations according to the percentage of excessive moisture over straight grade tolerances. "Dried," "scoured," or "washed" are added to the grade designation when moisture has been reduced; or, in the judgment of the inspector, these designations may be omitted when the grain complies with the straight-grade standard sample. "Rejected" is added as a grade designation to the recognized grades on account of mixtures of cereal grains, or "sample" is added when there is an excess of other factors.

Oats grades are numbers one, two, extra-three, and three

Canada Western, extra-one feed, one, two, three, and mixed-feed oats. Test weights per bushel range from 40 pounds for extra-three Canada western down to 28 pounds for number-two feed; there is no test-weight requirement for lower grades of oats. The oats test weight is per-imperial-bushel, but as the weighted bushel is 34 pounds compared with the United States Winchester bushel of 32 pounds, care must be exercised when calculating comparative price relationships between the two.

Barley grades of numbers one, two, and three Canada western six-row and numbers one and two western two-row must have pearling and malting qualifications. Other barley grades are numbers one, two, and three feed barley and several commercial grades of six- and two-row barley.

Rye grades are numbers one through four Canada western, Canada western ergoty rye, and a grade of Canada western ergoty rye and other grains.

Mixed grain has a number-one Canada-western grade when wheat predominates, a number-two Canada-western grade when rye predominates, number-three Canada-western when barley predominates, and number-four Canada-western when oats predominate. Other grain grades include flax, soybeans, buckwheat, corn, and some seeds—mustard, sunflower, etc.[3]

When Canadian grain is exported from United States ports on the Canadian grade, the grain moves in transit through the United States in bond and the grain is kept "identity preserved." Railroads carrying the grain and elevators loading the grain on ocean steamers certify that it is the identical grain named in the inspection certificate. There is only one inspection of the grain, which is made at the time it is loaded on a lake steamer at Fort William or Port Arthur, Ontario, at the head of Lake Superior. Inspection certificates are issued in units to match the export shipping documents. Thus there are a number of identical inspection certificates to a total equaling the number

---

[3] *Consolidated Catalogs, Edition No.* 7, National Miller (Dawson Richardson Publications, Ltd., Winnipeg, Manitoba), 1949.

of bushels loaded on the lake steamer, each bearing the steamer's name and the date of loading, in addition to the statement of the grade. These same inspection certificates follow the movement of the grain and accompany the ocean-shipping documents when presented to the buyer in the foreign country. When grain is inspected on railroad cars in Canada, the inspection certificates likewise follow through and are certified as to identity of grain when it is loaded on an ocean steamer.

The same method of inspection certification is used when Canadian grain is shipped for export from Canadian ports, i.e., the western-lake-vessel inspection or car inspection is attested to for identity when the grain is loaded on the ocean steamer.

Similarly, when United States grain passes through Canada for re-export from their ports to a foreign country, the United States inspection certificate is attested to for identity of grain when the grain is loaded on an ocean steamer.

Under the system of selling grain on the Canadian "certificate final" the government of Canada guarantees importers abroad that grain so purchased is at least equal in quality to the official export standard of the grade called for by the certificate.

Sales on Special Qualifications

At times, United States grain may be sold on the basis of a type sample rather than on regular grade standards and may possibly be referred to by a trade name. In such cases each shipment may be certified by an independent authority, or the shipments may be on the basis of a submitted sample with a portion of the sample kept in a sealed condition in the possession of a disinterested party. Other sales are at times negotiated on the basis of a grade standard with special guarantees of certain grade factors, such as minimum test weight above the standard for such numerical grade, or lower moisture content, etc., or grading up to a numerical grade, except for certain named grading factors, which may be lower.

Other Commodities

Some commodities traded in futures markets have no established United States official standards, but are traded on the basis of standards stated in the futures contract and are subject to specified inspection methods.

Lard.—Lard delivered on a Chicago Board of Trade futures contract must be of the following standard: prime-steam- or dry-rendered lard only may be delivered on futures contracts and is to be solely the product of such selected fresh fat parts of the hog as are required by regulations of (and must have been inspected and passed by) the United States Department of Agriculture; prime steam lard is to be rendered in tanks by the direct application of steam, and dry-rendered lard is to be rendered in steam-jacketed tanks without subsequent change of grain or character by the use of an agitator or other machinery except as such change may unavoidably come from transportation. Standard lard must have proper color, flavor, and soundness for keeping. The names and location of the packer and the type of lard and the month and year in which the lard has been made must be plainly branded on each package at the time of filling. Each tierce, or drum, shall be properly filled, etc.[4]

The lard must be in a warehouse regular for delivery on the futures contract, and if received at the warehouse as lard, it must have been inspected and passed by the Federal inspector. The inspection for contract purposes is made by a Chicago-Board-of-Trade-appointed inspector who removes the heads of several drums or drills one or more holes in several tierces for each lot and probes the lard to secure samples which he inspects for odor, taste, and color. The inspection certificates remain in force for thirty days, after which a new inspection is required for further delivery on contract. However, lard delivered on and after December 1 of any year on futures contracts can include only such lard as has been made on or after the first day of the previous October. Thus, lard cannot be older than fourteen

[4] Chicago Board of Trade, Regulation 1479A, amended May, 1947.

months when delivered on a futures contract. Lard may be sold in the trading pit as cash lard, and if the trade is made during December the lard may have been made on or after October 1 of the preceding year. Thus, the lard may be fifteen months old when delivered on a cash lard sale during December.

Crude Soybean Oil.—The crude-soybean-oil futures contract of the Chicago Board of Trade provides for the licensing of samplers by the Board of Directors of the Exchange and the appointment of official chemists by the Crude Soybean Oil Committee whose certificates for quality analysis are binding on all parties, except for the right of appeal. The regulations state that the sample should be taken by trier method within 24 hours after the loading of a tank car; specifications for taking samples are set forth in the sampler's license application. Also, it is stated that two of the three one-gallon containers of the oil sample should be forwarded to the official chemist, who retains one container of oil in a sealed condition for the purpose of referee.

Because of settlement of sludge in crude soybean oil during storage, the warehousemen are licensed or otherwise qualified by the various states in which deliveries are made and under the Board of Trade futures contracts to mingle or store together oil which is tenderable with other oil of like type, and to deliver on loading orders oil of any one of the four contract types. This permits warehousemen to add to their oil stocks or to withdraw oil from their storage stocks, provided the stocks are in balance with the oil represented by outstanding warehouse receipts. The contract also permits the warehouseman to ship any one of the four standard types of oil against any warehouse receipt. There is no provision for a quality inspection of oil while it is held in storage against outstanding receipts, but the warehouseman must deliver oil of contract standard at the time it is loaded out of the warehouse into a tank car.

The official chemist must follow the methods of the American Oil Chemists Society and the National Soybean Processors Association in his tests for quality analysis, but the contract provides for the limitation of crude oil factors as follows: maximum moisture and volatile content, color, maximum refining loss, minimum flash point; and oil to be one of four types—expeller pressed, expeller pressed degummed, solvent extracted, or solvent extracted degummed.[5]

Soybean Meal.—Another different inspection of a commodity is provided for in the Soybean Meal Regulations of the Chicago Board of Trade, in which delivery is accomplished by a Soybean-Meal Shipping Certificate. In this contract, standards are specifically stated, but no sampling or grading of the meal is provided for prior to its shipment or at the time the meal is loaded into the boxcar at the time of shipment. However, if when the car of meal arrives at its destination the owner does not agree that the meal conforms to the standards and he does not come to an agreement on an adjustment with the issuer of the shipping certificate, there are provisions for sampling and analysis. A sample is drawn with a double standard-tube eleven-compartment bulk-grain probe in the manner that a car of bulk grain is sampled. The sample is placed in an airtight container and forwarded to an official chemist together with an affidavit as to its correctness, etc.

The chemist analyzes the sample by testing methods approved by the Association of Official Agricultural Chemists and the American Oil Chemists Society. Certificates for quality analysis by any official chemists appointed by the Soybean Meal Committee are binding on all parties. On the basis of official quality determinations the meal is accepted or replaced or adjustment made according to the terms of the futures contract.

The contract standard is of 44%-protein soybean meal with specifications of minimum percentage of protein, fat, and nitrogen-free extract, and maximum percentages of fiber and moisture.[6]

---

[5] *Chicago Board of Trade Rules and Regulations,* Chapter 38.
[6] *Ibid,* Chapter 40.

Board of Trade Sampling

Commodities handled by the grain trade are inspected by qualified agencies authorized to determine grades of government standards or standards set by an exchange. The Chicago Board of Trade has a department for sampling commodities, and through this service and its laboratory analysis, merchants can check on the official grain-grading of government-licensed inspectors. The Board of Trade Sampling Department does not assign grades on grain for which standards have been established under the United States Grain Standards Act. It does, however, check on certain grading factors used in determining government grades which may help the seller obtain a higher price for the car of grain. Or it may indicate that the grade assigned by the State Inspection Department is likely to be raised if Federal appeal is called.

In some markets resampling is performed by a commission merchant, while in others it is done by private sampling organizations.

CHAPTER IX

Purchasing and Processing

Purchasing Grain From Country Locations

The great bulk of the grain handled by country elevators is merchandised through the large terminal grain markets or is shipped to processing plants, and a small share stays in country locations. This does not account for the disposition of all the grain which farmers sell, as there is an increasing amount marketed direct from farms by truckers to various buyers. Country-elevator grain may also be purchased by truckers who merchandise it, or the country elevator operators may engage trucks in the selling part of their business.

The grain offered for sale by the country shipper need not yet have been bought from the farmers, or it may be in the country elevator. In either case, it is available for sale and shipment via rail or truck transportation to the most desirable buyer; it may be in cars en route to market, or it may be in a terminal-market railroad inspection yard. For grain in any of these positions the country shipper needs guidance in locating the highest bidder. Inasmuch as country shippers of the grain cannot be in direct contact with all buyers in the terminal markets or buyers in other locations, it is desirable for them to have representatives who are in constant touch with all these interests, but more particularly with those who buy rail grain. Buyers in the terminal markets also consider it desirable to make their trades with these representatives, who are fewer in number than country shippers and who, being responsible to the buyer, eliminate the buyer's having to contact a great number of country locations. Thus both shippers and buyers have an intermediary in the "cash-grain commission merchant," to whom and with whom responsibility rests.

The commission merchant may have offices in several locations, being in position to contact many shippers and to locate buyers in various places so that at any moment he can sell unshipped grain to the highest market. Though there is considerable trading between country shippers and terminal buyers in some markets, commission merchants handle a good share of the grain that comes to market. When grain has been loaded into a boxcar and a bill of lading issued to a terminal market, it may be consigned to a commission merchant for later sale. After the grain arrives, the commission merchant examines the graded sample and, being familiar with the qualities of each grain and the desires of different buyers, sells it to the buyer most interested. There are elevator buyers, processor buyers, and "order buyers." The latter are those who buy on terminal inspection, but may ship grain to another destination and, if such is the case, customarily pay higher prices because of the greater time the car is in transit and the privilege of giving outside weights when the car is unloaded.

There is usually a price advantage in selling a car of grain on consignment, because the spot price is almost always higher than the "to-arrive" price. The spot buyer is willing to pay premiums over the current to-arrive price because of the opportunity of examining the graded sample of the car, knowing the railroad billing, and having the car available for immediate use.

The commission merchant can sometimes secure special advantages for the country shipper when there are outstanding grading factors or by carefully selecting the buyer when the grain in the car has poorer factors that will be overlooked by the buyer. "Best buyers" quickly change as one fills his requirements and withdraws or as another enters the market. At times after consulting with the shipper, the commission merchant carries the unsold car over to the next day, especially when it comes within the free time for ordering the car to the unloading elevator.

If the country shipper has some grain sold "to arrive," he may upon arrival of a car at the terminal sell it as a consignment rather than applying it on the to-arrive sale, provided there is still time to ship another car. The commission merchant serves the country shipper also by ordering unshipped grain to an uncongested market in times of heavy movement, especially when there is danger of quality deterioration while the car is in transit. Another service advantage is that the commission merchant may recommend calling Federal appeal of the grade, which may result in a higher grade and a better consignment-sale price or less discount on application of the car on a to-arrive sale.

To-arrive grain carries with it the shipper's privilege of applying grain of a lower than basic sale grade (sometimes within grading limits) at a price scale of discounts, either as arranged at the time of sale or at the prevailing market discounts upon arrival of each car at its destination. The shipper may choose the date within the contract time on which to ship the grain, or even choose to buy cars of grain from others for shipment or to buy grain on the spot in the terminal market if he desires or is unable to ship grain from his own elevator as originally intended.

The contract time of shipment of to-arrive grain may range from "cars in transit" to a period of time ending several months later. The actual shipping period may be of several days' duration or it may stretch over several months. The country shipper may make purchases from farmers as an offset at the time he sells to-arrive, or he may put these sales on his books and either hedge them or not in anticipation of purchases from farmers who haul grain to his elevator. Buyers in terminal and other locations like to buy some grain ahead of the shipping time, especially for shipment at harvest time as an assurance that they will accumulate a workable stock of grain to fill their elevator or run their processing plant. In accumulating grain some time ahead of the time of shipment to market on to-arrive purchases, there exists the uncertainty of the quality, but most buyers can handle the average run of quality even though some of the grain may have to be conditioned. Other buyers, lacking grain-drying or other necessary elevator facilities to condition the grain, delay buying until harvest time and may even wait to buy consigned grain after examination of the graded sample.

Cars of grain arriving at a terminal market are held on the inspection track of the arrival railroad where the samples are taken. Railroads permit sufficient time after sampling for grading analysis and sale of the grain before the car has to be ordered to the buyer's elevator for unloading and before demurrage charges on the car begin. Railroad tariffs assess shippers no switching charges for moving incoming cars to any elevator within the switching district, even though they may be handled by several railroads. This affords the seller of the grain a free hand in choosing the best buyer available at the time each car of grain is sold. It also permits the larger buying firms with several elevators to order cars to whichever elevator they are using to stock a particular kind of grain. Freight is billed by the arrival railroad regardless of which railroad the unloading grain elevator is located on. The paid freight bills must be registered with a railroad agency and carefully preserved to protect the application of billing on the outbound movement, which may be via a different railroad. Traffic requirements are most important to terminal buyers. The grain firm's traffic man sorts the railroad billing on hand and keeps the firm's merchandiser informed as to its most advantageous use concerning destination in the sale of the grain.

Terminal-Elevator Buying

Terminal elevator buyers are interested mostly in buying grain that they can again load out of their elevators on the basis of a normal commercial grade, or grain of a higher quality which they segregate in storage and expect to resell for special uses on the basis of its premium features. If the grain which they receive on "to-arrive" rail contracts and by truck or barge is not of an average quality that will be a commercial grade (usually number two) after conditioning in the elevator, the operator buys sufficient grain "on sample" to average out the quality of his stock. The grain marketed from United States farms, being from good seed and grown and harvested under careful supervision, is mostly of commercial grade when it arrives at marketing centers, but quality varies because of area and soil in which it is grown and the weather during the season. Care of the grain while held in former storage also affects its quality prior to shipment to terminal markets. Poor quality grain, however, is frequently the result of weather conditions.

All the grain that comes to a market finds buyers regardless of its quality. It is mostly the elevator buyers who take the low-quality grain; they can segregate it in their elevators, and by the nature of their business can put it to the best use in resale. If there is a large percentage of low grade grain moving from farms to market, its disposition is spread out in many directions. Years of a wet harvest require widespread artificial drying of grain to prevent its deterioration and spoilage. When grain is damaged from other causes, its final distribution is spread among many buyers in different markets. Even though elevator buyers originally buy the low-grade grain, condition it, store it, and even out its distribution, finally the food grains are sold to processors for conversion into food products and the feed grains to buyers for their respective uses. Some grain may go for industrial use, particularly when the quality makes it unfit for human or animal consumption. However, some inferior wheat may have to be sold as feed. Grains salvaged from fires, floods, etc., are reconditioned as much as possible, and, if at all fit for use, find buyers on the basis of their quality. It may take more than a current season to dispose of all the inferior-quality grain harvested in an unfavorable season. Export outlets aid in the absorption of some low-quality grain when it is priced attractively as compared with the normally commercial export grades. The length of time that grain has to stay in the holds of a ship during the ocean voyage and temperatures in the country of its destination require that the grain be of a low-enough moisture content and high enough in other quality factors to permit its safe transportation.

PROCESSOR BUYING

Processors must be more discriminating than terminal elevator operators in selecting low-grade as well as high-grade grain, for unlike the elevator operator, who has the choice of different kinds of outlets, they need grain to produce the desired end product or products of their manufacture. Some converters produce feed as a by-product in the operations of their food-products plants, so that, provided the low-grade grain can be purchased at a satisfactory price, they can use it. The proportion of separation of food and feed products in relation to the selling price of each determines the price they can afford to pay for low-grade grain as compared with higher grades. The kind of damage in the grain is a governing factor in its pricing, because each kind of damage may affect a different end product in its processing. Grain with damage that will result in a smaller percentage of production of a high-priced product must be bought at a greater discount than grain with damage to a portion of the grain kernel that stays in a lower-priced end product.

The different types of processing industries employ varying methods in the purchase of their grain; and in addition, varying methods are employed even within the same industry. A small but increasing amount of grain is purchased by processors from farmers or truckers moving grain directly from farms to processing plants, and more is bought from country elevators. Considerable grain, however, is purchased by processors in the terminal markets. Some processors have plants located in surplus-grain-growing areas and are able to draw their grain requirements from the immediate vicinity. The larger processors, however, who have plants located in production areas and other plants in heavily populated areas, draw a sizable portion of their supplies for all plants from considerable distances. Some of the larger processors have their own buyers in the terminal markets to buy grain from cash-grain commission merchants or terminal elevators, wherever the most advantageous purchase can be made. Other processors purchase supplies in terminal markets in this manner through brokers, while a third group buy solely from terminal-elevator operators or grain merchandisers and do not have their own representatives in the market.

Processors, like elevator operators, usually do their largest buying for storage at the harvest time when crops are moving heavily. The processor is limited in his harvest purchase to the extent to which he is able to store the grain in his elevators or in storage space he may rent from other elevator operators.

Most processors are in the market buying grain throughout the entire year, but because of individual peculiarities, this may not be true of certain processing industries. The malting industry is more seasonal, and soybean processors, because of the large percentage of the crop sold by farmers in the months immediaately following harvest, of necessity fill a big share of their crushing requirements early in the season.

With its population increase, it has taken more and more grain production to satisfy the food requirements of the United States. Per-capita consumption of most grain products for direct usage has decreased, and the total number of bushels used in producing these products has increased only moderately over a period of years. The per-capita consumption of wheat flour has shown an almost uninterrupted reduction—from 207 pounds in 1909 to 121 pounds annually at the present time—and this reduction has mostly offset the total-use increase from the rise in population. With the addition of 3 or 4 pounds of cereals consumed per person our annual, use of wheat for these purposes has increased from 475,000,000 bushels to somewhat under 500,000,000 bushels between pre-World-War-I years to now. The per-capita use of rye flour has been cut two thirds during this period, so that now we grind less than 5,000,000 bushels of rye, compared with more than 10,000,000 bushels formerly. Principal corn food uses are lower per capita, the chief reduction being in corn meal. They more than offset minor increases in direct processed food uses, such as syrup, sugar, starch, etc., so that

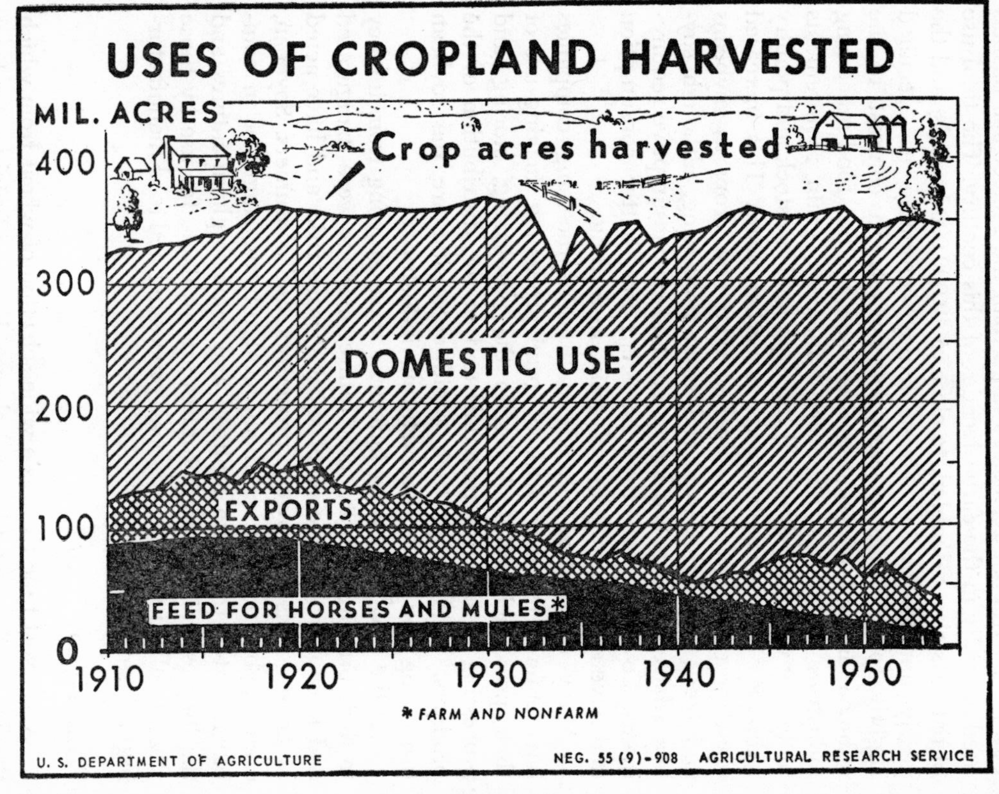
USES OF CROPLAND HARVESTED
MIL. ACRES
400
300
200
100
0
Crop acres harvested
DOMESTIC USE
EXPORTS
FEED FOR HORSES AND MULES*
1910
1920
1930
1940
1950
* FARM AND NONFARM
U. S. DEPARTMENT OF AGRICULTURE
NEG. 55 (9)-908 AGRICULTURAL RESEARCH SERVICE

Figure 6

the total number of bushels of corn consumed for all such purposes is only about 10,000,000 more than the 140,000,000 bushels used annually in the early decades of this century. The total use of oats has about doubled, to close to 40,000,000 bushels; and the yearly number of bushels of barley consumed has declined slightly to 6,000,000 or 8,000,000 bushels. In contrast to the reduced amount of some grains used by the food-processing industries and the small over-all increase, grain requirements including wheat used to feed the expanded livestock and poultry industries are substantially above earlier years. This increased need for grain has also absorbed such new crops as soybeans and feeds recovered from industrial processing, although soybeans have also satisfied larger fat- and oil-consumptive requirements. Soybean derivatives have cut into butter consumption and have extended the use of grains in feeding.

Many established oilseed- and grain-processing companies have entered the new fields of grain processing, making use of their personnel and facilities in the purchasing, storing, and processing of the raw materials and in the distribution of the products. Notable for their rapid expansion are the soybean processing and feed-manufacturing industries.

As the new processing industries were growing from infancy to their present maturity, new futures markets were inaugurated and have provided means of shifting price risks and have acted as price guides to growers, processors, and consumers. Soybean, crude-soybean-oil, and soybean-meal futures, singly or in combination, together with millfeed and grain-sorghum futures and the long-established grain futures are available for use by those who are allied with the soybean-processing and feed-manufacturing industries.

Wheat-Flour Milling

At harvest time there is a wide selection of wheat from which the flour miller may pick and choose. Because freight rates from producing to consuming areas are the same on wheat and flour and because milling transit privileges are widely available,

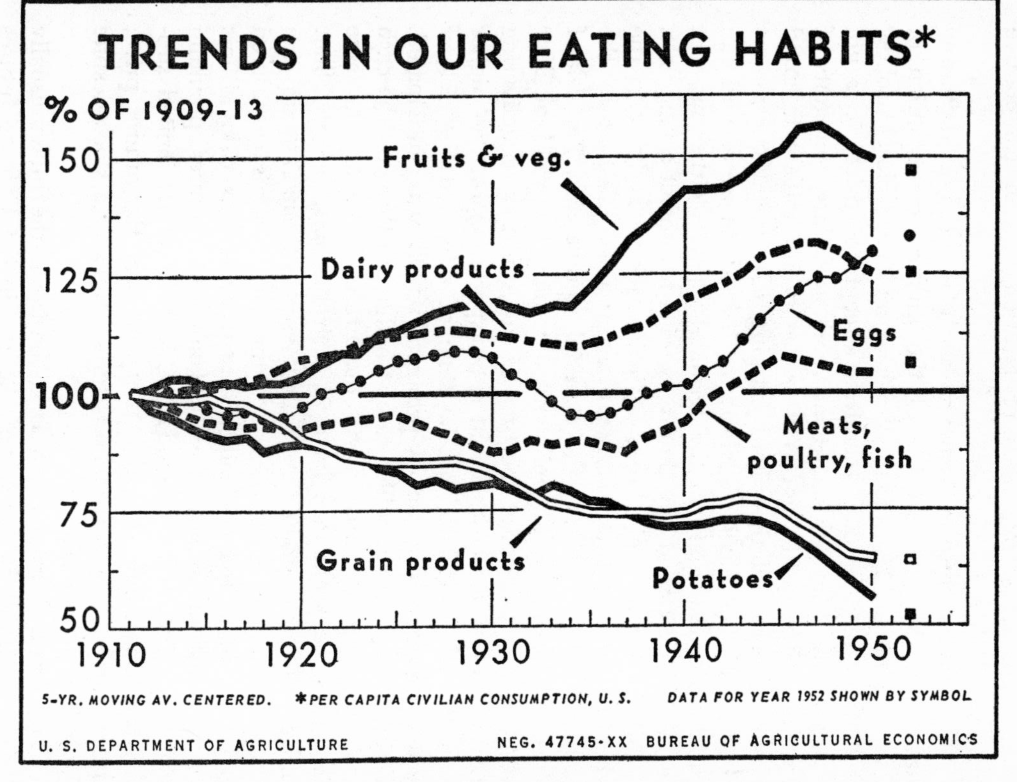
TRENDS IN OUR EATING HABITS*
% OF 1909-13
150
125
100
75
50
1910
1920
1930
1940
1950
Fruits & veg.
Dairy products
Eggs
Meats, poultry, fish
Grain products
Potatoes
5-YR. MOVING AV. CENTERED.
*PER CAPITA CIVILIAN CONSUMPTION, U. S.
DATA FOR YEAR 1952 SHOWN BY SYMBOL
U. S. DEPARTMENT OF AGRICULTURE
NEG. 47745-XX
BUREAU OF AGRICULTURAL ECONOMICS

FIGURE 7

milling centers are located in both producing and consuming areas. Thus mills, regardless of location, are in competitive positions.

The manufacture of flour takes place rather uniformly throughout the year because of the uniform consumption of flour and bread. The prices of wheat and flour closely follow each other day by day; therefore, except for price, it is not necessary for flour buyers to buy and stock large amounts of flour ahead of needs, nor is it necessary for millers to grind wheat far ahead of their flour-shipping schedule. Flour millers carry a sufficient stock of wheat for immediate needs and can usually purchase grain in the terminal markets either on spot or out of elevators at any time they wish to protect a flour sale.

Millers try to avoid inventory price risk by hedging in the wheat-futures market. There are many risks inherent to the milling business, such as the material storage risk, the risk of physically operating the mill and obtaining the yield of flour which was calculated at the time of sale, the risk of delivering the product to the customer at a transportation rate no higher than the one calculated at the time of sale, and the risk of recovering the value on by-products which was anticipated. Grain risks which the miller cannot hedge are those on the cash basis of the grain compared with the futures. These are the same risks that the grain men have in their business, but the flour miller, unlike the grain firm, cannot escape them. A grain firm can avoid buying grain on which the cash basis is considered to be too high, but the miller cannot avoid this risk. Millers must furnish flour buyers with flour that requires premium wheat in its manufacture and that, because of its limited supply, may be selling at a high premium over the futures price; although it may be scarce, he is forced to carry a stock despite the risk of a price decline.

Like grain firms doing a large business, the miller usually finds it advisable to carry some hedges in the Chicago futures market, which is broader than the Kansas City or Minneapolis markets, so that when hedges must be bought in against the sale of flour the impact will be less likely to bring about a sharp change in price. A risk in having hedges out of position in Chicago may arise from the fact that the miller's stock of wheat is Kansas wheat, which will follow the Kansas City futures, or spring wheat, which will follow the Minneapolis futures, while the Chicago market may be affected by conditions in the soft-red-winter-wheat trade. A widening of a premium for Chicago futures over either of these markets would be costly to the miller on his short hedges.

To produce a certain grade and quality, flour millers must have a specific type of wheat, and they take great care in selecting their wheat. Generally speaking, there are two types of flour —bread flour and cake flour, and bread flour may be further divided into baker's flour and family flour. Bread flours are ground largely from hard red spring and hard red winter wheats, while cake or pastry flours are usually ground from soft red winter and white wheats.

In buying grain for all types of flours, the miller is constantly confronted with the problem of quality. Consumers of flour expect a given flour to perform in the same manner in the same formula at all times. This expectation makes it necessary for the miller to produce a flour that consistently has the same chemical and physical factors for a given grade. Wheat selection is doubly difficult because of the fact that the baking quality of wheats of like grade and appearance may vary widely from one to another; even wheat grown in one locality may vary greatly from year to year in baking quality. From year to year a miller's supplies of wheat may be drawn from entirely different sections of the country and his mix composed of entirely different types of wheat, although from year to year he produces essentially the same type of flour. Thus it is important that the miller know in advance of the movement of the crop where the type of wheat he needs for his flour may be obtained. Some of the larger mills make a survey of wheat territories by sending into the wheat-growing areas survey crews which move northward with the harvest. Hundreds of samples may be obtained for milling and baking tests, and the results are mapped and used by buyers in purchasing supplies. Smaller mills also study wheat territories but on a less comprehensive scale.

If there is a revision in a miller's standard of flour, he advises his bakery trade so that they can make the necessary changes in their mechanized handling. The miller may draw wheat of one variety with a certain percentage of protein from one part of the country and another variety from another area. Keeping the various varieties, classes, grades, and proteins in balance with the sales of flour becomes a very complex operation. Flour may have been sold ahead of wheat purchases, thus creating a short position for certain classes, etc., of wheat, while at the same time the miller will be "long"—hold other wheat in excess of like flour sales. While grading factors are important to the miller in his selection of wheat, other considerations are often of greater importance. Probably the most important single factor in purchasing wheat of milling grade is the protein—both percentage of content and quality—for a proper blend of strong and mellow glutin to meet the mixing-time requirements of modern bakeries.

Yield value of wheat as compared with the price paid is a factor for the buyer to consider. The yield value varies directly with the test weight per bushel of wheat and inversely with the moisture percentage in the grain. As each lot of wheat may yield different amounts of flour, the price which a miller can pay for each test weight rests upon the buyer's experience and judgment.

To manufacture 100 pounds of flour, about 140 pounds of wheat, or approximately 2.35 bushels, are required. Forty pounds of millfeed, which includes the bran, middlings, and shorts, are obtained from the 140 pounds of wheat milled. Of the 100 pounds of flour obtained, all the flour streams in the milling process can be combined to make a straight-grade flour. In many cases a miller sells a higher grade of flour, a patent or a short patent, which may take from 2.5 to 2.7 bushels of wheat or from 150 to 160 pounds of wheat to make 100 pounds of flour. In this case the miller will have 45 to 50 pounds of mill-feed and some "first clear" and "second clear" for each 100 pounds of flour. It is difficult for the miller to keep his raw-material position in balance with his products, because he can not always sell millfeeds and "clears" at the same time as flour.

The flour miller keeps his stock of wheat segregated according to protein, baking quality, type, yield value, or other considerations which may be important from time to time. Percentages of the various lots are blended together preparatory to milling and are delivered to the cleaning machinery of the mill to remove the impurities in the wheat. In order to facilitate grinding and to make possible a cleaner separation of bran from flour, the wheat is tempered. Tempering is a process whereby water added to the wheat toughens the bran coat and causes it to separate more completely from the flour. The first grinding is done by a series of break rollers of corrugated iron rotating opposite to each other at different speeds. The first rollers, for cracking the wheat, are quite far apart, and the others successively closer until a fine separation of bran from flour is made. After each break the cracked and broken wheat is "bolted" by large devices which separate the fine flour particles from the coarser bran. The coarser particles of each break are returned to the next set of break rolls for further reduction. This grinding and sifting process results in three general groups of products: the coarse fragments which are reground until nothing but the bran remains, the fine particles which are the flour, and an intermediate group known as "middlings." These middlings are further reduced by grinding between smooth rolls, recovering some additional flour, and reducing the middlings until what is left is suitable only for feed.

In the distribution of flour, sales are usually made for delivery within 120 days, beyond which time mills customarily charge for the expense of carrying the wheat in storage, and in addition they charge interest and insurance. Some mills have established their brands of flour in foreign lands. The sale of such flour is handled in the same manner as domestic flour sales. Other foreign sales made on certain specifications make desirable business and give the mills running time, but as they are not as steady as home outlets they are not sought after too eagerly by some mills.

Rye Milling

The present quantity of rye flour milled in the United States is small, only half of the amount milled around the time of World War I, despite increase in population. One of the Federal grading factors of rye is size of kernels, which is an indication of the starch content. Those kernels which will pass through sieves with perforations of a certain size are classed as "thin." The percentage of thin kernels may determine the numerical grade and whether it is plump rye or ordinary rye. As the rye-mill buyer must purchase rye with enough starch content to produce a satisfactory yield of flour, he avoids rye containing too much "thin." Rye flour may be either light or dark in color according to the grain used and the process. The light color is usually preferred in the trade. (This does not refer to the light rye bread made in the United States, which is generally made from a mixture of rye flour and wheat flour, whereas European black bread is made from all-rye flour.)

In buying rye for milling, care must be taken to avoid rye that is musty, weevily, or has odors, and most especially rye containing ergot, which may grow in the rye. Rye grows principally in the Dakotas and the adjoining states, and small amounts used by United States millers often originate in Canada.

The milling system for rye is similar to that of a wheat mill, though little or no tempering is required. Usually corrugated rolls are used for the first break and for subsequent reductions. Smooth rolls cause rye middlings to flatten and flake. Rye flour also requires more bolting surface than wheat. Rye flour is lower than wheat flour in gluten—it has a heavier texture.

The rye market has hedging facilities in the futures markets located in Chicago, Minneapolis, and Winnipeg, Manitoba. Each of these three markets depends more or less on conditions prevailing in the others. At times delivery may be taken in the Winnipeg delivery points of Fort William or Port Arthur on Lake Superior and the rye shipped to mills located in the United States and hedged either in Minneapolis or Chicago on a competitive basis with domestic-grown rye. The Minneapolis rye-futures price at times permits the transfer of hedges from that market to Chicago at a premium about equal to the cost of shipping rye from that location to Chicago or shipping it from locations in which both markets buy rye competitively.

Wet Corn Processing

The buyer of corn for wet processing has in mind the recovery value of the end products derived from the corn. Starch is the principal constituent of corn, from which is made almost endless varieties of products; other portions of corn are gluten, hull, germ, and water. The outside covering, or the hull, of the corn kernel is of fibrous material; the main interior portion of the kernel, called the endosperm, is a mixture of starch and gluten; and the germ, at the point of the kernel, is made up largely of oil and fibrous material with some gluten. There are also some invisible solubles consisting of minerals and nitrogenous materials found on or near the surface of the corn and in the germ. The color of the corn makes little difference, although most corn is yellow; nor does the origin of the corn enter into the choice of the buyer. The buyer watches the Federal standard of grade and factors within the grade as well as types of damage, etc., in appraising the value of each corn purchase. Moisture in the corn may affect its quality in storage but is not objectionable otherwise, as the corn is steeped or soaked in water during processing until the moisture content is 40% to 55%. Damage to the kernel, if in the germ, reduces the amount of oil recovered in processing. As oil is a high-priced product, germ damage is costly to the processor. Other damage or cracked corn sends a larger portion to the feeds, which are priced lower than starch products. Test weight per bushel should be discounted, as the covering or hull of the kernel is about the same for light or heavy test weight and the processor pays for more fiber and less starch in lightweight corn; and the fiber is a feed and sells for less than the starch products. Natural-dried corn, like corn of different percentage of moisture, does not mix the best with kiln-dried corn. Kiln-dried corn does not give as sharp a separation—starch adheres to the bran—and the oil yield is somewhat affected. Competitive products such as cane sugar may affect the sale of corn sugar or syrup. Because corn processors have to make a certain amount of the latter products in their activities, competitive products have a bearing on the permissible price of corn purchased.

Each wet-corn-processing plant has practically nationwide outlets and may compete for export. Most of the plants are located in the Corn Belt. Because corn-grain railroad rates do not apply on all the products when they are shipped out of the plants, they are not too much of a factor. Processing plants do not have large corn-storage capacity in comparison to the large amount of corn used in their operations. One reason is probably that when corn moves in the largest volume it is high in moisture, which may be a storage hazard. Therefore, buyers are nearly always in the market for corn. They buy "on spot" or for "to-arrive" shipment up to about 90 days, and at times for shipment out of terminal elevators, or they may take delivery of futures. They may use the futures market to buy in anticipation of purchases of cash corn, but they would be less likely to have occasion to hedge their stock of corn in view of their large turnover and their practice of buying almost continuously. More often, the problem is to keep large quantities of corn rolling or in sight to supply the large capacity of the plants.

Wet-corn-processing plants may use grain sorghums in place of corn, and wheat starch has also been used by a modification of the wet-milling process. There are plants in operation for wet-processing grain sorghums making products similar to those of corn.

After incoming corn is weighed at a processing plant it goes either to storage bins or is cleaned to remove dust, chaff, cobs, stones, rodent excreta, insects, broken grain, and foreign material. Cleaned grain then goes to the steep tank. Steeping, or soaking, is the most important step in wet milling; it loosens the bond that holds the starch granules together in the kernel, removes solubles, mainly mineral matter, from the germ so that it is lightened and can be floated off in the germ separators, and softens the kernel for grinding. Steeping does not harm or modify the starch very much. The shelled corn is steeped from 30 to 40 hours in tanks of warm water circulated countercurrently through the steeps and slightly acidified with sulphur to prevent fermentation and to keep the product sweet. Steep water gathers soluble matter from the corn and, concentrated by evaporation, is an important constituent in corn-gluten feed and is also used in the manufacture of drugs and yeast.

From the steeping tanks the soft kernels go through degerminating mills which free the germs without crushing them. Washed into tanks called separators, the floating, oil-laden germs are skimmed off, dried, and run through screw-type oil presses or a combination of oil presses and solvent extractors. The dry germ contains 42% to 50% oil, and after the oil content is removed the oil cake or corn-germ meal remaining contains 19% to 22% protein. Most of the oil is refined and goes largely for food uses, though the crude oil may be used industrially.

The torn corn and starch milk which have been drawn from the bottom of the germ separators pass either through stone mills practically the same as those of ancient times or through vertical hammer mills. These mills thoroughly disintegrate the harder portions of the corn and rub the starch and gluten from the hulls. Subsequently the hulls are separated from the starch and gluten by means of shakers or reels covered with silk or nylon bolting cloth; the extremely fine particles of starch and gluten pass through the pores of this cloth, leaving the hulls within the reels or shakers to be discharged at one end, from which they pass on to be dried for mixing into the animal feed.

The starch is separated from the gluten by tabling and centrifuging. Starch tables are long, shallow, slightly tilted troughs over which the starch-gluten flows. The starch granules, being heavy, sink to the bottom, and after several hours of steady but gentle flow of the liquid across the tables a layer of starch a few inches deep is formed. The starch is removed by sluicing it off with water, and then it passes through centrifugal machines to remove any trace of gluten. The liquid with the gluten passing over the starch tables is collected and is piped to settling tanks and then dried for animal feed. The trend is to replace tables with centrifuges, because there is less chance of any contamination, processing time is shortened, less floor space is required, and the results are better.

The starch is dried and prepared for market as starch or converted into dextrin, syrup, or sugar. The uses of starch in the home and in the manufacture of food and industrial products are many and varied. When starch is heated under proper conditions it is chemically changed to dextrin. By combining dextrins with water, a wide variety of glues, pastes, and gums is formed. Corn syrup is made by heating starch in closed tanks. In the process, hydrochloric acid is added, when the conversion has reached the right point it is stopped; the acid is then neutralized and the syrup filtered and reduced by evaporation to various consistencies. Nearly all of syrup is used for food, but the slight remainder used for nonfood and industrial purposes is none the less important.

The process of starch conversion used in making corn syrup, if extended for a much longer period of time, results in corn sugar. So nearly complete is this conversion that the end product, a highly refined corn sugar, is 99.5% to 99.8% pure dextrose. When the process is arrested at an earlier stage the degree of conversion is expressed as "dextrose equivalent"; those of 70 to 90 dextrose equivalent are dextrose syrups from which sugars are isolated by crystallization. Dextrose has many uses in the production of foods and pharmaceuticals. Corn-sugar molasses, or "hydrol," a by-product of corn-sugar manufacture, is used as an ingredient of sweet feeds for livestock and as fermentation material in the production of alcohol.

Corn-gluten feed is about 23% protein, and its content of corn hulls gives it the bulk desirable in dairy feeds. Corn-gluten meal, containing no corn hulls, has a higher concentration of protein —41%—and is a valued ingredient in poultry rations. Corn-oil meal is relatively lower in protein—20%—but high in fat. It commonly forms part of corn-gluten feed, but may be marketed separately.

A specially prepared gluten very high in protein also finds use as a material for plastics and lacquers. Virtually all of the tonnage of gluten, germs, and hulls, however, is returned to the farmer in the form of feeds—much more efficient feeds than is the original whole grain.

Dry-Process Milling of Corn

Both white and yellow corn are used in this process. The miller attempts to select corn of true color, because the color of the finished products is an important element of quality, particularly in the products made from white corn. Millers prefer thick kernels rather than kernels that are thin, and attempt to avoid round kernels because they are more difficult to process. In purchasing corn, millers also avoid corn which contains kernels damaged by molds or fermentation, because of the effect on the quality of the finished product.

Typical dry-milling products derived from yellow corn are granulated corn meal, bolted corn meal, and flour; those made from white corn are pearl hominy, brewers' grits, hominy grits, granulated corn meal, bolted corn meal, and flour.

The process of dry corn milling is very much like that of flour milling; the essential difference is the objectives of the two processes. In corn milling the products in the early stages of reduction are worth more than the products in the final production, namely flour; thus, the less flour that is produced the better—and that is the opposite to wheat-flour milling.

After the corn is cleaned, the first step in processing is tempering. Next the corn is degermed—the germ and bran separated from the remainder of the kernel. Corn oil is extracted from the germ, and the residue forms a by-product from which corn-oil meal is made. In the process the products pass through bolting, separating, and sifting machines, and the corn is reduced further by corrugated reduction rolls similar to those used in flour milling, except that the corrugations are larger.

A high percentage of the dry-milled corn products are used for food, with small amounts going for animal feed and industrial purposes. Important food uses are corn meal, grits, and breakfast cereals; industrial outlets include core-binder and adhesives.

"Old process" meal is made by grinding whole corn between closely rotating stones. Usually the germ is not removed before grinding, because its presence in the meal improves the flavor and nutritive value; its keeping quality is limited, however.

Oats Milling

The oats miller has to consider his product from the point of view of edibility. Therefore, oats to be milled must not contain unfavorable factors that will show up in the end product. Because a small amount of the bran or hull may be present in the final product, it is essential to buy oats grading white on the Federal grades or possibly slightly colored, and not oats that are badly weathered. Heat-damaged oats are also avoided. The oats must be plump, sound, cool, and sweet and must contain only a small percentage of objectionable foreign material or other grains. Number-two numerical-grade oats generally meet the requirements. The test weight per bushel does not necessarily have to be high; on the other hand, it cannot be low, and thin-hulled oats may be of a lighter test weight than those with the thicker hulls. A plump berry means that the groat is meaty and a good milling recovery will be obtained.

Oats-milling companies have large oats-storage capacity; therefore, they carry a stock of oats for some time before it is milled. For this reason, the moisture content must be low—not over 14%.

Cleaning and preparing oats for milling is an intricate process requiring a number of steps which include separating by aspirators, grading or screening by diameter and length, and blending. Chaff, light or "pin" oats, double oats, hulled oats, and other grains and seeds are separated by special machines. The oats thus separated as suitable for processing are dried, and at the same time, because of the toasting, acquire a flavor.

Oats are graded into three classes—large, slim, and stub—and each class is milled separately. In one hulling process the oats are placed between two milling stones, one of which revolves while the other remains stationary. The oats themselves stand on end and spin, tearing the hull from the groat. After the hulling process, oats that have not had the groat separated from the hulls are returned to the hulling stones. Other oat-hulling machines, replacing milling-stone operations, use an air current carrying the oats into a hulling chamber of metal that may be lined with rubber or an abrasive so that the air rotating the oats inside the chamber will separate the groats from the hulls. Some machines have rotors which beat against the oats, causing the separation.

Groats for steel-cut oatmeal are cut by special steel rolls, and those for rolled oats are passed through steaming machines so that they will roll into flakes without breaking.

The pin or thin oats cleaned out of milling oats are graded "thin" on Federal standards. These are suitable for feeding. Some are pulverized and used in a bulk feed mixture, and the hulls from the processing plant also go into bulk feeds. Variation in the price of hulls permits their sale for the manufacture of furfural which, normally made from corncobs, is used in making plastics, in making lubricating oils from petroleum, and in producing other important chemicals derived from it.

Even though Iowa is normally the largest oats-producing state, mills there and in Ohio and western New York rely on purchases from northwestern surplus states for a good share of their supplies. During some seasons the price of Canadian oats permits payment of duty on them and their importation into this country for feeding and milling uses, thus putting them in competition with varieties grown in the United States.

Barley Malt

Malt is a grain the starch content of which has been converted to a form of sugar through a process of sprouting, or growing. It is used primarily in the brewing and distilling industries.

There are fewer than a dozen acceptable malting-barley varieties out of several hundred different varieties of barley grown in the United States. Great care is taken in seed selection and in the growing, threshing, and storing of malting barley. Good malting barley is more than just malting and high-test-weight barley; maltsters want plump, even-sized kernels of malting-variety barley with few or no skinned or broken kernels. Federal grain grades allow in barley to be graded "malting" only 10% skinned and broken kernels—by "skinned" is meant hulls loosened or removed over the germ, or a third of the hull removed.

The reason for careful selection of barley is that in malting it is first steeped in water and then sprouted. Sprouting results in the activation of enzymes that break down the starch granules in the grain so that they may be subsequently converted into dextrines and sugars in malt-using processes. Sprouting must be uniform and complete so that the resulting malt is completely modified.

When undamaged barley kernels sprout, the sprout, or acrospire, grows from the germ end underneath the hull of the kernel and emerges from the beard end. The hull protects the sprout so that its growth is normal and modification is complete, producing a high-grade malt. Skinned kernels sprout faster because they take up water faster and the sprouts grow out of the breaks in the kernel unprotected by the hull, but when the maltsters stir the sprouting barley to areate it and keep the roots from matting, these unprotected sprouts are broken off; sprouting stops and the quality of the malt suffers.[1]

The task of buying malting barley is very exacting, but the buyer is aided by knowing the origin of the barley. Most of the six-row varieties come from the upper Mississippi River Valley and the two-row varieties from the Pacific Northwest. Barley that is not suitable for malting is used for pearling or feeding and customarily sells at a very large discount below the malting-quality price. For this reason great care is taken in selecting barley to be sure of its malting qualifications. The buyer is aided in determining the soundness and mellowness of barley through a pearling test; in pearling barley the entire husk is removed in a scouring machine, disclosing more readily the percentage of mellow and sound kernels. The color of a pearled sample of malting barley is white or blue and white.

Buying malting barley usually starts early in the crop-marketing year or as soon as the crop starts moving after harvest. Barley purchased shortly after harvest is not immediately suitable for malting and must be stored until it has been cured—the barley must go through a rest period during which it will not germinate. It is necessary that the barley be low in moisture content so that it will store safely and have no odor. Stored barley should be of one or of similar varieties.

There is no futures market in the United States that is a satisfactory hedge for malting barley. It is a specialty grain comparable to high protein wheat but normally selling at higher premiums over ordinary grades of barley than protein wheat sells over ordinary grades of wheat. Malting-barley trade requirements are very technical and concentrated in too few firms, and not enough malting barley is readily available to be suitable for futures trading. The barley-futures contracts in Minneapolis and Chicago are on the basis of feed-grain-quality

[1] From literature of the Midwest Barley Improvement Association, Milwaukee, 1950.

requirements, although malting barley may be delivered if sellers desire.

Prior to malting, barley is cleaned, as are other grains, to remove dockage, etc., before it is processed. In the cleaning operation of malting barley, a separation machine removes oats, wheat, broken kernels, skinned barley, and seeds from the whole barley kernels. The barley is then graded according to size so that uniform grains may be processed together. Four sizes emerge from the sizing operation: the two larger used for brewing purposes after malting, the third size for distillers malt, and the fourth for feed. Again, when skimmings are recovered by floating off lightweight kernels from the steep tanks into a collecting trough, a further amount of barley is recovered for feed.

The type of malt required by brewers is one that will produce beer that is palatable and tasty as well as of good color and aroma. High extract yield is important for malt in the brewing trade. In distilling, the principal requirement for malt is that it be high in diastatic power, or the capacity for converting starches to sugar.

Malting barley is next steeped for two to three days until white tips of the rootlets appear; at this stage the barley contains 45% to 50% water. It is then transferred to drums or compartments, where it is grown under controlled conditions for from five to six days, until the acrospire reaches from three fourths to full length up the kernel. The root meanwhile reaches away from the the tip of the kernel to a length about equal to that of the kernel. At this stage it is known as "green malt." The growth is then stopped by kilning—gradually increasing the heat for about two thirds of a day's stay in the kiln. Then it is transferred to a second kiln for an equal length of time when greater heat is applied for a few hours. Moisture is reduced to 3% or 4%; the malt is cooled and cleaned to remove the rootlets, then is stored for aging. The sprouts are sold for feed.

A 48-pound bushel of barley produces somewhat more than

a 34-pound bushel of malt; and it takes about a bushel of malt to produce a barrel of beer. Malt makes up about 70% of the grain in most beers, to which adjuncts of corn, rice, grain sorghums, wheat, grits, etc., or syrup are added in the brewing process together with the hops, yeast, etc. Finally, after the liquid is drawn off in both brewing and distilling, there remains a by-product which is valuable as a livestock feed.

In distilling, bourbon whisky must contain at least 51% corn and rye whisky at least 51% rye. Distillers buy high-quality grain low in moisture for distilling; it is the starch content of the grain in which they are interested. They pay good cash premiums to obtain what is generally known as "distillers' rye" and are careful in the selection of their corn supplies. Distillers do not have much grain storage capacity; therefore, they require their suppliers to follow a strict schedule in shipping cars of grain to their plants.

After the grain for distilling is cleaned, it is ground into meal. The meal is cooked with water, which ruptures the starch cells to facilitate conversion of starch into sugar. Next the malt is added, and the mash is converted into sugar. Yeast is then added, which brings about the fermentation process. In the distilling industry the fermented mash is referred to as beer. Through heating the alcoholic content is first vaporized and then condensed. The residue left in the still after the alcohol is distilled is called "spent mash," which is the material used in the manufacture of animal feed. During the distilling process the material is cooled several times and the heat controlled at other times.

It takes about 1½ pounds of malt to produce each 100-proof (50% alcoholic content) gallon of liquor.

Pearling Barley

Pearling barley, used in soups, etc., requires a barley that is plump and of a white or creamy color after the outer layers are removed. Mostly two-row barley is used for this process—likely larger-berried barleys such as the Spartan or Campagna varieties, the former grown in the northern section of the plains states and the latter in the plains states generally. Barley is pearled by gradually removing the hull and the outer portion of the kernel by abrasive action. Uniform kernel size is important, because the finished product must be produced in definite sizes.

A common type of pearling machine consists of a cylindrical millstone revolving rapidly within a perforated cylinder which turns more slowly in the opposite direction to that of the millstone. The holes in the cylinder are smaller than the grain, their purpose being to turn the grain over and over while the revolving millstone grinds off the hull. Each charge of grain is held in the machine until the desired stage of milling is reached.

After the grain is discharged from the pearler, the mixture of offal and partly hulled barley is sent to a reel, which removes the hulls. The series of operations is repeated until a product of desired size and purity is obtained. After the third pearling, the product may be classed as pot barley; after five or six pearling operations the resulting barley is small, round, and white.

Barley hulls from the pearling operations are used by the feed trade.[2]

Soybean Processing

The soybean-processing industry in the United States is entirely different from that of the Orient, the land of the soybean's origin. In China, where meat is eaten only several times a year by most of the population, soybeans are used less for livestock feed than for human food. In the Chinese diet, probably only 5% of the protein is animal protein, the remaining 95% being vegetable protein, as contrasted with the

[2] Production and Marketing Administration Miscellaneous Publication No. 692, Oct., 1949.

fact that in the United States over half the protein eaten is animal protein and less than half vegetable protein.

China uses soybeans for the production of soy sauce, the result of a fermentation process in which the liquid is filtered out. The sauce is used in the daily preparation of food and as a table condiment. Another product is soy or vegetable milk, produced by soaking beans, grinding them, and filtering out the milk, which is consumed as is our cows' milk even though its flavor is not too popular even with the oriental people. The residue, containing considerable protein, goes for animal feed. Yuba, another product, is made from the milk by heating and skimming off a protein film from the surface. Yuba is used as a wrapper for other foods, or broken into smaller pieces, or cut into ribbons and fried, or used in soups. Soybean curd, or *tofu,* is a cheeselike product made by adding magnesium or calcium to soy milk; it may be added to soups or eaten as a meat substitute. Another soybean product is soybean cheese made by pressing the soy curd hard enough that it can be cut into small cubes. The cheese varies with the process, a fact that is due probably to the influence of climatic conditions on the activity of the fermenting micro-organisms.

Some soybeans are processed in China to obtain oil and meal, the processing being done by screw or hydraulic presses. The cake from hydraulic-processed soybeans is a flat disc about 5 inches thick and 24 inches in diameter. Soybean cake is very hard, but farmers prefer to purchase their soybean meal in this form, because it assures them that it is unadulterated. Oil for domestic consumption is unrefined and is retailed in small shops for home use.

The Japanese make a product from soybeans called *miso,* which has a flavor like that of soy sauce and is made in a similar way, except less water is used, and the entire product is eaten rather than just the filtered liquid. Its largest single use is in soup, which some Japanese eat three times a day. It is also spread on bread and vegetables to add flavor. Along with sugar and oil, it is used in cooking fish, meat, and vegetables.[3]

In the United States, that which is harvested as beans rather than as a plant cut for other purposes is almost exclusively processed for oil and meal. Statistics indicate that a very minor amount of harvested soybeans are used on farms for purposes other than to seed the next crop. Nearly the entire crop is accounted for by the amounts processed, used for seed, exported, or carried over at the end of the crop year. Because soybeans are said to produce soft pork when fed to hogs before the oil has been extracted or, if fed to cows, the milk produces soft butter, farmers market practically their entire production. After the oil has been extracted from soybeans at processing plants, the remaining meal becomes a high protein supplement that is a valuable ingredient in feed for livestock and poultry. It saves considerable grain feeding and shortens the time it takes to make animals and birds ready for market. The oil extracted from soybeans is used mostly for food, largely in shortening, margarine, salad and cooking oils and mayonnaise. Used inedibly, it is an ingredient in paint, varnish, and soap.

There is much similarity between the marketing of soybeans and of grains. However, there is a sharp difference in the movement of soybeans into actual consuming channels as compared with the movement of wheat, corn, and other grains because of the proximity of soybean-processing plants to the areas of heavy production. A substantial portion of the soybean crop never does pass through what is known as a primary market. Instead, soybeans go directly to interior processing centers.

It might be well to realize that, despite the fact that much of the soybean crop that passes into commercial channels necessarily does not come to Chicago, it is the soybean futures market at the Chicago Board of Trade that is called upon to

[3] Allan K. Smith (Northern Research Laboratory, Peoria, Ill.), "Notes on Oriental Farming Practices," *The Soybean Digest,* 1949.

absorb the hedging activities of processors, merchandisers, exporters, and interior elevators throughout the country.[4] Of soybean receipts at the primary markets, particularly Chicago, much of the run is sold on a "to-arrive" basis or is shipped to Chicago via barge, and a small share on a consignment basis or by truck. Some move to Chicago directly to processing plants and the balance to terminal elevators.

While processors buy a considerable share of their soybean requirements directly from the country elevators, commission merchants handle some for processors as well as for terminal elevator companies and exporters. Like all grains, soybeans that move to terminal markets are held until such time as they are disposed of to processors or exporters. Meanwhile, soybeans stored in regular delivery elevators in Chicago may be delivered on futures contracts to "longs" who pay for them and ship them out of the market or sell them through merchandising; or they may carry them from one future-delivery month to the next or redeliver them on the same future as received.

Chicago is so situated in relation to national soybean production that it is not often an export outlet, except to Canada. Soybeans grown in the Mississippi-delta states or along the Atlantic seaboard furnish most soybeans for export as soybeans. The soybean oil that is exported, however, may move from plants in Chicago or other marketing areas. Exports of soybean meal are small in comparison to those of oil and soybeans.

Practically all soybeans inspected under United States standards are of the yellow class. Soybean purchasers judge quality mostly by the grading factors and area in which they are grown, inasmuch as nine latitudinal areas of the country govern the varieties planted. Though a mixture of soybeans in a processor's purchases gives an average oil recovery in mill operations, each one's purchases are made largely in one section of the country. Oil content varies somewhat from year to year, but is mostly a characteristic of bean variety, as is also the iodine

[4] Chicago Board of Trade, *The Story of Soybeans,* 1951.

number of the oil. Oil of maximum iodine number is preferred in the drying-oil trade for use in paints and varnishes. The edible oil trade prefers oil of a minimum iodine number because it requires less hydrogen in the hardening process and because the final product has better keeping properties.

Railroad freight is a consideration in purchasing soybeans, because there is no transit billing on the oil when it is extracted from the soybeans. Thus processors try to buy soybeans originating close to their plants to save this unrecoverable portion of the in-freight on soybeans purchased for processing, considerable amounts of which are bought for truck hauling to the processing plants. Soybean oil itself has transit privileges when it moves from its point of origin as oil. Outbound meal moves on the soybean-transit billing. Processors make a practice (although not exclusively) of buying soybeans "basis track country station" and paying freight to their plant rather than buying on the basis of "price including freight paid to destination," as is done on the grains. Since meal shipped from processing plants moves in many directions, whatever railroad billing is on hand can usually be worked off by finding buyers in favorable locations suitable to the billing. Selling of meal is usually based on the "free on board cars Decatur, Illinois," price, and on most of the meal shipped from the large processing area in central Illinois the buyer has an unrestricted choice of destination. The seller prepays the freight and charges the buyer the rate from Decatur to destination, no matter where the meal is shipped from. Usually the seller knows the destination at the time the meal is sold. Meal sold from plants from which there is a freight penalty to certain destinations or a saving to other destinations is sold on a "restricted destination" basis. Freight rates on soybeans in some cases differ from grain rates and take a higher railroad export rate than the grain rate.

There are three types of soybean processing—the hydraulic-press process, the continuous-expeller or screw process, and the solvent extraction process. Hydraulic presses handle only a small percentage of the quantity of soybeans crushed; such mills are engaged principally in crushing other oilseeds, such as cottonseed and flaxseed. Their unit crushing costs are said to be higher and the recovery of oil per bushel of soybeans less than in the other methods. The expeller, or continuous-screw-press, method recovers somewhat more oil than the hydraulic process but considerably less than the solvent extraction process. The solvent extraction process, although more costly to install, is displacing the expeller technique because it separates more of the higher-priced oil from the soybeans and leaves less oil in the meal to be sold at the lower meal price. At times expeller meal commands a premium over extracted meal, compensating for at least part of the difference in processing recoveries.

In the hydraulic process, soybeans are ground, then mashed into thin flakes, and cooked, after which the hot flakes are formed into rectangular cakes and wrapped with a hair or wool mat. Very high pressure is applied to the wrapped cakes with a plunger or ram slowly squeezing out the oil, which runs into a trough and is piped into tanks. The residue is a hard, compact mass called "oil cake," which is ground to produce soybean meal.

Soybeans are rather coarsely cracked in the expeller processing method and then dried to a low percentage of moisture. They are then held at a relatively high temperature in order to cook the protein. The hot material is fed into the press and compressed by means of a powerful rotating screw and forced through a cylindrical cage composed of steel bars spaced a few thousandths of an inch apart. The oil is squeezed out of the soybeans and the residual material is forced onward and discharged as irregularly shaped fragments which are cooled and ground to produce soybean meal. The crude oil is filtered before storing and subsequent shipment to the refinery.

In the solvent extraction process the soybeans are cracked, heated, and flaked, and then are passed through the solvent extraction apparatus. There are many kinds of apparatus in use, but in all of them the flow is countercurrent; that is, the fresh flakes meet a mixture of soybean oil and solvent, and as the flakes pass along the solvent encountered is progressively fresher. The oil removed from the soybeans and mixed with the solvent is called "miscella." The miscella is filtered, and then most of the solvent is removed by passage through a series of evaporators. Final traces of solvent are removed from the oil by scrubbing it with steam. The solvent is returned to tanks for further use and the crude soybean oil is put in storage. The residual solids are discharged from the extractor into driers which evaporate all the volatile solvents, and the deodorized flakes are toasted and ground into meal.

In official feed-ingredient definitions, the product is named "soybean-oil meal," preceded by the type of processing to differentiate from "soybean meal," which could be made from the crushing of whole beans with oil included; but in futures trading the product is known as 44%-protein soybean meal. The 44%-protein meal deliverable on futures is described as produced by conditioning ground soybeans and reducing the oil content of the conditioned product by use of solvents to 1% or less on a commercial basis. The minimum fat content of the meal must be 0.5%, and the maximum moisture content when shipped 12%.

There is a certain amount of soybean pressing and extraction to make, respectively, medium-fat and low-fat flour. In addition, some soybeans are ground without prior removal of the oil, the products being either full-fat soy flour or ground soybeans, depending on whether it is for human or animal consumption.

The products of soybean-processing plants are marketed in separate commercial channels. Oil resulting from plant operations is crude oil, in which form most of it is sold by the processors. Crude oil is the only oil deliverable on futures contracts, although it may be degummed or non-degummed. Soybean crude-oil and meal futures-contract standards are equal to the products of most of the processing trade.

The soybean and products contracts are designed to afford protection by hedging and to offer price guidance for those who produce soybeans, those who merchandise them, those who store them, those who process them, and those who use the products in refining, feeding, and many other uses. By use of the crude oil or meal futures market, each tradesman may hedge either by buying or selling. The soybean processor may protect his crude-oil output by a sale of an equivalent quantity of oil futures and sell his meal output as cash in commercial channels, or vice versa, when the oil is merchandised and the meal is not. Or if neither oil nor meal is merchandised, he may sell the equivalent amount of his soybean stock in oil and meal futures contracts when their combined prices relative to the price of soybeans is high enough to cover the conversion costs. The crude-oil price is influenced by supply-and-demand conditions in the fats-and-oils market; at the same time, the meal price moves from the influences of a different set of conditions largely allied to the livestock-feeding trade. The same opportunity of hedging or buying soybeans and oil or meal is available to consumers by use of these futures. Each of the three futures contracts—soybeans, crude oil, and meal—have a definite place in the economy.

Feed Manufacturing

Raising marketable livestock and poultry in a shorter feeding time saves considerable grain and consequently reduces the costs of the feeding material required per livestock unit. For this accomplishment livestock and poultry men owe a lot to the feed manufacturers. Much credit is also due to those who do basic nutrition research and to breeders in developing livestock and poultry which have the inherent ability to be more efficient users of feed.

Feed manufacturers employ many ingredients in addition to grains in formulating specialized feed mixtures in such a way that the finished product supplies all essential nutrients in the correct proportion to meet the needs of the class of livestock or poultry for which the feed is designed. Ingredients such as grain are used as sources of energy in feeds; other additions are proteins, vitamins, minerals, and antibiotics. Feed formulas differ for each kind of animal and bird. Those for the livestock vary according to the age of the livestock and the purpose for which they are being raised and with the part of the country in which they are raised. In addition to formula feeds for hogs, cattle, and chickens, there are turkeys, ducks, rabbits, goats, dogs, and also small animals used for laboratory purposes to be supplied by the feed manufacturers with feed for balanced diets. Before anything can be used in feed manufacturing, it must be approved by the Association of American Feed Control officials and be distinctly defined by them. They have a list of well over 200 feed ingredients.

Most states require feed manufacturers to register the brands of feed that they wish to sell in the respective states. It is also necessary to guarantee the chemical analysis in respect to the fat, fiber, and protein content. This requires that the manufacturer maintain the quality of his feed within the limits of the guaranteed analysis; and this in turn limits to some extent the substitution of one grain for another. There is considerable room for substitution, however, because various grains have similar feeding values. The feed manufacturer therefore utilizes as fully as possible those grains that from time to time are the cheapest and will result in the most economical production of feed. For this reason the use of the different grains in the production of commercial feeds varies from season to season. Many feeders buy manufactured feed in the form of a high-protein supplement to be used with home-grown grains to add the feeding essentials that their grain lacks. Some feeders buy pelleted feeds which contain the right proportions of ingredients and are of the correct size for the livestock or poultry they are to feed. By feeding pellets, they are assured that the bird or the animal consumes every bit of feed ingredient that it should have for its development. Birds, for example, to a certain extent select those particular items in the feed formula that especially appeal to the eye; in a pellet they get all or nothing. However, some feeders break the pellets before feeding.[5]

Grains are prepared for feed manufacturing first by recleaning; then they are cracked, screened, ground, crimped, crushed, pulverized, or whatever else is necessary. Some feed manufacturers buy some grain products already prepared. Ingredients used in relatively small quantity are premixed or blended carefully to insure their uniform distribution; there are two types of mixers—continuous process mixers and batch mixers—which thoroughly blend all the ingredients so that each 100-pound sack or other small portion of feed will have all the ingredients present.

Mixed-feed manufacturing is the principal use of soybean meal as well as the other meals from the oilseed crushing industry. By-product feeds of the various processing industries also find their way into this trade. Formerly many of these were wasted.

The Midwest is the only area which produces a net surplus of feedstuffs and ships substantial quantities of grain and meal to each other region in the country, but it does bring in relatively small quantities of cottonseed meal, fish meal, and alfalfa meal. The Southwest ships out grain sorghums, cottonseed meal, and alfalfa meal to other regions, but such shipments are overbalanced by in-shipments of grain, soybean meal, and other feedstuffs for consumption there. Pacific Coast manufacturers obtain corn from the Midwest and grain sorghums from the Southwest as well as other ingredients from these areas and elsewhere, but produce some of their own grains and other materials, such as cottonseed meal. The New England States are very deficient in grain and oilseed production, but are large feeders; they have to buy practically all their supplies in other areas of the country or import them from Canada. The Southeastern States

---

[5] Production and Marketing Administration Miscellaneous Publication No. 692, Oct., 1949.

obtain large quantities from other areas. There are many feed manufacturers in scattered locations throughout the country, and some of the larger firms with many plants cater to particular needs in each area. This is economical, as it avoids paying freight on bulky material and enables them to use locally grown crops in the preparation of their feeds.

In applying railroad billing to shipments of mixed feed going out of a plant in most areas, the amount of billing for each commodity must be applied according to the percentage of that commodity contained in the feed. It may take several shipments to use the inbound billing on one car. Pool cars are shipped to several firms at one destination, or cars may contain several feeds for one customer. Trucks handle small-lot shipments.

CHAPTER X

Statistics and News

The grain trade gathers news from all over the world and follows statistics of prices and quantitive data compiled in daily, weekly, monthly, quarterly, and annual form. Except for some of the records that were destroyed in the great Chicago Fire in 1871, there is a continuous statistical and news record of the grain trade in Chicago dating back over a century to 1848.

Crop Reports[1]

Of all the statistics available to the grain trade, probably none are more important than those on the size of the crops, estimated privately and, more importantly, by the Crop Reporting Board of the United States Department of Agriculture. The nature and scope of our agriculture are reflected in the almost daily reports of the Crop Reporting Board on some crop or another, and in many daily reports of other official agencies.

To America's millions of farm people these statistics are direction finders. They help processors and distributors to iron out some of the kinks in the tortuous road a product travels from the farm to its ultimate consumer—to the benefit of both producer and consumer. They help manufacturers of farm machinery and supplies locate their best markets. Other users of the crop reports who might be named are agencies, transporta-

[1] U.S.D.A. Crop Reporting Board Miscellaneous Publication No. 703, Dec., 1949.

tion systems, newspapers, farm and trade publications, radio and television systems, etc., of both national and international scope.

The statistical work carried on by the Department was established by Congress in 1862. To aid the farmers in their bargaining position in the sale of their crops, the Federal Government first provided a census for agriculture to be taken in 1840 in connection with the sixth decennial census of population. Since that time a census of agriculture has always been taken in conjunction with the census of population in each decennial enumeration. Since 1925 a mid-decennial agricultural census has been taken. Thus, since 1920 the United States Department of Commerce has taken a census of agriculture every five years. When data from this census becomes available, final revised estimates are made of acreage, yield and production of crops, numbers of livestock, etc. These are primarily revisions of the levels of the annual estimates for crops, livestock, etc., for the previous five or six years, and census data are adjusted for incompleteness when commercial or other check data are available. Census data are especially useful for agricultural products for which commercial check data and other information are not adequate or available, such as agricultural products that are mostly consumed on the farm or are shipped primarily by motor truck rather than by rail. From the census and the other data, errors made through mistakes in judgment in reporting crops are eliminated, and a fresh start is made with each census.

In general, acreage estimates are based upon two types of information: (1) absolute acreage data for a given crop season, ordinarily obtained from the quinquennial United States census of agriculture, a state assessors' census, or some other complete or nearly complete enumeration, and (2) indicated changes in acreages of individual crops from one year to the next obtained by questionnaire from samples of farmers or processors. Acreage data of the first type are called "acreage bases" or "bench marks," while the sample data are called "acreage indications."

An almost ideal method of obtaining accurate acreage information would be to make a complete enumeration by mail, by personal interview, or a combination of both. This would provide a means of obtaining figures on both planted acreage and harvested acreage by the method of utilization. This ideal is hardly approached even in those states where assessors' censuses ask for acreages in the current rather than the preceding year, for ordinarily only one type of acreage information, either planted or harvested, is available. Furthermore, insufficient time elapses between harvesting late crops and the date of the final acreage and production estimates in December to make possible the use of assessors' censuses, even if they were taken in the late fall after harvest, as they never are.

Because of the rigid time schedule and limitations imposed by costs and available personnel it is necessary to derive, from sample data, acreages as percentages of acreages of the previous year. These percentages are applied to the previous year's acreages to obtain indications of current acreages. For example, the indicated percentage that the acreage of corn for all purposes this year is of last year's acreage, is applied to last year's acreage to obtain an estimate of the acreage this year.

The sequence of acreage forecasts or estimates for most spring-grown crops is (1) acreages intended for planting ("prospective plantings") as of March 1, released late in March, (2) acreages planted and acreages for harvest, released with the July General Report, and (3) acreages planted and harvested, released in the Annual Summary in December. This sequence is not followed for all individual crops, however; estimates of the acreages planted to fall-sown wheat and rye are released in December of the year preceding harvest, and acreage remaining for harvest is estimated in May.

A forecast of crops is a statement of the most likely yield or production on the basis of known facts on a given date, assuming weather conditions and damage from insects and other pests during the remainder of the growing season to be about the same as that of previous years in which reported condition on the given date was similar to the present reported condition. The yield potentialities of the current condition may be appraised accurately, but if the weather or other conditions between the date of the forecast and the time of harvest are not similar to those experienced in the past seasons used in the determination, the actual yield may differ somewhat from the forecast. As the season progresses, the forecasts made at or just before harvest merge into estimates of accomplished fact.

The first forecast of the production of winter wheat is published by states at about December 20 of the year previous to harvest largely on the basis of the reported condition as of December 1 and precipitation from August through November. Monthly forecasts of production of winter wheat are made from April through August; monthly forecasts of the yield of rye are begun in May; of oats, barley, and spring wheat in June; of most other spring-grown field crops in July; and of a few crops including cotton, soybeans, peanuts, sorghums, and broomcorn as late as August.

The Crop Reporting Board does not forecast yield solely on the basis of reported condition and meteorological data. As a crop nears maturity, crop reporters are asked to estimate the probable yield in their localities, and the average of these crop reporters' forecasts are translated into yield forecasts by the Crop Reporting Board by means of regression charts in which "true" yields are plotted against reported probable yields. When there is either an upward or a downward trend in yields over a period of years, crop reporters tend to lag in their appraisal of the situation.

The sources of information upon which forecasts and estimates are based are many and varied. The information is generally of two kinds: (1) sample data and (2) presumably complete census or other complete enumeration data such as quantities processed or shipped. The sample data are obtained from farmers in two ways: (1) by means of a mailed questionnaire, called "voluntary mail sampling," or (2) by personal interview, sometimes using "preselected-interview (or probability) sampling." The latter method has many advantages, but because of certain disadvantages, including its high cost and slowness, it has not been adopted for making forecasts or estimates of agricultural production but has instead provided lists of names for mail surveys. Methods of voluntary mail sampling predominate in the work of the organization.

In the use of voluntary mail sampling, farmers who are willing to co-operate are requested to supply information about crop acreages, crop yields and conditions, farm livestock inventories, milk and egg production, farm employment and wages, and other items closely related to their farming and about which they have intimate knowledge. This information may relate (1) to agricultural conditions in the locality in which the farmer lives or (2) to the operation of the farmer's own farm.

Voluntary mail samples fall into four general categories:

1. Regular monthly reporters receive a schedule the first of each month. The questions concern crop and pasture conditions, yields per acre, etc., and also the rate of milk and egg production and farm stocks (quarterly). A return of about 30% is obtained from a list of about 80,000 farmers. Similarly, about 30,000 monthly reporters receive price questionnaires and about 30% are returned.
2. Direct-mail individual-farm reporters receive crop-acreage questionnaires in March on intentions to plant, in June on crop acreages for harvest, and late in the fall on acreage harvest and on production. About 80,000, or 25% of the 320,000 farmers, reply.
3. Rural mail carriers of the Post Office Department distribute about 600,000 unaddressed individual-farm questionnaire

cards to farmers along their routes three times each year—in June and December on livestock and in October on crop acreages planted and harvested. About 160,000 cards, or 27%, are returned and tabulated.

4. A fourth type of "special-purpose" mail sampling is used in making estimates of acreage, condition, yield and/or production of commercial crops, numbers of livestock, and production of livestock products, etc. Examples include fruit, nut, and vegetable crops; such field crops as cotton, tobacco, seed crops, cattle and lambs on feed, etc.; and grain stocks in mills and elevators. This also covers areas where a small percentage of farmers produce a large percentage of a crop, the feeding of livestock, and portions of states where a small percentage of the farmers produce a certain crop.

Although the goal is not always reached in practice, an attempt is made to obtain the services of at least one general crop reporter in every agricultural township in the United States.

It has long been obvious that farms tend to differ from one part of a state to another; consequently, a geographic stratification was adopted long ago and is still in use. Every state is subdivided into crop-reporting districts, the boundaries of which tend to follow the lines which mark off differences in farm characteristics but do not cut across individual counties. The general pattern calls for nine such districts per state, but the number is smaller in some states and slightly larger in others.

In reporting the condition of crops, farmers are asked to report on the basis of 100 representing a normal condition:

A normal condition is not an average condition but a condition above average giving promise of more than an average crop. Furthermore, a normal condition does not indicate a perfect crop or a crop that is or promises to be the very largest in quantity and the very best in quality that the region reported upon may be considered capable of producing. The normal indicates something less than this and thus comes between the average and the possible maximum, being greater than the former and less than the latter. The normal may be described as a condition of perfect healthfulness unimpaired by drought, hail, insects, or other injurious agency and with such growth and development as may be reasonably looked for under favorable conditions.

Procedure in Making a Crop Report

In the preparation of a particular crop report, procedures are standardized in Washington, but statisticians in charge of state offices have considerable latitude in choosing the method to obtain information and expand it into statewide estimates. Washington procedures grow out of field experience and suggestions, but Washington prescribes the questionnaires to be used and the methods of summarizing and analyzing the information obtained by the questionnaires. All transcriptions, except those from the original questionnaire, to the listing sheet are verified. To be of value, publication of reports for each of the forty-eight states and of all the states combined must be issued as early as possible. For example, monthly crop reports relating to conditions as of the first of the month are issued between the eighth and eleventh of the month.

All individual information furnished is kept confidential and is never made public outside the estimating service—the reporter is confident that his information will never been seen by a local tax assessor or any other person who is not a member of the Agricultural Estimates staff. The Crop Reporting Board also keep its reports of forecasts and estimates in strictest confidence until their release to the public. Personnel both in Washington and the field offices are forbidden to speculate in agricultural commodities. Fines up to $10,000 and imprisonment up to ten years are provided as penalties.

The procedure in an August Illinois general crop report is generally as follows: About the middle of July Washington mails to the state statistician a set of instructions and forms for individual reporters for the next month's crop report. Illinois has mailing lists that include the names of about 4,000 crop reporters. Forms for reporters are mailed out between the twenty-fifth and the twenty-seventh of the month and about the end of the month begin to come back to the state offices, where they are sorted by crop-reporting districts, then by counties within each district.

The reports are painstakingly listed on uniform sheets. Any questionable reports are carefully edited, but are maintained if apparently representing some minority situation in the county. By the third or fourth of the month, listings must be closed and entered on district summary sheets from which weighted and unweighted state averages are computed. Approximate predetermined weights are used for computing each weighted state average. Except for speculative grains, all district summaries are placed on a state-summary form. These speculative grains (soybeans, corn, oats, and winter wheat for Illinois and other states and spring wheat and cotton for still other states) are listed and reported on separate forms for compilation in Washington.

During the last few days of one month and the first two days of the next month, several state statisticians travel in the more important crop-producing sections of their states or sections where weather or insect damage is of potential but previously unknown significance. They also talk with well-informed persons such as operators of grain elevators, county agents, local dealers and representatives of farm management services, as well as with the farmers. Reports of these statisticians' recommendations are entered on the summary sheet, which is prepared in duplicate. Comments of effects of weather, etc., are written on special forms separately for each item or group of related items. The summary sheets and comments are placed in an envelope marked "C" and mailed to the Crop Reporting Board in Washington in time to be received about four days before the issuance of the report.

Such crops as corn, oats, wheat, and cotton have been designated as speculative because of the large volume of futures trading in them on the organized exchanges. Individual states in which the production of a given speculative crop is so great that forecasts or estimates of production for those states, either singly or in the aggregate, are highly correlated with the country's total production have been designated as speculative states for the crops in question; all other states are called non-speculative with regard to that crop.

After non-speculative summaries have been mailed to Washington, the state statisticians turn their attention to speculative items. These are mailed in a special "A" envelope addressed to the Secretary of Agriculture. These are mailed so as to be delivered in Washington at 10:00 A.M. the day before the issuance of the report, which is due to come out at 3:00 P.M., for grains. Much preparation of work sheets is done prior to receipt of the state summaries; i.e., acreages estimated in July are on the August sheets. Also, accompanying data of the past year and 10-year averages are prepared. All these are assembled in a folder for each state.

The "C" envelopes containing non-speculative reports received in duplicate and statisticians' recommendations are divided between computing units and a member of the Crop Reporting Board. In the first phase, the latter reviews the data much as the state statisticians do and arrives at his own recommendations, making out a "change slip" if he does not agree with a state or field statistician's recommendations. After review, all material is placed in a state folder and returned to the secretary of the Crop Reporting Board. In the second phase of the non-speculative review, which is called the commodity review, members of the Crop Reporting Board are assigned individual commodities to review. Using the same techniques as formerly, they review all estimates for all states and approve or disapprove changes made previously and make changes if they believe the data warrant them. These changes are discussed with the board member concerned, everything being approved or disapproved by the chairman of the Crop Reporting Board. Changes are mailed to each field office concerned. Necessary computations are made, including the United

States total production and yield; also, comments on non-speculative commodities are prepared by board members for the report to be published.

In the meantime, the "A" envelopes addressed to the Secretary of Agriculture are given special handling. Immediately upon receipt, the envelope is delivered to the chief of the Secretary of Agriculture's records section, who has the responsibility of placing the report in a mailbox that is secured by two locks and kept in a locked room, and of then checking the reports off on a list on top of the box bearing the names of the so-called "speculative states."

On the day of release—about 6 o'clock in the morning—the chairman of the board, who has the key for one lock, and one other member with a representative of the Secretary of Agriculture who has the key for the other lock, go to the locked room accompanied by an armed guard. They unlock the box and take the speculative reports to a designated room where window blinds have been closed and sealed and telephones disconnected; there they are locked in with others so that neither they nor any who enter later carrying special passes may leave until the appointed hour of release.

Each board member makes his own interpretation of the data for each of the speculative items for each of the states. The secretary of the Crop Reporting Board records the recommendations of all members of the board on a separate summary sheet for each speculative item. These are reviewed and discussed until agreement is reached or the chairman has exercised his authority to set the official estimate. They are entered on the computation sheet that already contains the data for non-speculative states. The necessary computations are made and national production and yield per acre are computed. Stencils are made and board members write comments on the speculative commodities for which they are responsible. These are edited for accuracy and style and then are stenciled. Finally, shortly before the time of release the report is assembled.

The Secretary of Agriculture enters the locked quarters

about 2:45 P.M., reviews the report, discusses it with board members, and signs it, thus approving it for release. Two or three minutes before 3:00 P.M. the chairman and the secretary of the board, accompanied by a few members, leave the locked quarters under armed guard to proceed to the release room. Here telephone and telegraph instruments are already connected with the outside world, but their operators are out of reach of the instruments. The reports are placed face down beside each instrument, and at 3:00 P.M. when the word "go" is said the reporters for newspapers, press services, and brokerage houses rush to their instruments and begin sending out the report.

A telegram is dispatched to each state office that requests it, containing all of the changes in recommendations for that state differing from the statisticians' recommendations and all the United States estimates. Mimeographed releases are mailed to all field offices by air mail and made available to the public.

Other Government Reports

Governmental agencies issue many reports useful to the grain trade. One is the weekly report of *Commercial Stocks of Grains in Terminal and Sub-terminal Markets.* Another is the quarterly report of grains in all positions, except for grain sorghums, which is given semi-annually; this report is very informative. One item which concerns commercial stocks of grain in terminal markets is available for reports at the end of the quarter. About the tenth of the month after the end of the quarter, a report of the stocks of grains on farms is published; it is also a guide to the disappearance of grain from the farms during the quarter and since the start of the season for each grain. It, however, does not disclose the disposition of the grain if the grain was not consumed on the farms, because it may have been moved to another location without being sold for commercial purposes or it may have been processed or exported. The final portions of the quarterly reports are issued about the twenty-fifth of the month—or later for soybeans and flaxseed—giving the amount of grain in merchant mills if it is wheat or in processing plants if it is other grains, the amount in interior mills, elevators, and warehouses, and the amount in Commodity Credit Corporation storage structures and in transit. These quarterly reports contain information as to the carryovers of grain—July 1 for wheat, oats, barley, and rye and October 1 for corn, soybeans, and grain sorghums. By application of the quarterly reports, the periodic disappearance of grain is ascertained, and after deduction of exports during each period the remainder represents total domestic uses of grain.

There are further reports for milling, processing, distilling, feeding, grain used for seed, etc., that break down the disappearance of each grain into many uses. For wheat, the largest use is in flour milling, and next in volume is usually the amount exported, followed by the amount of wheat fed as grain. Feeding uses of all grains combined varies from year to year with the number of animals and poultry in the country. Statistics are available for each quarter's feeding of grain. The by-products feeds produced from milling, oilseed crushing, animal proteins, etc., are reported monthly. To assemble the statistics for application to any business purpose requires some conjecture because of substitution of materials and location and price influences, but there are many sources of information for bases of calculation.

The exports of all agricultural products are published each month, with special releases for grain exports. Other reports issued at intervals cover livestock, cattle on feed, pig crops, lamb feeding, etc., as well as slaughter of various livestock. Milk, egg, and other products reports having a direct bearing on grain uses are regularly published. There are government-compiled statistics on each of the grains and reviews of situations in wheat, feeding, fats and oils, livestock, dairy, marketing, and farm income and other regularly released publications that give complete statistical information on the grains.

Agricultural Statistics issued annually by the United States Department of Agriculture—a book of over 700 pages—contains statistics on probably every important agricultural activity in the United States and on foreign trade as well. The book covers other phases of agriculture, including many prices, income, support programs, soil conservation, and financing, as well as farm resources, population figures, employment, weather information, etc.

Agricultural Prices, published monthly, contains parity prices, prices paid and received by farmers, and miscellaneous price information. Some of the tables in the publication are by states, giving monthly average state prices for each of the grains, the dairy industry, and livestock, and livestock products.

Foreign Crops and Markets, a weekly release, covers world agricultural products, and its articles are on agriculture in the United States or any other part of the world. Detailed tables of grains produced in each country of the world are published with comparisons for recent years and averages for earlier periods together with acreages and yields per acre. Many descriptive articles on conditions of trade and production of crops and allied foods, feeds, and fibers throughout the world are contained in the weekly booklet.

The government conducts a service for market news, reporting daily and weekly on prices, quantities, and activities in different trades. All the government statistics and services are available to those who are interested. Some of the publications are mailed out of Washington, D.C., but others are compiled and issued from the many field offices.

Grain Exchange Prices

The organized grain and other commodity exchanges perform a service to the economic system by the widespread dissemination of prices of trades made in futures and cash grain on the exchanges. Futures prices are recorded each time there is a change in the price; as fast as the handling system permits, each quotation is sent on hundreds of tickers throughout this country and Canada to subscriber members of the exchange and to nonmembers. The quotations received by the tickers may also be telegraphed or teletyped on the private wire systems of futures commission merchants serving many points not subscribing to the ticker-quotation service.

Special quotations are put out frequently by private wire firms "quoting the market" by direct quotations from the trading pits even though there is no change in the price. This is handled from the exchange floor by phone men who "flash" the price to the wire room, from where it is immediately sent to the branch offices and particularly to the cities where there are other grain-futures markets. These particular quotations are usually accompanied by the statement that the price is "bid" or "asked." Their transmission is very fast, as in the telegrapher's code there are symbols for the grain, the month, and "bid" or "asked" which permit rapid handling. These flash "quotes" are used mostly in connection with spreading operations when the spread must be executed at a guaranteed price difference between two markets. A broker handling intermarket spread orders is usually located in the least active of the two markets and works closely with a broker in the other market who continually sends flash quotes. When he receives a favorable flash quote he sends a "quick" (fill or kill) order back to that market. In a very short time he receives a report as to whether or not his order has been filled. If the order is filled he then makes a trade in his own market to complete the spread. Sometimes, on the basis of the flash quote, he immediately trades in his own market and sends a "market order" to the other market. If his order is filled at the flash-quote price all is well and good, but if not he has missed his spreading limit and cannot apply the trades on the spreading order.

There are other quotation services for grain futures. One gives nationwide continuous quotations by electrically controlled boards. This service emanates from a central office as the quotations appear on the tickers of the grain and other commodity exchanges. Radio broadcasting stations quote grain futures during the trading session, and by tuning in different stations word of frequent price changes may be secured. News tickers also carry grain quotations several times a day. The public telegraph furnishes "C.N.D." service at regular intervals to subscribers, and cables quote the market in foreign countries. With all the telephoning that is done from market centers, branch offices, etc., in addition to regular services, it can be realized that there is quite a complete coverage of grain-futures price changes.

Many newspapers throughout the country print futures opening prices, high and low, of the session and closing prices and either the previous closing prices or the amount of change in price for the day. Periodicals and trade journals as well as trade annuals print the daily range of futures prices, making them available as permanent public records.

Dissemination of quotations gives widespread knowledge of the price of futures on which growers, merchandisers, and consumers trade their grain. No one need be uninformed as to the market price of futures; therefore, grain and products in all locations can be bought and sold at their proper relation to this price-basing medium.

The prices of cash grain are quoted less often than futures, but they are available throughout the day to those interested. They are printed several times a day on the same ticker that records futures quotations. These are the spot trades posted on a "cash"-quotations board on the trading floor within a reasonable length of time after each trade is made. Further detail as to the grading factors of each car is listed elsewhere on the trading floor. The range (highest and lowest prices) for each grade of cash grain is broadcast over the radio during the day and furnished to the press. The exchange keeps a permanent record of the daily range of each grade for all grains that are traded in the spot market but no record of to-arrive or shipping sale prices.

Grain Exchange Statistics

Two important reports for the grain trade compiled by grain exchanges are the daily "Primary Receipts and Shipments" and the weekly "Visible Supply." Each day thirteen prominent grain centers of the Midwest report the number of bushels of each grain received and shipped. The trade refers to these as the "Primary Receipts and Shipments." These are tabulated and posted on the blackboards of the exchanges and reported regularly where grain statistics are quoted. Although there is some duplication when grain is shipped from one market to another in general this report represents the size of the original movement of grain from country points to primary markets and the amounts shipped out of these markets for consumption. Each Monday a great many markets report the stock of each grain on hand at the close of the previous week. This statistical compilation, known as the "Visible Supply," includes the grain in many of the market centers east of the Rocky Mountains. In addition to the terminal markets it lists smaller interior concentration points, the grain on the Great Lakes in transit between ports and in boats "afloat" at the ports (not yet unloaded), and grain at export ports. The report lists each grain by cities so that definite locations of the grain are known. A few locations do not disclose their stocks because they have elevators operated by only one concern. In most cases the report does not include grain in processing plants, but only stock in elevators which receive and ship grain without converting it into products—grain that is potentially in merchandising channels.

The "Visible Supply" differs from the *Commercial Grain Stock Report* issued by the U.S.D.A., which includes many cities throughout the United States (the Pacific coast included) but lists the stocks by areas and not by cities, as does the "Visible Supply."

A few of the terminals, such as Minneapolis, Duluth, and

Kansas City, publish their stocks of grain daily. Chicago publishes its stocks of grain in some detail once a week. Grain in federally licensed elevators is published collectively by each deliverable grade for each grain, and undeliverable grades are given in total without grade designation. Each Illinois state-licensed elevator in Chicago publishes its stocks of grain in detail by grade. Knowledge of the stock of each deliverable grade of grain in the Chicago elevators is something of a guide as to the amount of "contract" grades available for delivery on futures contracts. It is not conclusive, however, as some contract-grade grain may be held for non-delivery purposes and other grain may be put into delivery position after issuance of the weekly stock report.

The grain trade through the exchanges receives daily statistical data from some markets on inbound and outbound inspected grades of grain and also receives receipts and shipments recorded by individual railroads and by barges, steamers, and trucks. While general origins and destinations may be determined from the transportation system on which the movement occurs, actual origins and destinations of the grain are not disclosed except in cases where the movement is by water carrier.

As a convenience to members and for service to their members' customers, exchanges receive by telegraph many of the government reports as soon as they are released and keep many statistical records compiled by the various state and national agencies.

Private Statistical Agencies

Grain and other commodity statistics and news of use to the grain trade are gathered throughout the world by private statistical and news agencies which sell their services to individuals and to firms. The reports consist of official statistics or private estimates of crops, conditions, trade news, and prices in world markets as well as edicts, laws, agreements by or between governments, or anything in general that is interesting or informative to the grain trade.

News agencies and trade-publication organizations gather a great deal of trade data within the United States. Semi-confidential information such as private trades and prices thereof is secured by these agencies and circulated to their subscribers, but such information soon becomes public. However, the names of the principals involved in the trades are not always divulged. It remains for competitors to secure what information they can of what is lacking on any trade in which they may be interested. Usually after a trade is made and hedges are placed or removed there is frank discussion with competitors as to its conditions except where repeat business is probable. It is often to the advantage of an exporter to disclose the details of a foreign sale so that domestic shippers may offer him cash grain to suit the commitment. The grain business is so highly competitive that buyers solicit among several potential sellers before making a purchase; after the business is done there is usually no reason for withholding details.

Private news agencies call the attention of the trade to changes in the cash-grain basis, the amount of farmer selling, terminal receipts and shipments, domestic grain merchandising, mill flour sales, export sales, etc. While merchandisers may follow all the events in their sphere, they cannot observe what is happening elsewhere; so they and futures commission merchants who inform their customers must rely on these agencies for most of the trade news. In the constant seeking for and exchange of news, agencies and trade personnel very thoroughly cover events transpiring in the trade.

The Commodity Exchange Act provides penalties for transmission, etc., of false or misleading reports concerning crops or market information that affects prices; the exchanges may suspend or expel a member who, it has been determined, has disseminated false or inaccurate market information. Grain news is carefully screened by those who handle it and pass it along to others. The current news is often an important price-making factor and the interpretation of its market value may be the most important phase of its handling.

Canadian Data

Canadian statistics gathered by their government agency, the Dominion Bureau of Statistics, and by private statisticians permit a very informative analysis of the Canadian grain trade. Official and several private crop reports compiled for the three prairie provinces, Manitoba, Saskatchewan, and Alberta, are issued periodically during the growing season. The government also reports on grain in the eastern provinces. Moisture and temperature reports are tabulated to guide at-a-distance observers of crop conditions. A complete daily record is available of the amounts of grain which prairie-province farmers deliver to country elevators and the amounts of grain which these elevators load out. Weekly stock reports give the quantities of each grain on hand in the country elevators. Terminal arrivals at Fort William and Port Arthur, and shipments by lake and rail, are reported daily. The lakehead terminal stocks of grain are published by grades once a week. Reports on arrivals, shipments, and stocks of grain at Canadian Pacific ports are also available.

The Canadian weekly "Visible Supply" lists the stocks of grain in all commercial positions from country elevators to export ports. This includes the grain in transit, in store, and afloat in steamers in lake ports as well as bonded stocks in the United States, so that Canadian commercial stocks of western-grown grain outside of those held in private storage are published currently. Weekly export statistics keep the trade informed on overseas shipments. Twice a year there is a report of each grain in all positions, including grain grown in eastern Canada.

Canada has comparatively little difficulty in securing grain statistics, as compared with the United States, because their transportation movement is over few railroads and much of the grain passes through Great Lakes port terminals in transit eastward and through Vancouver, B.C., and several other ports in the west.

World Data

International grain statistics and news of crops and grain trading all over the world circulate rapidly so that their impact is felt upon all markets in the ever-changing grain world. The prices at which remote Australia sells to Europe or to Asia are likely to affect immediately the sale of United States grain offered in competition to the same destinations, so that repercussions are felt even in the interior markets of our country. Although the Southern Hemisphere harvest season is six months away from that of the Northern Hemisphere, prices at which international sales are made from each area influence all world markets. Prices of sales from any origin are usually compared on a delivered-destination basis because of differences in ocean freight rates from each port of origin. By applying shipping costs from United States ports to the same destinations to which other countries make sales, the relative values of each country's grain may be ascertained. This follows the same means of competitive pricing within the United States when one area can ship to any domestic destination or export port only when its price is lower than that of other competitive domestic origins.

A weekly statistical compilation is made of the amount of each kind of grain (but principally wheat and flour) exported from each group of United States ports—Atlantic, Gulf, and Pacific. This is combined with clearances of Canadian grain from Atlantic and Pacific ports and grain from Argentina, Australia, and the Black Sea (Russian and Danubian countries) and other countries less regular in exporting. This table is referred to as "Weekly World Shipments." The running record is kept throughout each season, starting at the beginning of the world crop year, August. Its total and comparison of amounts from countries within the table and with other years is followed closely by the trade. It is separated as to destinations, primarily to Europe and ex-Europe. Further division is made by destination to some individual countries for closer examination. In conjunction with the size of the European wheat crop, the trade judges necessary world shipments to that area in the light of an approximate annual quantity needed for normal wheat consumption, taking into consideration the size of the carryover at the start of the season. Shipments to ex-European countries vary for different reasons, often depending on the size of other food crops and the substitute foods.

International statisticians make close examinations of all factors which in their judgment will affect each country's ability to export and of the current amount remaining as surplus for export or carryover, and also of the amounts of grain which import countries will require for use on the basis of the current conditions. These estimates start as soon as the size of the crops are known, and are corrected from time to time as statistics and economic conditions change.

The volume of international trade in feed grains is more difficult to anticipate than is wheat because of the availability of other feeds such as root crops (principally potatoes in Europe), the many grains used in the feed trade, and the adjustment of livestock to the available feed and the prices thereof.

The amount of grain afloat on the oceans is recorded as "on passage" and is a valuable datum for importers. Approximately how much grain will arrive at various destinations within a given period is calculated from the sailing dates of steamers from certain groups of ports and the average length of time it takes for the voyages. Some grain cargoes clear their port of export "for orders" and are directed en route to any destination within range of ports; thus, this grain is available for whichever destination requires it.

The alternating seasons of Northern and Southern hemispheres, both embracing important wheat and coarse-grain export nations, provide the import nations with continued fresh amounts of grain in international trade. The crop news and statistical reports issued by both the export and import countries are a guide for both groups. It makes each aware of their potential markets and acts to cushion price movements through timely contracting. When there are extremes of shortages or surpluses estimated by crop reports or statistics of current supplies, expanded participation by other shippers or additional buyers levels off the supply-and-demand position.

Weather

Weather, to the grain man, is one of the most important news items in his daily routine. The amount of precipitation throughout the twelve months of the year is important even though the grain crops draw on the moisture in the soil only during part of this time. Wheat is grown in some areas where rainfall is scant enough to warrant summer fallowing—the practice of leaving the ground unseeded for a season but plowed and harrowed in order to catch and store up moisture for a crop to draw upon during the next season. This is practiced on many farms in the prairie provinces of Canada and just east of the Rocky Mountains in the United States. In these areas and somewhat toward the east, the largest North American wheat acreage is sown, and a normal-sized crop of wheat depends upon production in the scant-moisture areas.

Sufficient moisture is required in the early fall for plowing and seeding the winter-wheat crop and to provide moisture for germination and growth prior to the dormancy period. Probably more concern is felt over moisture supplies in the United States southwestern wheat states than elsewhere, because the wheat stays in the ground many months and a prolonged period of dry weather at any time might be damaging to the plants. In dry falls, a considerable portion of this acreage is "dusted in" and the seed lies ungerminated until moisture is received. Its chance to survive and produce a crop depends upon the vicissitudes of weather—moisture, temperatures, and winds. In the spring-wheat area where the annual moisture is also scant, rainfall need not be well distributed throughout the year provided the soil is moist enough after planting to sprout the seed and sufficient rainfall is received during the growing months. As the wheat plant draws heavily on moisture in the latter part of its growing season, if there is little reserve moisture in the soil and timely rains do not fall there are poor grain yields. Early fall moisture is essential to wheat production in western Canada, for late-fall and winter snows melt and run off the ground before the ground thaws in the spring. The average precipitation from April through July is not sufficient to provide moisture for a normal yield of grain per acre, but good crops may result if the rainfall is above average and well distributed during these months, even though there had been a dry early fall. Dry weather at harvest time is desirable, because heavy rains will delay the harvest and damage the quality of the crops.

As in the case of wheat production, climate and soil are the limiting factors in the production of corn. However, corn is more exacting than most plants in regard to these factors. It is not the total amount of water but the distribution of the season's rainfall that is considered important in the production of corn. Under ordinary growing conditions, the water-storage capacity in the soil is exhausted by the corn plant before the end of July, and therefore corn is dependent on the July and August rainfall to complete its growth.

The number of days without killing frost is also a factor in corn production, and temperatures in the early fall are watched very closely. Early frosts prevent the corn from maturing; and that, in some years, results in a considerable quantity of soft corn because of abnormally high moisture content and immaturity.

Temperatures are important to wheat production also. Too-cold weather may damage or kill winter wheat if the plant is unprotected by a covering of snow. Alternate freezing and thawing causes heaving of the soil, which may break the roots of the plants. Frost may be damaging to spring wheat in the early or late stages of the plant's development. Too-hot weather prevents adequate growth of winter or spring wheat and results in improper maturity.

Winds in the early spring may blow the soil from around the small winter-wheat plants in the southwest and soil-blowing may also damage the farmlands themselves. Summer storms may damage any of the grain crops. Southerly winds often carry rust-disease spores all the way from Mexico or Texas to the Dakotas. Hail, although localized, does considerable damage to crops.

It is not surprising that grain men are always interested in and often concerned about the weather. It is customarily the first business of the day for the grain man to inquire about the weather in crop-production areas. Merchandising and commission firms secure weather reports and scan the news for forecasts. Weather news is gathered and circulated through the co-operation of the Weather Bureau, grain firms having offices in the growing areas, the private wire systems, and the grain news agencies.

Grain exchanges secure official weather reports from the Weather Bureau and post them on large maps showing barometer readings, temperature, precipitation, and other weather-condition reports throughout the United States and Canada. In addition, official weather forecasts are published early in the morning and during the trading session. When the forecast indicates a change in the weather, it is often of market significance. The Weather Bureau three times a week publishes five-day weather outlooks for the grain belt, and twice a month they publish to subscribers the national outlook for precipitation and temperatures for thirty days ahead. Everyone is interested in weather; there are private weather forecasting agencies and various special reports of weather cycles, sun spots, etc. Some grain men through years of experience have become proficient in "reading" a weather map to forecast the weather.

It was Benjamin Franklin who found out in 1743 that

weather travels. He was all set to look at an eclipse of the moon at Philadelphia but a northeast storm cut off the sky; yet a few days later he was astonished to hear that people in Boston had seen the eclipse and that the storm did not get to Boston until several hours later. He saw the surprising fact that a northeast storm could travel backward from Philadelphia to Boston. He checked up on other storms and found that they acted the same way. The wind was one thing, the storm was something else, and the storm reached Boston later than it reached Philadelphia. In the Crimean War in 1854 a storm that sank many ships in the harbor of Balaklava was studied, and it was found that it had traveled across Europe and might have been foretold before it got to Balaklava to cause the disaster. Meanwhile, in the United States by the end of 1849 the Smithsonian Institute in Washington, D.C., was getting reports from 150 places in the country by Western Union and was putting up signal flags on their building telling what weather to expect. The first official weather bureau in the United States was established by the Signal Corps of the Army in 1870, and in 1891 it was moved to the Department of Agriculture. It was finally moved in 1940 to the Department of Commerce.

Now weather data is reported by private wire from hundreds of stations all over the United States and Canada and by radio from ships at sea several times daily. From these reports of wind, rain, temperature, air pressure, and the rising or falling tendencies of the barometer a weather map is quickly drawn. On other maps and charts are shown the winds and temperatures in the upper air at various points in the country. From these maps prepared at a number of centers throughout the country the forecasters make district forecasts, each covering about four to six states.

Scientists have to look for the causes of weather in the movements and changes in the atmosphere. In the United States cloudy or rainy weather usually comes in the neighborhood of a "low" (barometer), where the air pressure is less than the average and the air is rising off the ground. Actual winds are complicated by many influences such as the shape of the ground and the rotation of the earth. Some parts of the country have a wet climate and other parts are dry deserts. Most of these differences are caused by the way the sea and the mountains are arranged.

On the West Coast the winds blow in from the Pacific and slide up the mountains. Being forced uphill, the air comes under less pressure. It expands, cools off, and drops rain or snow on the western slopes of the mountains. Then the wind slides down the east side of the mountains and is compressed, making it hot. Having lost most of its water, the air is extremely dry. Accordingly, precipitation is more frequent and is heavier on the western slopes of Washington and Oregon than in other parts of the United States, while the land to the east of the coastal ranges is dry.

Mississippi Valley conditions are different. Each low that comes along has south winds on its east or front side, which often extend south far enough to draw moist air from the Gulf of Mexico and then climb over the colder northern air and make rain.

In the states where farmers depend on irrigation, the water supply for the summer depends on the melting snow on the mountains. Government men go high up on the mountains in the winter to measure the depth of the snow and take samples to see how much water it will give when it melts. These surveys aid the farmers in planning to plant as much as they are able to water and no more.[2]

Widespread Uses of Grain Information

The statistics of the grain trade present a composite picture of the immediate distribution of the world's crops and the potential deferred supply. Therefore, traders are enabled to

[2] "Weather," *The Modern World at Work,* No. 6 (Washington, Superintendent of Documents), 1940.

keep a constant flow of grain in commercial channels, and at the same time consumers can look ahead to where they may secure supplies for later use and merchants to where they may find suitable outlets for the production.

Grain statistics are useful to businesses outside of farming and the grain trade. There are direct connections between grain statistics and the shipping business. That branch of shipping devoted to the seaborne transportation of grain is the most important in the world trade of bulk goods, large variations occurring in crops in certain parts of the world are of special importance to the movement of ships. Awareness of changing conditions in the shipping business becomes known through the reports on crops of different countries. Unexpected adverse developments in the wheat situation in Argentina or Australia may result in leaving a large volume of ocean tonnage concentrated in those areas in anticipation of a normal movement but without prospect for employment because other cargo is not available in remunerative volume. So remote are these regions that such out-of-position steamers must be held idle, awaiting other cargo or travel in ballast for thousands of miles to some other market.

Of lesser import to shipping are abnormal crop changes in Canada or in the United States because of the relative ease with which such steamers can change their base of operations. At times "tramp" steamers while waiting for charters lie offshore within easy call of North Atlantic ports.

The railroads use the crop reports to estimate the need for equipment to handle the harvest movement of grain, and they concentrate thousands of boxcars on sidings awaiting the combining of the grain. Some railroads have their own crop-reporting organizations. The amount of wheat exported is generally related to the size of the crop and the railroads gauge the transportation needs to export sales. Great Lakes and river transportation expands with the necessity to move grain to export positions.

The business of farm-implement companies is closely connected with the size of the grain crops, and they plan their output on the basis of crop estimates. It is essential for them to have equipment available for farmers to purchase.

There is a relationship of grain prices to the general average price of all commodities; therefore, grain statistics are useful to other lines of business. Sales of many industrial products are governed by agricultural production. Sales forces for general merchandise are attracted to areas where good crops are secured. The size of bank deposits and bank financing activities in farming areas follow crop expansion and contraction. Also, bank trust departments must watch how the prospective size of crops and farm prices are likely to affect companies whose securities are held in their portfolios.

The pulse of the news of the world as it affects grain is reflected in price changes, planting of crops, and the movement of grain so that its distribution keeps food available to wherever transportation can move it for man's needs. The co-ordinated services of the grain trade, especially the service of reporting the prices of futures transactions, on which most grain trades throughout the country are based and which are used as a guide throughout the world, together with the various statistical services (government and private) and the news (grain, economic, and social) which are available to all in the open market make for a well-rounded and well-informed business.

CHAPTER XI

Exporting

Exports as a Balancing Item

The amount of wheat (and wheat products) exported from a country during a season is normally the surplus above domestic requirements and a normal carryover at the end of the crop year. Exports are a balancing item that keeps supplies within the country at a level sufficient for all needs without creating a shortage or a burdensome carryover. Feed-grain surpluses are consumed by the adjustment of livestock- and poultry-feeding activities, which also act to keep the carryover of grain at the end of a season at a normal level rather than the volume of exports controlling the supply and demand balance.

In the adjustment of supplies of all grains to the demand for them, the relative price level controls the amounts utilized and is a guide for the size of the acreages to be planted for production. Prices are sensitive to the forces of supply and demand and encourage or discourage production or consumption as is required. The number of acres planted to a crop does not wholly determine the number of bushels produced, even though it is the only short-term means of control. Fully as important as moderate adjustment of acreage is the probable yield of grain per acre, which varies with changing growing conditions while the plants are in the ground. This foretells the need to expand or contract outlets for the grain after it is harvested. The futures price of grain follows the probable production of each grain crop as it relates to the demand. Thus, export business for grain may be contracted between buyers and sellers well in advance of the harvest when the price level has adjusted itself to surplus conditions and to values from other exporting countries for a corresponding time of shipment.

The harvests of the principal countries participating in the world wheat-export trade come at intervals during the year, so that their port clearances are spaced to keep a rather even flow of wheat to the import nations. Each country in arranging shipments is likely to have its heaviest shipping schedule when other exporters are putting smaller quantities of wheat afloat. Importers can follow the sequence of harvests and buy for their requirements in advance with the assurance that there will be no sudden release of large supplies from unexpected sources.

While this is the general and normal pattern of international trade in wheat, there are constant exceptions. Russian participation has always been an unknown factor, especially the volume of wheat which they are likely to sell into the world's markets. That vast country in the past has exported from Black Sea ports to Western European countries while at the same time they were importing into Vladivostok in the east from origins across the Pacific Ocean. This was economical because of the trans-Siberian transportation distance involved and the proximity of markets to which to sell and from which to buy. During the war they opened up areas towards the east to the production of grain. The Russian wheat crop—above all spring wheat, which normally accounts for more than 60% of Russian wheat acreage—is strongly concentrated in the semi-arid zone. And most Russian cotton is grown under irrigation in the dry regions of central Asia. It is not surprising, therefore, that the problems of the semi-arid and dry zones have long been in the foreground of public and official attention, especially after every recurrence of a dry season. Russia has nothing corresponding to three of the most productive regions of the United States —the mid-latitude region (the area south of the Great Lakes region), the Corn Belt, and the Cotton Belt, all of which have been of tremendous importance in the production of the agricultural wealth of the United States.[1]

The small number of livestock, as contrasted with the marked increase in Russian human population, and the fact that Russian grain crops are little larger now than were their prewar crops would suggest that there is need for the use of grain for livestock expansion to aid in diet and clothing requirements.

Other exceptions to the normal pattern of world export trade are any deviations from normal growing conditions in all export and import countries. Prices adjust themselves to the vicissitudes of weather and encourage acreage expansion in Northern Hemisphere countries following crop reductions in Southern Hemisphere nations, or the sequence may occur in reverse. European fall wheat plantings are more productive than spring-sown wheat acreages, so that a poor outlook during the winter offers a larger potential market for North American spring-sown-wheat exports. Canada in particular, a large producer of spring wheat for export, and the United States, to a lesser extent an exporter of spring wheat or spring-wheat flour, may avail themselves of the opportunity to sow more acreage to provide for larger exports. North American spring-sown wheat is available for export in the northern fall season several months before Southern Hemisphere crops may reach European ports in competition. Western Europe prior to World War II received two thirds of all the wheat in international trade, part of which originated within its eastern countries. While this proportion of world shipments has decreased since about 1950, it is nevertheless important to wheat-export nations how much wheat and flour European countries are likely to buy from them.

Argentina and Australia, the Southern Hemisphere exporters,

---

[1] Lazar Volin (Region Specialist, Office of Foreign Agricultural Relations), *A Survey of Soviet Russian Agriculture,* Aug., 1951.

are the heaviest world shippers of wheat during the months following their harvests, which is during the nothern winter and early spring months. Even during their peak movement, however, quantities do not reach the seasonal volume or last as many months at a heavy rate as maximum exports from North American countries do. When Southern Hemisphere exports decrease during our spring months, navigation on the Great Lakes is about to open, and this releases the winter's accumulation of wheat built up in storage in United States and Canadian ports at the head of the Great Lakes. The exports resulting from these shipments down the Great Lakes, with the addition of old-crop wheat exports from United States Gulf of Mexico ports and elsewhere, continue the flow of wheat to import nations until the new-crop United States winter-wheat exports reach a sizable volume in July. The United States new-crop exports are then normally the most important amounts in international trade until late fall, when Canadian wheat exports become heaviest. There are many other export nations outside the so-called big four, some which at times put sizable amounts of wheat into the world's trade.

The importers, other than European countries, which have taken nearly half the wheat in world trade since about 1950 are principally the Orient and some South American and African countries. In addition, Mexico, the Pacific Islands, and countries that only occasionally import take the rest. Oriental wheat imports vary as they are needed to augment rice and other native food crops. Barley is also imported, as after pearling it is mixed with rice (they have the same boiling point); orientals prefer white barley because it blends with rice better than the blue barley. At times the Orient has increased its grain imports when prices have been low, but they cannot be considered a market for inferior-quality wheat, and especially flour, if for no other reason than its poor keeping quality in storage in the warm climate. This is particularly true where the people have been accustomed to a diet of white rice. Imports of wheat into the Far East have increased since World War II because of the rapid increase in population and because the supply of rice has not increased in proportion to the population. Wheat in many localities is a supplemental food rather than a direct substitute for rice, but wheat is clearly the first choice after rice. The Far East will continue to import wheat and flour in larger quantities than prior to World War II, even though imports by some countries will be less than the abnormal requirements of recent years.[2]

In general, when natural markets function, European consumption of wheat from their own production supplemented by imports of wheat and flour does not vary a great deal from year to year. Nor under these conditions has the carryover of wheat in exporting countries changed much historically from year to year. There has been so much world unrest and so many national laws in principal grain export and import countries conflicting with natural grain markets that these facts have been almost obscured during the past few decades. Nevertheless, free markets in this country have shied away from carrying the risk on excessive carryover quantities, so that the risk has been transferred to the government agencies administering the laws that have encouraged more than normal production quantities. Likewise, abnormal foreign demand following World War II resulted in high prices that for a few years encouraged exports and inspired large planted acreages. Other countries have had more unnatural wheat laws than the United States; nevertheless, exports continue to be the balancing factor in wheat-exporting countries.

The behavior of wheat-market prices necessarily follows the dominant factors, whether they are government laws or the influences of supply-and-demand forces. Exporting of wheat and flour is a continuation of the domestic physical movement of grain from farm to market in which the futures market conveys the risk protection to those handling merchandising.

---

[2] Henry A. Baehr, Edward J. Bell, and Archie M. Camp, *Market Potentialities for Wheat and Wheat Flour in the Far East,* U.S.D.A. Foreign Agricultural Report No. 50, June, 1950.

If export quantities are large, it brings more buying in the wheat futures, but if supplies in the exporting country are correspondingly large, they bring more selling in the futures. Conversely, if exports are small and supplies are also small, there is less use of futures for export purposes. Thus exports have an offset in the quantity of supplies, and exports tend directly to affect price levels only when the two are not in balance.

When the surplus of grain available for export is large, the export country's price tends to remain at the world's level until a sufficient amount of grain has been sold to reduce the remaining domestic supplies to normal quantity. When the surplus above domestic requirements and a normal carryover is small, or when no export surplus exists, the price level within the export country tends to remain above world levels, thus reducing or eliminating exports. When necessary, the price may even go high enough to encourage imports. The export business is one of practice rather than one of theory. Export firms continue to make foreign sales so long as they can buy the wheat at a price equal to their sales abroad. It is the price relationship in the world's market that permits or prevents exports. The price of old-crop wheat may be too high to permit export sales for that shipping period, but at the same time the new-crop-shipping-period price of wheat may be equal to the world's level, and a lively business may currently be contracted. This is a basic principal of the futures price structure that affects export and domestic business alike. In the domestic trade it reduces but does not eliminate consumptive business. Inventories of wheat and flour are reduced and wheat is marketed by stubborn holders because of the higher current price for old-crop wheat compared with the price for new-crop positions.

It is the price of wheat at which importers are buying that governs the price at which export nations may sell. The initiative may be either the exporters' or the importers', but there is always a meeting of prices between some of the nations of these groups that represents the world's level. It is this level of price that governs the domestic price of wheat within an export nation. Of course, consideration must be given to government support and export subsidy programs.

Feed or coarse-grain exports affect the United States price level to a much lesser extent than exports of wheat. Ordinarily the quantity of feed grain exported is much less than that of wheat and is only a small share of feed-grain production. The domestic price does not rely upon world levels. We do export, however, only when our price is competitive with that of others in international trade. The total world shipments of all coarse grains combined is less than wheat and flour alone. Corn exports constitute the largest share of the world's coarse-grain shipments, and Argentina is ordinarily the largest supplier of corn in this trade.

Routine of the Export Business

The entire facilities of the grain trade are available to the export end of the business. Railroad rates on export grain are lower than domestic rates from some origins or rate-break points, but inland water-transportation rates are the same as those for domestically consumed grain. United States grain standards are the same for export grain as for domestic grain, and they apply to any foreign grain that has been imported into this country on which the duty has been paid or which is passing through the country and is re-exported in bond, provided the foreign grain is sold and inspected on United States grain standards.

Exporters diligently use the futures market to hedge the grain which they handle even though they are required to offer large amounts overnight to several prospect buyers at equal-to-the-closing price of the futures for acceptance reply the next morning. Offering grain overnight at the closing price requires assuming an unavoidable risk similar to the one assumed by millers in selling flour at a price established daily which is based on the closing price of the futures market. A separate risk also exists on the cash basis until the exporter buys the actual grain to fill the sale. The exporter may contract to receive payment for his grain in a foreign currency, which necessitates some risk on the fluctuations of foreign exchange rate until the sale of the money is made to a banking institution; in postwar years, however, considerable United States grain was sold in dollars or in some cases bartered against other commodities or manufactured goods. Another major risk of the exporter on cost, insurance, and freight sales is ocean freight. A vessel of the proper size and in a suitable position to report for loading of the grain within contract time of shipment must be secured at the rate calculated in the sale of the grain. If the rate is higher the variance is at the shipper's expense. All these risks and the problems attendant on shipping grain from the interior of the country and loading it on the vessel at the port are normal in the business of a grain exporter.

Other risks in moving grain from one country to another in fulfilment of an exporter's overseas grain contract may be covered by sub-contracts. When documents covering the grain and all the risks involved are furnished, the exporter's responsibility ceases—official weight and inspection certificates certifying quantity and quality of the grain loaded on the steamer are final for him. The bill of lading signed by the captain of the ship or his agent fulfils his obligation of proof of shipment. Insurance certificates issued against policies with approved insurance companies covering marine insurance risks, and also war risk when required, are furnished by the exporter. Most export sales are made on the terms of "full out-turn weight guaranteed." In order to guard against any shortage of grain discharged from the steamer at its destination, the exporter can employ the services of an agent to supervise the unloading of the grain and to pay the buyer for any loss of grain compared with the amount loaded on the steamer. When a shipment of grain has been made in accordance with the terms of the contract and the seller has notified the buyer accordingly and all documents have been banked for collection, the seller's obligation ceases. However, there is the contract right of arbitration, which may be exercised by buyer or seller.

On "free on board" steamer sales the exporter has fewer risks. Although he must attend to the loading of the grain and issuance of the ocean documents, he has no risks pertaining to the ocean voyage of the grain on the vessel.

Types of Export Firms

The grain-export business is conducted by several different types of firms. The largest share of the business is done by international grain firms whose organizations consist of offices for handling different phases of the business in various parts of the United States and Canada and offices abroad which contact the buyers. While many export firms operate in both the United States and Canada, most of the international firms export and import in a number of countries and also employ arbitrage and barter not confining their activities to grain. Some of the international firms own or lease country elevators, terminal elevators, and port elevators; they also operate other facilities for handling grain. This enables them to accumulate grain very quickly or to have grain on hand which they may sell abroad or domestically, whichever is most advantageous. One organization reaching from the farms to foreign market insures savings which enables the international grain firm to compete with others on a close margin. Nevertheless, the business is so highly competitive that other types of export firms make the foreign sales unless prices are calculated at existing market levels for grain in the lowest cost location that can fill the sale.

The international firm in this country can quote prices of grain for each time of shipment and in each export-port location, which the foreign office can couple with ocean freight to any destination and satisfy whichever buyer is interested. Prices of grain fluctuate in the foreign markets where buyers are located, so that there are changes in prices in those markets several hours before the exchanges in this country open in the morning. This gives the international grain firm advantages not enjoyed by those firms who cable their offerings from this country and cannot change the price or conditions before the time expires for their foreign agent to reply. There are also opportunities to perform financial or other services for buyers that bring business in return. Each international firm operates differently; each firm has different kinds of facilities on this side of the ocean, and they may cover markets in different parts of Europe and elsewhere more intently than their competitors. They overlap each other in their activities here and abroad, but each one has some limitations on each end.

Some of the domestic grain firms compete in the export trade abroad but not as steadily as the international firms. These domestic firms may have extensive organizations in the United States and in Canada or they may confine their activities to one section of the country and export only from ports in that area. Export trade offers expanded outlets for the grain which they concentrate in their elevators, and being suitably located to the ports, they have opportunities for special services, such as bagging grain, and they are in close touch with the local ocean-freight situation.

Other export firms use public-grain-elevator services exclusively in their business. They may buy grain in the interior either from local inland shippers in carlots or from terminal elevator operators in carlots, or for shipment by barge or Great Lakes vessels. This grain may be bought in lots suitable to fill identical export sales, or it may be accumulated at the seaboard public elevators for blending of grades and be exported as the sales are made.

All the different methods of purchasing grain are available to each type of export firm, and there is no regular pattern that they follow. Each exporter trades as the opportunities appeal to him.

Some domestic grain firms are known as "fobbers." The conduct of their export business is to sell the grain which they have bought in the interior on the basis of "free on board ocean steamer" to exporters and not to contact foreign buyers at all. The fobber is likely to sell "f.o.b. steamer" only at one port, or at ports located only in one area.

Contracts

N.Y.P.E. Contract—For f.o.b.-steamer sales to exporters it is customary to use the New York Produce Exchange contract specially drawn for Gulf business. Buyer and seller are usually brought together through the services of a broker working for a fee, whose responsibility ceases upon furnishing satisfactory principals. Thereafter buyers and sellers contact each other. Margins for adverse market changes may be called by either party to the contract. The money is deposited in a bank as security and released by the secretary of the Exchange with the approval of both parties.

These contracts are usually for a half-month period, during which time the seller must load the grain on the buyer's ocean vessel. If the steamer does not load the grain within contract time there are contract provisions for payment for the grain against warehouse receipts, or for reselling the grain, or the seller may agree to carry the grain at the buyer's expense until the steamer calls for it. Before the seller is required to load the grain on the ocean vessel he must be furnished with an insurance guarantee which protects him after the grain leaves the export grain elevator. This is the same insurance that protects the buyer on the terms of his sale abroad. Payment for the grain may be made by the fobber taking out ocean-shipping documents as instructed by the buyer and presenting them through the banks at the buyer's domestic office. Or the buyer may pay for the grain upon presentation of the ship's "mate's receipt" for the grain loaded on the steamer, and the buyer or his agent at the port of loading attend to the issuance of the ocean documents.

An exporter may buy grain from several fobbers in a total quantity sufficient to furnish the grain for one ocean shipment. Sometimes one such contract is enough for the entire cargo or for part of a cargo, which latter amount may be termed a "parcel." The contract is in bushels equaling a number of long tons of 2,240 pounds each. The seller must furnish a quantity of grain 2% more or less, which variation is to suit the vessel's loading convenience (although the exporter sells in terms of 5% more or less, to his foreign buyer).

These quantities conform to export sales abroad. When parcels are sold they are shipped on general cargo steamers (liners) carrying part of the cargo as grain, or if the steamer carries only grain it may consist of a number of parcels for the account of several foreign buyers and most likely all be shipped by one exporter. The ocean steamer's documents are issued in units of tons with separate bills-of-lading and corresponding certificates of inspection for the grade and weight usually for each 250 tons. Bills-of-lading and all other documents are issued in duplicate with each set of bills-of-lading bearing a distinguishing letter or number. Issuing duplicate documents, marked as such, is the custom for all export documents whether for parcels or cargoes.

When an exporter sells a cargo of grain and charters the steamer, it consists of the steamer's full cargo. If the foreign buyer charters the steamer, he buys the grain "free on board the steamer" and may (although not usually) load other cargo in addition to the grain. The sale of cargo lots is the sale of a capacity load of a certain size of steamer, say 9,000 long tons, but the grain loaded may be 10%, more or less, to suit the convenience of the steamer. The exporter in supplying the amount of grain needed to accommodate a vessel for either parcels or a cargo settles part of the excess or deficiency from the sale quantity at the contract price and the balance at the market price when the grain is loaded on the steamer. The fobber, however, when selling on the New York Produce Exchange broker's contract must furnish within 2% of his contract quantity.

N.A.E.G.A. Contract.—Another contract is one used between the exporter and the foreign buyer on free-on-board-steamer trades—the North American Export Grain Association contract. There are provisions in this contract covering percentage of loading differences, type of certificate for quality, time of delivery of the grain to the steamer, payment for the grain, insurance, extension of shipping time, cancellation of contract, arbitration, strike clauses, default of shipment, etc.

Payment is a most important feature of this or any grain contract. Payment for the grain according to the N.A.E.G.A. contract is to be by confirmed irrevocable letter of credit in exchange for shipping documents, or for warehouse receipts when the grain has not been loaded on the steamer according to contract, or for an extension of the letter of credit and inclusion of payment of charges for carrying the grain to the end of the extended expiration date of the credit. The buyer must furnish marine and war-risk coverage to the exporter, which the exporter can in turn pass to his supplier of grain. Arbitration is provided for before a New York Produce Exchange committee.

L.C.T.A. Contract.—The London Corn Trade Association has a number of forms of contracts for use in different parts of the world under varying conditions. There are separate contracts for parcels and cargoes shipped from North American ports to European destinations. The terms are cost, insurance, and freight to destination (C.I.F.). When shipment is made from any eastern Canadian port or United States Atlantic or Gulf of Mexico port to a United Kingdom port, the payment is to be made in British sterling by sight draft in exchange for shipping documents. The draft is for payment seven or twenty-one days after sight, according to the port from which the grain is shipped. There are different rates of foreign exchange for each of these drafts which affect the conversion of the United States price to sterling price.

When grain is sold in the currencies of European continental countries the drafts are sight drafts. Payment may be made in dollars by banker's credit when the export sale is priced in United States dollars. European buyers may purchase grain for destinations other than their own country and may arrange for the financing through various sources.

An exporter works on a standing agreement with his foreign

correspondent; the agreement states the usual port of destination, unit of price and currency, and the method of payment and other standing terms. The conditions of the agreement may differ from the regular terms of the printed contract. The existence of an agreement makes it unnecessary to repeat the full terms each time a bid or offer is made.

Insurance

Exporters carry an open insurance policy against which they issue certificates, sending a copy to the insurance company. One certificate (in duplicate) accompanies each set of ocean documents. The insurance must be effected with approved companies and/or underwriters, and the policies must carry certain stipulated clauses. Under C.I.F. contracts, when the buyer pays the draft and takes up the shipping documents, title to the grain is acquired, and if there is a loss he recovers under the insurance policy whether the loss arose before or after the title was acquired.

A marine insurance policy is an ancient document drawn up in old-world phraseology and adapted by additional clauses to meet modern needs. Some of the wording may seem quite out of harmony today but the meaning of each word has been questioned and determined in the courts. Underwriters believe it is better to keep known policy wordings than to risk further lawsuits.

The premium for the insurance is paid at a basic rate which may be adjusted at intervals for varying destinations or insured conditions. Normally, the basic insurance policy excludes war-risk clauses, which when desired are added to the insurance.

Vessels

Cargoes.—On C.I.F. contracts the seller must ship the grain in vessels of a high classification. The contract for the steamer, called a "charter party," is made between the owner of the steamer and the charterers. It names the steamer, the year it was built, etc., its classification, and the tonnage, as well as the guaranteed quantity of grain it will carry, within 10% more or less. The charter party states the location of the steamer and that it is to proceed to the port of loading and report to load the grain after being passed by the Board of Underwriters' Surveyor as ready to receive the cargo. Loading, if required by the charterers, shall not commence before a day named in the charter party. If the steamer should not report ready for loading by a day named, the charterers or their agents have the option of canceling the charter party. This is a hazard with which the grain exporter is faced in making his shipment on time. However, it is seldom that the steamer misses its cancellation date.

The charter party provides five days, Sundays and holidays excepted, for the loading of the cargo, after which demurrage is assessed if the delay is caused by default of the charterers or their agents. When the cargo is loaded the captain calls at the charterer's office and signs the bills-of-lading. The signed bills-of-lading on a customary form for such voyages for grain cargoes supersede the charter party.

The customary bill-of-lading is the "Baltimore Form C," which goes with the charter party of the same name. The B/L acknowledges receipt of the grain, states its stowage in the ship, and names the port of destination and the rate of freight. The bill-of-lading gives title to the cargo of grain and is a negotiable document. It is usually made to the "shipper's order" and endorsed in blank by the shipper. Some of the clauses contained in the charter party are also in the bill-of-lading. One clause states that the cargo shall be received at the destination as fast as the vessel can deliver it during ordinary working days, but receivers of the cargo are not obliged to take delivery at night without their consent. "The charterer's liability under the charter ceases on 'cargo being shipped,' but the vessel has a lien on the cargo for the freight, dead freight, demurrage, or average."

At times grain firms use a "time charter" for steamers, paying freight on the basis of the vessel's deadweight carrying capacity at a monthly rate. The charterers have the privilege of employing the vessel in trade between various world ports.

When an exporter makes a "free-on-board" sale of grain, he performs about the same duties at the port of loading as he would on a "cost, insurance, and freight" sale. The same set of shipping documents except for the insurance certificates must be secured and the required banking operations followed. The buyer furnishes a copy of the charter party to the shipper to guide him in the loading of the grain.

The grain exporter is not required to handle the port needs for the steamer itself, as there are vessel agents who attend to fuel, provisions, repairs, or other requirements, including United States Custom House clearance.

Parcels.—In addition to cargo sales of grain, exporters sell in "parcel" lots. Although parcels are usually shipped on "liners," steamers making regular trips between ports, the exporter may charter a steamer and ship an accumulation of parcels as the cargo and make up separate sets of documents for each 250 tons or unit of sale. Ocean freight rates for grain vary for parcels as well as for cargoes. There is an open market for both. Vessel brokers handle the booking of parcel space for the operators of the steamships. Usually the period allotted in the sale for loading grain on a ship is half a month, either the first half or the last half of a calendar month. The first half of the month includes the first and the fourteenth for a 28-day month, the fifteenth for 29- and 30-day months, and the sixteenth for 31-day months. The last half is the balance of the month for 28- and 30-day months, but includes the fifteenth for 29-day months and the sixteenth for 31-day months. The grain shipper must have his grain ready to load when the ship calls for it any time during the period for which the freight was booked, but the ship must load the grain so that the B/L are dated within the period. The B/L for grain carried on a liner are the same as those in use for the other cargo of the ship and have clauses which do not pertain to grain, but there are clauses covering essential grain requirements.

Sales of grain vary in the length of the shipping period. The first and the last half portions of a calendar month are the customary periods named in sales, but the time of shipment may be for a 16-day period (tenth to twenty-fifth inclusive) within a month or it may overlap two months. Sales are also made for a full month's shipping period and at times even for two months'. The latter may be the case when grain is sold well ahead of the harvest for shipment during the new-crop period. Some sales are for shipment of equal quantities per month over a period of several months. At times the shipment is "per a named steamer" expected to sail near a certain date with or without the option of "substitution of steamer." The seller has the option of shipping the grain any time during the period named in the grain contract. The requirement is that the steamer bills-of-lading be dated within this period of time and from such port or ports as are named in the contract.

Ocean freight bookings or charters for grain may stipulate that the freight is to be prepaid at the time of the steamer's loading on the quantity of grain loaded on the steamer. Other terms are that the freight is to be collected at the port of discharge on the amount of grain discharged from the ship. The shipper of the grain on a C.I.F. sale must cover insurance on the freight if it is prepaid, but if the freight is booked on the basis of "collect" there is no insurance involved.

Out-turn

The "out-turn guarantee charge" by the company settling with the grain buyer for shortage between the loading and discharge weights of grain is on the sale value of the grain at a percentage rate according to the port-of-loading and the port-of-discharge of the vessel. While most grain export sales are "full out-turn guaranteed," which covers the entire shortage, other sales are "out-turn within 1%" of loading weights. When the sale is within 1% the exporter may guarantee this himself, in which case there is no calculation for a guarantee charge in the sale price. As the buyer purchases the grain cheaper, he saves enough in price to offset some loss of grain while the vessel is on the ocean voyage.

Export Ports

Ports from which grain is exported from North America start in the north at Churchill on Hudson Bay, from where grain is shipped during the summer months when the route is free from ice. Most of the grain exported from Canada leaves St. Lawrence River ports, exportation from these ports also being limited to the months during which the river is navigable. Steamers may ply this route from April until the ice forms late in the fall—until about the end of November. Montreal handles the heaviest tonnage, but there are other ports such as Quebec and Three Rivers. The winter ports used for eastern Canadian grain exports are Halifax, Nova Scotia, and St. John, New Brunswick; Portland, Maine, may be used for Canadian and United States grain.

The interior routes over which grain is shipped to these Canadian ports are via railroad to Churchill, and an all-water, a water-and-rail, or an all-rail route to the other ports. When Canadian grain exports from eastern ports are considered, they are almost all of western origin and pass through the terminal of Fort William and/or Port Arthur, Ontario, on the western shores of Lake Superior. Small amounts may originate in eastern Canada and move to the export ports by rail.

The grain loaded in railroad cars in the Provinces of Manitoba, Saskatchewan, and Alberta for eastern consumption or for export through the eastern ports is practically all unloaded at Fort William or Port Arthur. It is from this point that the export business actually starts; west of that it is considered to be the country-elevator portion of the trade, but obviously there is a close connection between the two movements. From the time navigation opens on the Great Lakes, sometimes in March but usually in April, continuous large quantities of grain are loaded out of elevators located in these twin port cities into lake vessels carrying bulk cargoes of grain. Hundreds of millions of bushels of wheat and large quantities of other grains clear these ports during the season in an uninterrupted flow until midnight of December 11, when navigation officially closes. In occasional years when the weather is mild there is an extension of time and ice-breakers are used in the rivers and harbors to aid late-sailing vessels in their passage.

Smaller-sized boats may carry the grain right through to the St. Lawrence River ports, but the larger boats, by far in the majority, unload their cargoes at eastern Lake Erie ports or Georgian Bay ports and some at Lake Huron ports. Canadian Lake Erie port elevators transfer their grain mostly to smaller river-sized steamers, or they may ship out some by rail. The Georgian Bay elevators ship out the grain by rail. Some of the Canadian lake steamers unload their cargoes at Buffalo or other United States ports and forward the grain to St. Lawrence or to United States ports along the Atlantic seaboard.

After the close of navigation on the Great Lakes, there is a railroad movement of grain out of Canadian Lake Superior ports during the winter months. Its volume may be governed by the requirements for export to augment the amount of Canadian grain in eastern lake and seaboard ports. The higher cost of moving the grain all-rail in relation to the price at which earlier water-transported grain may be purchased from owners in the eastern position is also a governing factor. More feed grains are likely to be moved from this Canadian shipping point for consumption in United States or in eastern Canada than is wheat for export during the winter months.

Any Canadian grain moving into the United States for ultimate re-export, while in warehouses or en route to ports via carriers, is held in bond. Canadian wheat milled in the United States for re-export is likewise held in bond. Millfeeds from this wheat may enter the country on an ad-valorem duty, but wheat of milling quality and flour, except for a very small amount, must according to United States law be re-exported. There is no lawful limit to the quantity of wheat of feeding quality imported into the United States; this enters on an ad-valorem duty.

Canadian grain or United States grain moving out of eastern United States lake ports moves to the Atlantic seaboard via railroad on special rates called "ex-lake" rates, or it is referred to as "at-and-east" rates. It may move for export to a range of ports including Boston, Albany, New York, Philadelphia, and Baltimore. There is a movement of barge grain which may terminate at Albany, New York, or go on down the Hudson River to New York City. At either of these ports the grain may be elevated and transferred to ocean vessels. Some barge-received grain goes through a grain elevator at the port of New York, but most of the grain moving for export through New York is loaded into the ocean steamers by means of floating grain elevators which go to the steamer's loading berth. These elevators load the grain straight from the barges and lighters, or if they are required to do so they blend grain from several barges in the course of its elevation. The grain received at the port by railroad is transferred to lighters for storage, and when ordered to be unloaded onto a steamer, the lighter is towed to the steamer. Railroad rates include unloading the grain from the cars, putting it into the lighters, and free lighterage service, but storage on the grain is charged after the expiration of a period of free time.

United States grain originating in the northwestern grain area—the Dakotas, Montana, and Minnesota—after a railroad haul to Lake Superior, moves for export through Duluth-Superior via the Great Lakes on lake boats and from the eastern end of the voyage on other carriers to the port for export, except when it can reach the seaboard cheaper via all-rail from the Northwest. Normally lake and rail transportation is the cheapest, but that depends upon the grain rate charged for transportation by the lake boats. This is a free, fluctuating rate market. The water route is similar to that which is used for Canadian grain moving east for export. United States grain uses the same Canadian Lake Erie ports, Georgian Bay ports, St. Lawrence River ports and Canadian Atlantic export ports as Canadian grain. Also, United States grain is transferred through the United States eastern lake ports of Buffalo, Erie, Oswego, etc., and forwarded to the seaboard. Railroad rates are the same for either United States or Canadian grain moving over the same routes.

Great Lakes boat rates vary between Canadian and United States vessels. Each country's boats have their separate grain, ore, coal, and other trades to serve, so that the demand for boats governs the rates. According to law, neither country's boats may ply between two of the other country's ports, but with some exceptions they may move between one of each. In most of the lake-grain business one shipper takes the entire shipping space on the boat for one trip. Lake boats vary in size so greatly that there is a choice of boats to suit the shipping quantity. Sometimes, however, if the lake-vessel broker can arrange it, he contracts with two or more parties to take shipping space and load their grain in separate holds of the same boat. The vessel brokers representing the boat-owners work closely with those who are interested in lake shipping. While one trip is the usual contracting time for lake steamers, it may be arranged to take a certain quantity of space for different periods of time. Lake shipping is quite different from ocean chartering, as the vessel brokers may switch their available tonnage to suit the convenience of the contracted dates and the dispatch is very fast; there is no bagging to top off the bulk grain in each hold, as there is in loading an ocean steamer.

When lake shipments originate at Lake Michigan ports, the grain may have come from the northern portions of the Southwest grain-growing area or from the Central States. At times it is cheaper to export grain via St. Lawrence ports than via Gulf of Mexico ports. This is governed by the cash basis of the grain in the interior markets in combination with the lake-freight and ocean-freight rates to its final destination. There is also a breaking point which governs the exporter's decision to use either "lake and rail" to the Atlantic seaboard ports as compared with the fixed railroad rates. If lake rates tend to be high the traffic is diverted to the railroads. This is different from domestic business originating in the West for eastern movement, as in forwarding the grain from an eastern domestic distribution point the through rate to the final point of consumption governs. Illinois proportional rates apply on grain moving by rail by way of Chicago for export via the Atlantic seaboard, whereas the investment in the freight between the proportional and the local inbound rate to Chicago is lost if the grain is shipped out by lake.

Considerable grain that originates east of Chicago and is not in position to use the Great Lakes route leaves the country via Atlantic ports. Grain that moves from farms in that area at harvest time or in the months following may be held in terminals near the originating area, or in Buffalo elevators, or in terminals further east. Some grain moves on small barges via inland waterways from near-by points of origin to Baltimore. Atlantic ports south of Baltimore and Norfolk do not handle much export grain.

New Orleans on the Gulf of Mexico is favored with a natural low-cost route of transportation from the interior. Grain, principally corn, is trucked from farms in the heart of the Illinois Corn Belt to river elevators and loaded on barges for the long trip down the Illinois and Mississippi rivers. This grain may also go to St. Louis for conditioning before proceeding to New Orleans or Mobile at a higher rate, or to other river ports south of St. Louis for domestic distribution. Because of the low barge rates to New Orleans, which apply to either export or domestic movements of grain, the railroads have put in competitive export rates for grain originating in many parts of Illinois and also for grain moving from the St. Louis area to New Orleans and competing ports. These railroad rates permit the use of the drying facilities of many of the inland elevators so that in the fall and winter months corn arrives at the ports ready for export. Otherwise, corn arriving at a port in a wet condition and having to stay in the boxcar "on track" awaiting its turn to be unloaded into the elevator for drying may go out of condition. There are times when grain, mostly wheat or soybeans for export or oats for domestic use, moves out of Chicago via barge to the Gulf or lower-Mississippi ports. The low water rate permits the movement to New Orleans or even via the intercoastal waterways to Galveston and Houston, Texas. Other origins of river traffic may be Minneapolis–St. Paul area for movement down the river, and at times grain moves from Kansas City via the Missouri River to St. Louis and up the Mississippi and Illinois rivers to Chicago. Grain moves east past New Orleans to Mobile, Alabama, via the intercoastal waterways, and via coastal vessels to Florida, or enters the West Indies and South American and Mexican trade.

The ports in the Galveston-Houston area of Texas are the closest export outlets to the large hard-winter-wheat-growing area of the Southwest. More of this class of wheat is exported than any other from the United States. Grain sorghums growing in the western part of Texas, Oklahoma, and Kansas also use these export ports, and some corn is exported. The exports of grain that move to Mexico via water are handled largely through Texas ports but some go by way of New Orleans. Large portions of our grain exports to Mexico, however, move by railroad through such railheads as El Paso and Laredo. As the cash-basis premium paid for Gulf-export wheat advances, the area which can be reached by payment of higher freight rates stretches farther north and finally puts the Kansas City market on an export-shipping basis.

Under extremely unnatural market conditions with Kansas City prices at a premium over Chicago and the Kansas City market on an export basis to Texas ports, there has been a movement of wheat from Chicago to Texas ports via Kansas City and to other southwestern ports. Soft red winter wheat is shipped from Chicago to Kansas City, where it remains for consumption or reshipping, and hard red winter wheat is shipped out of Kansas City on the railroad billing using a low railroad rate which applies from Chicago to the Gulf for export. Hard red winter wheat could not move out of Chicago on this basis because it could go to New Orleans cheaper. This rate also permits the movement of Canadian wheat through Chicago for export via Gulf ports. There are also tariffs published from northwest markets at correspondingly low rates available for the movement of spring wheat, permitting the spring wheat to be milled in the southwest area and the billing carrying hard winter wheat to the Gulf for export.

Pacific Northwest ports and Californian ports receive their grain from the interior, and it is exported to the Orient across the Pacific Ocean or to Europe by way of the Panama Canal. Vancouver, B.C., is the principal western port for Canadian grain, but Victoria and Prince Rupert, B.C., also handle some. Canadian grain moving west originates mostly in the province of Alberta. There is a considerable quantity of grain exported from Pacific ports.

Inspection

Export grain elevators are equipped to condition the grain preparatory to shipment and to blend it to secure the desirable grade. The final sampling for inspection of the grain is made during the elevator operations in loading a steamer. An exporter may buy his grain at country points and forward it to the port, where it is stored according to grade factors in the export elevator so that when it is loaded out the best grading use is made of the grain on hand. If the grain has been bought from an interior terminal or sub-terminal market, the exporter is likely to call Federal appeal of the grade when the grain is loaded into cars, barges, or lake vessels. This usually makes it certain that the grain will grade according to his sale requirements of grade when it is loaded on the ocean steamer.

If there is some special analysis of quality outside government standards, such as protein, included in a foreign sale, it is customary to state the name of the agency under whose authority the service is to be rendered. If export grain is sold on the terms of an interior market inspection, the identity of the grain is preserved from the inspection point and certified by those who handle it that the identical grain has been loaded on the steamer.

When United States grain passes through Canada in bond for re-export from one of their ports, it is kept separate from other grain so that certification may be made that it is the grain called for in the United States grain-inspection certificate under which it was sold to the foreign buyer. The same preservation of identity is sworn to on Canadian grain moving through the United States when it is re-exported. Canada also preserves the identity of its western-inspected grain within their own country. The lake-steamer inspection certificate at Fort William or Port Arthur is the one certified to for identity of the grain when it is exported from an eastern Canadian port.

Official weights, of course, are only those taken at the time the grain is loaded on the ocean steamer.

Selling Abroad

An exporter has all the domestic avenues of the trade and the favorable railroad export rates available to him, and he uses whichever combination figures the cheapest to get the grain to the port from which the best ocean freight rates are available to ship the grain to the desired destination. The cheapest port position is not always the most favorable, if there is elevator congestion or if ocean freight is not obtainable to suit the prospective buyer's required time of shipment. It is not always possible to obtain grain and freight in the right combination.

There are other reasons why business is difficult to secure. For instance, when there is a foreign demand for a deferred time of shipment, some exporters may be willing to sell the cash basis "short" and wait until the shipping time approaches before buying the cash grain from domestic sellers. Such trades may be unattractive to other exporters who lose the opportunity to effect sales. Later, when such sales are covered in the cash market, it may not be possible to sell abroad. However, such a fact has no bearing on whether or not the cash basis is covered profitably. Or at times exporters sell abroad from a previously acquired "long" cash-basis position of grain or a "long" ocean-freight position at a cheaper price than the cost of replacement, thus excluding competition.

It may be that when an export inquiry develops, a domestic firm which works on and off in export channels will decide to offer grain that they had previously held off the market; in their competing for the foreign business, their price is lower than other potential sellers', so that the newcomer secures the business. After accumulation of a stock of grain, it is normal for elevator firms to hold the grain for as long as several months, especially if there are good carrying charges in futures; and when they decide to sell, those who do not have foreign connections offer the grain to domestic and export buyers. This keeps the export price in line with the cheapest offers of grain from any source. Exporters follow all price changes in the domestic market and make offers of grain from various shipping positions to different foreign destinations every night that there are likely to be buyers. Because of this and because of the competitive nature of the business there is not often the opportunity to sell grain to a foreign buyer at a price higher than the going domestic price plus the ocean charges.

Even though exporters make sales from a long cash-basis position—and at times with the intention of staying "short" the cash basis for a while after making a foreign sale—most of the business is done prior to owning the cash grain and before securing the ocean freight. Forward-shipment sales are made at a calculation of price that will permit the exporter to buy the grain futures, charter the ocean freight, and sell the foreign exchange if the sale is priced in a foreign currency, so that when all this is accomplished it will leave him in a short position on the cash-grain basis below which he believes the grain can be bought at a profit. There are times, too, when exporters cover all but the ocean freight in anticipation of lower rates. Forward sales may be made months ahead of the shipping time, particularly for a new-crop position.

The price at which an exporter sells the grain abroad may also be closely connected with the method which he intends to use in buying the grain in this country. The one making the sale may figure on buying the grain over a period of time in small lots in country locations until the required amount is accumulated. Such a market may be currently cheaper than large lots offered in terminal positions or by f.o.b.-steamer sellers who are securing their stocks through the same method in country locations.

The first operation in connection with a foreign sale is that the exporter buys a quantity of futures equal to the number of bushels sold abroad. In doing this the exporter eliminates the important risk of the grain-futures market fluctuations. The exporter is then in the position of being short the cash-grain basis (unless he had owned the cash grain before he made the sale abroad). The exporter retains his long futures position until such time as he buys the cash grain which he intends to ship on his foreign sale. When the cash grain is bought it is usually purchased on a cash basis with "futures in exchange." To complete the transaction the exporter "gives up" the "long" futures to a futures commission merchant representing the seller of the cash grain. In making this exchange of futures, neither the buyer nor the seller enters futures orders for execution in the pit. The trade is an "office trade" made at the current market quotation or at a price mutually agreed upon by both buyer and seller. The price at which the futures are exchanged in combination with the cash-grain basis (premium or discount) sets the actual price at which the seller invoices the buyer for the grain. There may be a number of "giveups" before this is completed, each at the time that partial amounts of grain are bought, but in total they will equal the grain required by the exporter to fill his foreign sale. The prices of futures may vary over the period of time during which the exporter makes the various cash-grain purchases, but if the cash basis is the same for all of them, the adjustment between the exporter's original purchase and the various "giveup" sales of futures will balance profits against losses—the higher or lower futures have a compensating price variance in the cash grain which he buys. If when purchasing the cash grain he buys it at a flat price, the exporter immediately sells a corresponding amount of futures in the pit. Thus he divests himself of his holdings of futures and in their place he has acquired the cash grain which he will ship abroad.

This is the customary way exporters operate, and it is the same way in which a great deal of the domestic business is handled. It avoids the necessity of each buyer of cash-basis grain sending futures-selling orders to the pit and simultaneously the seller of cash-basis grain sending futures-buying orders to the pit. Buyers and sellers of cash-basis grain merely exchange the futures with each other in opposite transactions. The buyer of cash-basis grain "gives up" or sells the future and the seller of cash-basis grain "takes" or buys the future. In this way they both eliminate the futures position they were carrying against their respective sale or stock of grain.

It is not necessary for the domestic seller to have the grain on hand when he makes a sale. His, like all grain trades, is a contract to furnish the grain of a stated grade in a position and for a time of shipment agreed upon. Should the domestic seller not own a stock of grain to ship on his sale he retains the "long" future taken in exchange from the exporter until a later time, when he exchanges them against a cash-"basis" grain purchase or until he sells them out in the pit if he buys the cash grain at a "flat" price.

In the course of time after an exporter has sold grain abroad, the ocean freight must be chartered or booked. This may be done immediately after the foreign sale or as it suits the exporter's convenience. Often there is a choice of ports from which the grain can be shipped, so the freight has to be arranged for the port to which the grain is forwarded. The exporter's decision rests upon an advantage of a fraction of a cent a bushel between ports. As the export elevators provide a period of time of free storage, the exporter tries to have his grain reach the port so that it will be loaded on the steamer before the storage charges start. If the grain is bought "f.o.b. steamer," the shipping dates and steamer-loading period are booked to correspond with each other.

When grain sales are made in a foreign currency the exporter is mostly likely to sell promptly to a banking institution an amount of foreign exchange equal to his drafts. The sale of foreign exchange is for a time of delivery of the drafts that are accompanied by the shipping documents that correspond to the steamer's loading date. If the payment is by "irrevocable letter of credit," the grain contract provides for a date by which the bank credit is to be established.

An exporter buys his grain in the currency and on the unit terms of quantity of the country of its origin and (at times) sells the grain in the currency and weights of its destination. The conversion from one to the other is sometimes an involved calculation. It is necessary to figure this conversion on each cable offer which the exporter makes. The prearranged agreement on which the exporter and importer work sets the terms of conversion from one basis to another. The number of pounds of grain per ton is agreed upon, as is also the number of pounds avoirdupois to a certain number of kilograms in the metric system.

When grain is offered to the United Kingdom in British sterling it is priced in pounds, shillings, and pence per ton. The rate of exchange used in the export calculation is that which is quoted by the banks for the time of shipment of the grain and corresponds to the time the drafts, with shipping documents attached, are presented to the bank for collection. These rates also differ for the seven- or twenty-one-day sight drafts. A calculation for wheat to the United Kingdom is as follows: price in dollars and cents per bushel, divided by 60 (pounds per bushel), multiplied by 2,240 (pounds per long ton), divided by the exchange rate (in British sterling). This gives a price in pounds sterling and decimals of a pound, which decimals are then reduced to shillings and pence. The exporter has short methods of figuring, and as a means of checking his figuring he has books of calculation tables for each grain ranging in prices and exchange rates which show both currency equivalents. These books save time and insure accuracy.

When grain is sold in kilograms it is usually agreed that the price of 112 pounds equals 50¾ kilos. This is 1,015 kilos per 2,240 pounds (a long ton), but the price of the grain is quoted per 1,000 kilos (a metric ton). The figuring in this conversion is more involved than from bushel to long ton but the exporter has short cuts and calculation tables to aid him.

In arriving at the offering price of the grain the exporter must start with the futures price and the cash basis for the grain in the position he will buy it. Then he must add the charges to put the grain in the position corresponding to his offering. If the price is f.o.b.-steamer there are no ocean charges. If the price is C.I.F. there are different rates for the marine insurance and out-turn guarantee charge from different loading ports and to different destinations. If the ocean freight is prepaid it must be included in the items insured, but if the freight is "collect" and is not payable until the grain is discharged from the vessel it is not insured and this results in a slightly lower offering price.

The working agreement between the exporter and his foreign correspondent may stipulate that the offering is understood to give the seller the option of shipping the grain from one or more of a number of ports and that the destination is understood so that it will not have to be stated in the cable offering. Some correspondents work on a percentage commission to be paid by the seller, and when a sale is made, the name of the foreign buyer is given to the exporter on whom he draws his drafts; other correspondents are the principals and receive no commission.

The working agreement states either the time the foreign correspondent is to dispatch his cable of acceptance or the time it is to be received by the exporter. If the reply is late the exporter may reject an acceptance. Other means of contact may be by telephone.

The export business requires the exercise of judgment in purchasing grain prior to its sale abroad or in the contracting of ocean freight in anticipation of continued foreign demand or, if the exporter judges so, in withholding action on either until an anticipated more-favorable opportunity exists after sales are made. If there is a tight situation the exporter may not offer unless he has a "refusal" in hand for either the grain or vessel space. A "refusal" is an offer good for acceptance until a stated time, so that if the exporter makes a sale he is assured of the grain or freight, having only to accept the refusal. An exporter sometimes buys grain futures at the time an offer is made abroad if he considers it less hazardous than waiting until the next day when he has sold. This method is similar to the actions of a domestic merchandiser in lifting some hedges in anticipation of grain or product sales after the close of the market, or in selling some futures as a hedge in anticipation of overnight country grain purchases during the heavy harvest movement.

There is no set pattern which the exporters follow, but their continual seeking of the cheapest route for grain from any interior position keeps the domestic markets in balance just as the over-all price of grain in any export country controls exports which keep its over-all position in balance with its domestic requirements.

CHAPTER XII

Mechanics and Behavior of the Market

Transference of Risk

The "mystery" of a merchant owning and controlling a stock of grain and transferring the major risk of price change to others is accomplished through futures trading. Actually the merchant sells an equivalent quantity of grain for delivery in the future. In its simplest form, if the contract were consummated when the futures month became current, the merchant would deliver the title to the buyer of the futures and receive payment. The buyer receiving the delivery would ship the grain to his mill or make other disposition of it according to the nature of his business. Even when this is done, the merchant may keep his futures contract for many months, but the original party to the other side of the contract (when the merchant sold) may offset it quickly or at any later time, so that there may be many changes in contracting parties before the merchant makes his delivery. A buyer of futures may also keep his contract until delivery is received and the selling contracting party may and does change from time to time. So long as one contracting party maintains his position of necessity there must be someone having an opposite contract (both parties being responsible through the clearing house). Finally, all futures contracts are settled either by "offset" trades or actual delivery. In most grains less than 1% of the futures contracts are settled by actual delivery of the grain. Instead of the simple procedure of selling futures and making delivery, the merchant knowingly makes a contract to deliver grain of a grade and in a location that he does not necessarily possess, but with the belief that the price of his grain will approximately follow the price of the futures. The merchant also knows that, if he later buys the same futures contract that he has sold, it will offset the original sale. Meanwhile he retains possession of the cash grain, keeps it in condition, blends it with other grain, moves it to a more advantageous merchandising position, or whatever is considered necessary to enhance the value of his over-all cash-grain position; if none of these are possible and the cash basis declines, he nevertheless keeps the futures sale as long as he retains his cash grain. While there is no assurance of a profit to the merchant in selling futures against a stock of cash grain, he considers that his risk lies in the change in the cash basis rather than in the outright change in the cash-grain price, and therefore he does not consider the fluctuations of the futures market except for spreading differences between months and markets.

The procedure followed by a merchant who sells cash grain "short" or a processor who sells products "short" is to buy an equivalent amount of futures and to retain this position until the cash commodity is purchased, at which time the futures contract is sold to offset the futures purchase.

As it is the business of those active in the grain trade to take the farmer's grain whenever he wishes to sell it and to have grain available for whoever wishes to buy, by use of the system of futures trading the merchant is able to transfer part of the risk of price change to whoever is willing to assume it. Because the merchant does not carry the risk of futures market fluctuations, his price to the farmer allows no margin for protection against this risk.

The independent country-elevator operator who buys the farmer's grain customarily does not hedge it in futures, although the use of futures is available to him as it is to everyone. His handling charge includes an operating profit. When country elevator grain is sold, the price will be the same to a grain merchant as to a processor and possibly also to a commission merchant. Inasmuch as processors are also buyers from grain merchants, the grain merchant must receive his compensation for handling grain from the performance of services or correctly analyzing the changes in the cash-grain basis.

The hedge which a grain merchant places against his stock of grain is not usually a perfect hedge that would permit the payment of storage, insurance, and interest charges to the time of delivery on the futures, nor is the grain always of a quality or usually in the proper position to make delivery. To the extent that delivery conditions cannot be met, the hedger is undertaking a risk. There are several risks commonly assumed on hedged grain. Cash grain located in the delivery city may be purchased at a price higher than that at which the hedge is sold; or if the cash grain is bought at a discount, the discount may not be sufficient to absorb the charges to carry the grain to the delivery date. It may be that the grain is out of position for delivery on the futures so that it will necessitate payment of an excessive freight to the delivery point. The class or the grade of the grain may not be of deliverable quality. Even though not all, or even any, of these conditions may be regularly met by many participants in the handling of grain, hedging in futures is the general practice within the trade.

When grain is purchased at a flat price, all the risks belong to the buyer, but in hedging the major risk of fluctuation is transferred to the futures market. When the grain is hedged, the merchandising risk remains with the merchant and the larger risk of major price fluctuations is transferred to the futures market. No matter what course is followed, a speculative risk exists for someone to assume until the grain is consumed.

From the time the farmer plants the seed in the ground each year he is creating a risk that continues until the final buyer consumes the grain in some form. Prices of commodities, in fact probably prices of everything, have changed ever since the use of barter or money has been known. For crops, as long as the farmer is the owner of his production, he is the speculator and bears the risk. As each truckload of grain is hauled to the country elevator and sold to the operator the speculative risk

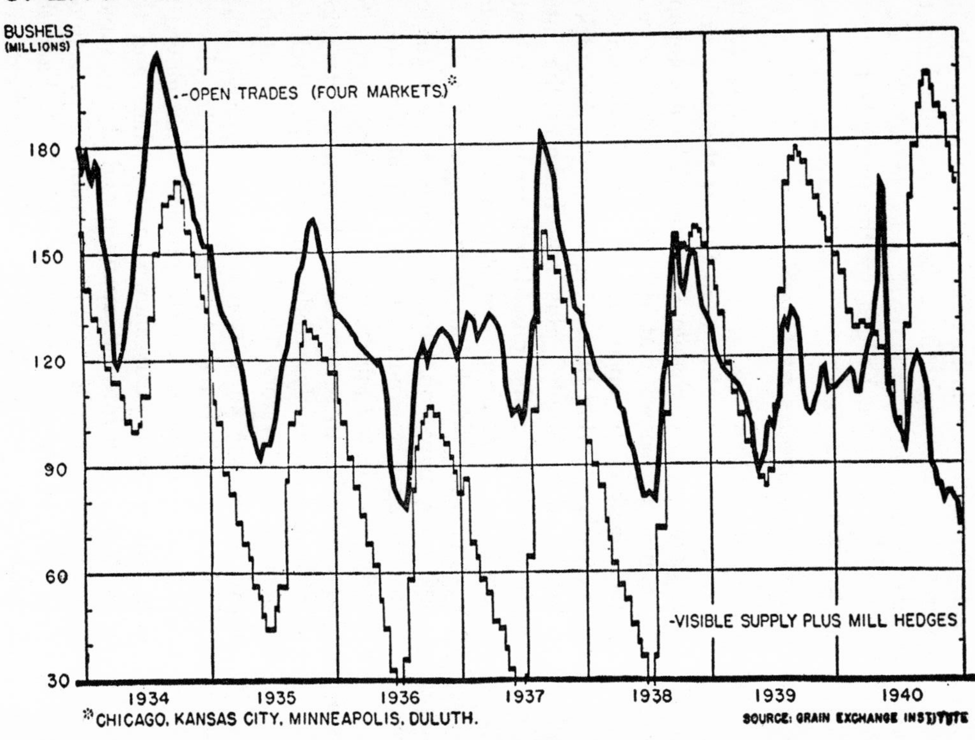
OPEN INTEREST IN WHEAT FUTURES VS. STOCKS OF WHEAT
BUSHELS (MILLIONS)
180
150
120
90
60
30
-OPEN TRADES (FOUR MARKETS)*
-VISIBLE SUPPLY PLUS MILL HEDGES
1934
1935
1936
1937
1938
1939
1940
*CHICAGO, KANSAS CITY, MINNEAPOLIS, DULUTH.
SOURCE: GRAIN EXCHANGE INSTITUTE

FIGURE 8

follows the grain. Someone has to own the grain and bear the price risk. If the farmer had contracted the sale of his grain with the country elevator ahead of the time he hauled it to market the risk would have been transferred earlier. If this had been the case the risk might have been transmitted to the terminal market through a "to-arrive" sale, in which case it invariably would have been hedged by the terminal buyer in the futures market.

Open Interest vs. Stocks of Grain

When the speculative risk is transferred to the futures market it creates an "open interest" in futures that is recorded daily by the Commodity Exchange Authority. The accompanying chart (Figure 8) shows that during the first few years shown on the diagram the open interest did not decrease as fast or decline as low during the spring months as the stock of wheat in the "Visible Supply" plus mill hedges (the latter approximately representing the unsold mill supply of wheat). This may have been due to open interest created by the placing of hedges against wheat which had been bought to arrive for shipment during the new-crop harvest movement and the exchange of futures against export sales, which at that time of the year largely precede the purchase of cash wheat in country positions; in combination these were more than an offset against the amount of hedges currently withdrawn against the declining stocks of wheat in the elevators. The futures exchanged against export sales of this nature are customarily sold out later when the farmers' cash wheat is bought through the country elevator or a subsequent terminal buyer. As the physical grain moved to the elevators during those years shown on the chart and the stocks increased, the open interest expanded and always stayed above the stocks and mill hedges. This expansion of open interest continued until the harvest was completed in the fall and the storage stocks reached their peak. As the stocks of wheat were reduced later in the season the open interest declined. In the winter of 1936 and the spring of 1937 the open interest did not

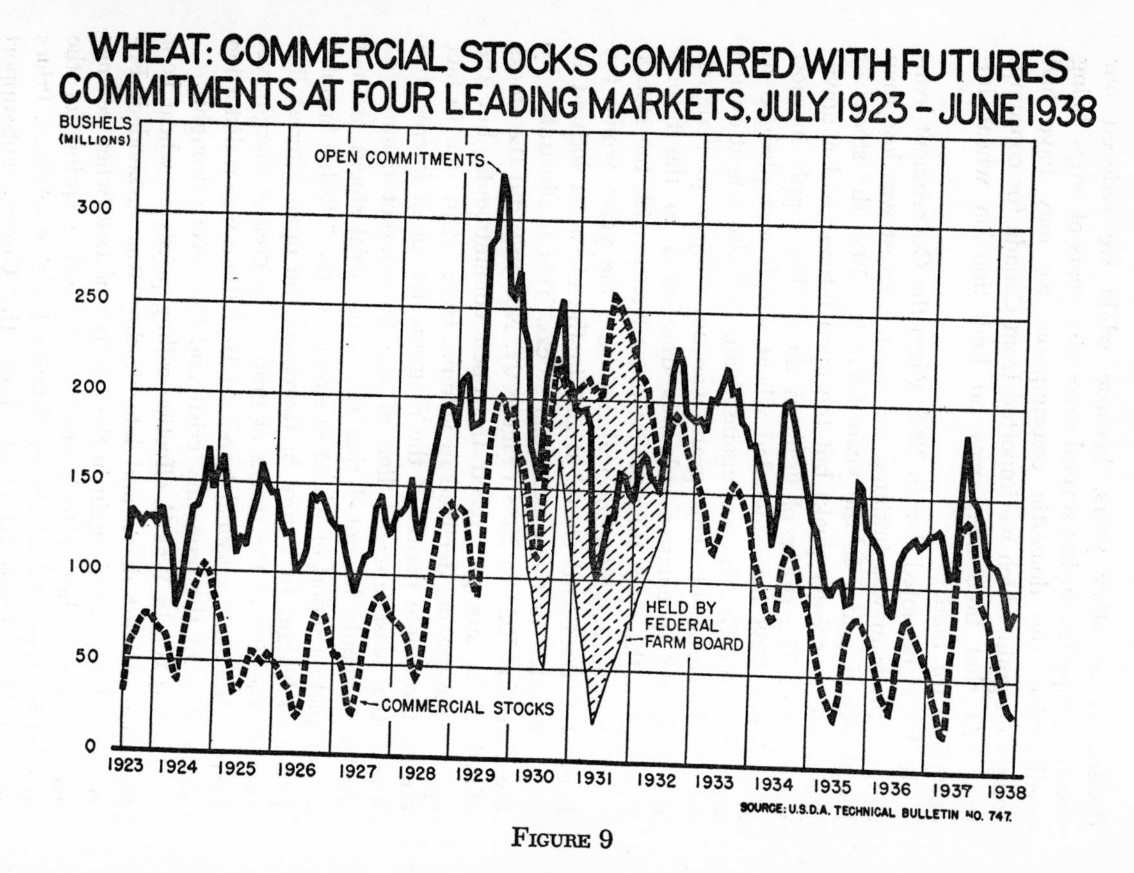
WHEAT: COMMERCIAL STOCKS COMPARED WITH FUTURES COMMITMENTS AT FOUR LEADING MARKETS, JULY 1923 - JUNE 1938
BUSHELS (MILLIONS)
300
250
200
150
100
50
0
1923
1924
1925
1926
1927
1928
1929
1930
1931
1932
1933
1934
1935
1936
1937
1938
OPEN COMMITMENTS
COMMERCIAL STOCKS
HELD BY FEDERAL FARM BOARD
SOURCE: U.S.D.A. TECHNICAL BULLETIN NO. 747.

FIGURE 9

decline as in other years, because while we reduced our domestic supplies during several successive years of crops' being smaller than the domestic consumption, we may have had hedges on grain which we imported from Canada for consumption. (At that time there was no limitation on wheat importations for food.)

It should be noted that in 1938, when the Government loan-support program was initiated, the open interest was less than the stocks of grain. In the years following 1938 the stocks of grain rose to greater peaks but the open interest had a downward trend. The stocks of grain in the visible supply in most years since 1938 have included wheat which was pledged as security to the Government against loans and also wheat owned by the Government. This grain was not subject to hedging; therefore, no speculative risk was transferred to the futures market and the open interest did not advance with the stocks.

This same condition prevailed during the years which the Federal Farm Board stored wheat in the elevators located in cities included in the commercial stocks. This is illustrated by the chart for 1923 to 1938 (Figure 9). Not only did the stocks of wheat in storage exceed the open commitments, but the open commitments declined in volume. Here again, and in fact during the whole period of the diagram, the open interest followed the seasonal-trend line of the free-market commercial stocks. It should be noted that the commercial stocks are not as complete a report of wheat in storage as the "Visible Supply" plus mill hedges in Figure 8; therefore, the open interest line exceeds the line of the stocks of grain by a greater margin, yet there is the same seasonal trend. In 1933 there was a distortion at the time of the monetary crisis and the severe drought.

During World War II effective ceiling prices on wheat kept the open interest down and later trading was suspended. Futures trading started again in the summer of 1946 when ceilings were removed, but it took until the following spring for the market to develop into a representative hedging medium. Prices were high (Figure 10) and above the Government-support

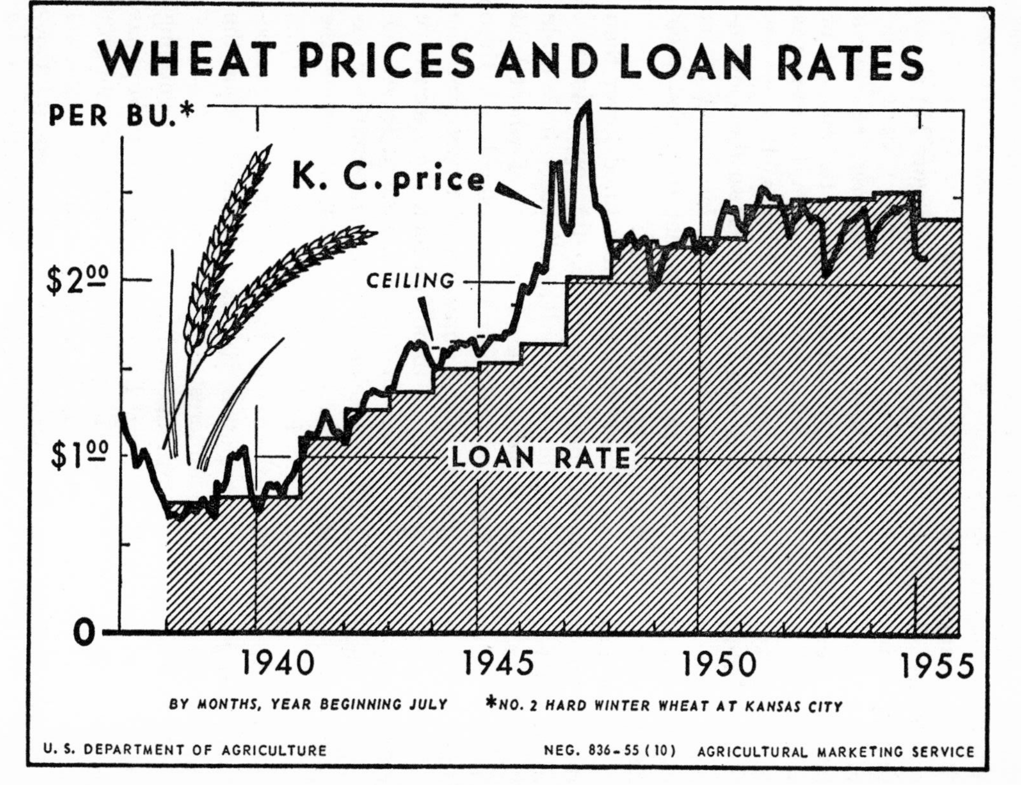
WHEAT PRICES AND LOAN RATES
PER BU.*
$2.00
$1.00
0
K. C. price
CEILING
LOAN RATE
1940
1945
1950
1955
BY MONTHS, YEAR BEGINNING JULY
*NO. 2 HARD WINTER WHEAT AT KANSAS CITY
U. S. DEPARTMENT OF AGRICULTURE
NEG. 836-55 (10)
AGRICULTURAL MARKETING SERVICE

FIGURE 10

level, so that little wheat went into the loan and it was redeemed; nothing was turned over to the Government. It was a period when the market was free to function on supply-and-demand principles—during the spring of 1947 and the 1947–48 crop season. The chart for that period of time (Figure 11) shows that open interest and stocks of wheat resumed a better relationship, and in the fall of 1947 the open interest reached a fair volume. Although it was about as large as the amount of wheat in the "Visible Supply" (only) the open interest was less than an amount including the mill hedges. It was less than the stock of wheat plus mill hedges because the Government had bought large quantities of wheat far ahead of its exportation, against which the merchants had removed their hedges or had placed no hedges at all.

In the next season, 1948–49, market prices ruled lower than the Government-support price; therefore, the open interest expanded very little despite the very large increase in "Visible Supply" stocks, which included a large quantity of wheat held as security against Commodity Credit Corporation loans. Here again it is demonstrated that futures markets perform the function of furnishing a medium through which the speculative risk of price change is carried on the grain after it leaves the farmers' hands and until it reaches the final consumer or exporter. When hedges are placed in the market to protect the price risk while the grain is being merchandised, the open interest expands; and as the requirement for this price protection disappears the speculative risk is withdrawn from the futures market—the open-interest contracts.

Soybeans have been little affected by large amounts entering the Government support plan. Each year the whole crop has been consumed so that soybeans pledged as security for support loans were released when farmers redeemed the collateral and sold the soybeans. (In years of unredeemed loans the Government quickly sold what they received.) The ineffectiveness of the loan to permanently contain the price risk left this futures market free to carry the hedges.

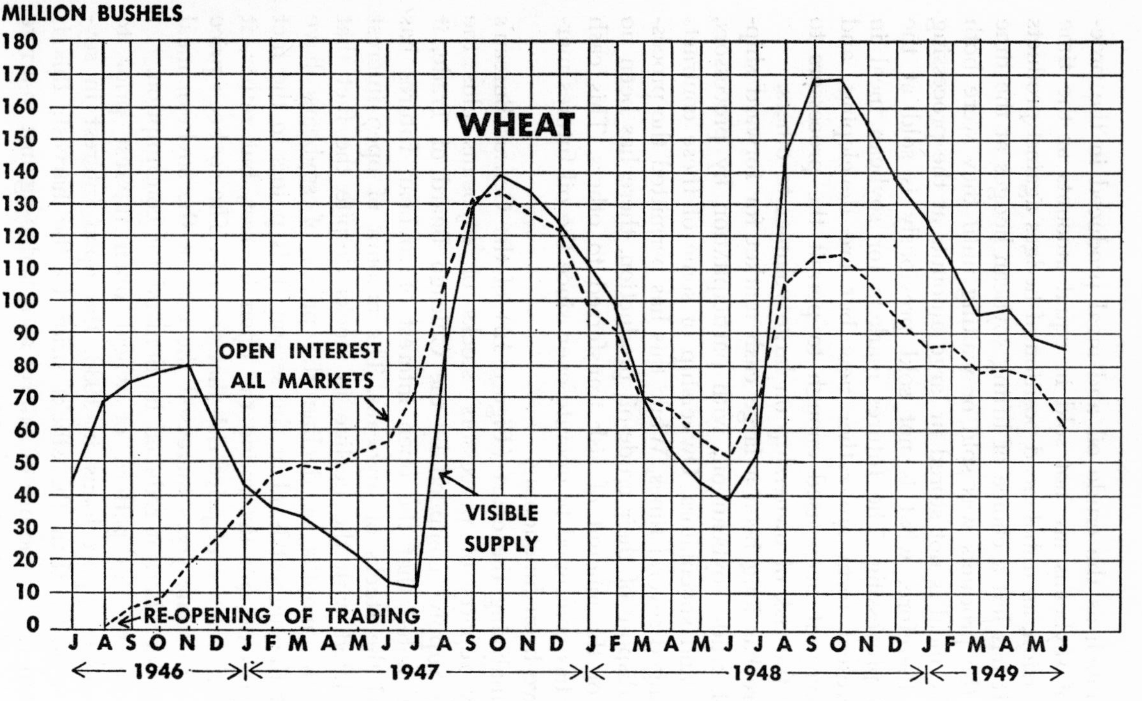

SOURCE: OPEN INTEREST—COMMODITY EXCHANGE AUTHORITY
VISIBLE SUPPLY—CHICAGO BOARD OF TRADE
(BEGINNING OF THE MONTH FIGURES)

FIGURE 11

Inasmuch as the crude oil and meal produced in the processing of soybeans are not sold in equal amounts at the time of conversion, an unbalanced position of hedges against products is left. It has left a choice of lifting soybean hedges at the time one of the products was sold or waiting until they were both sold. The meal is not stored in large amounts at the processing plants; therefore, what is not sold previously is sold at the time of processing. The futures markets for soybean meal in their present form are rather new but are developing, and they have not been used enough to permit the processors to transfer the risk of ownership on large volumes to others.

There has long been a large cash market for forward shipment of crude soybean oil, with participitation by processors, refiners, and speculators. Ownership of some of these contracts has changed several times. While this has permitted the processors to dispose of their crude-oil production, there has been no record of the amount of risk transferred to others. This cash market has continued to operate even since the oil futures markets have been functioning.

In analyzing the chart (Figure 12) of the Census Bureau's monthly reports of processors' stocks of soybeans plus the "Visible Supply" compiled by the Chicago Board of Trade, it may be noted that the open interest of soybean futures has followed the stocks of soybeans. The amount of open interest has declined with the decline in stocks despite the fact that during the months of decline the prices of soybeans have been at the highest level of the season. This points to the fact that prices do not determine the open interest, but rather, it is the transference of price risk that governs. The soybean price advance in some years increased the cost of the soybean meal to the point where it reduced its demand for consumption.

Similar to the pattern of wheat open interest prior to Government-support loans in 1938, the open interest in soybeans is larger than the stocks prior to the harvest; this is accounted for by the use of futures as a hedge against to-arrive purchases of new-crop soybeans.

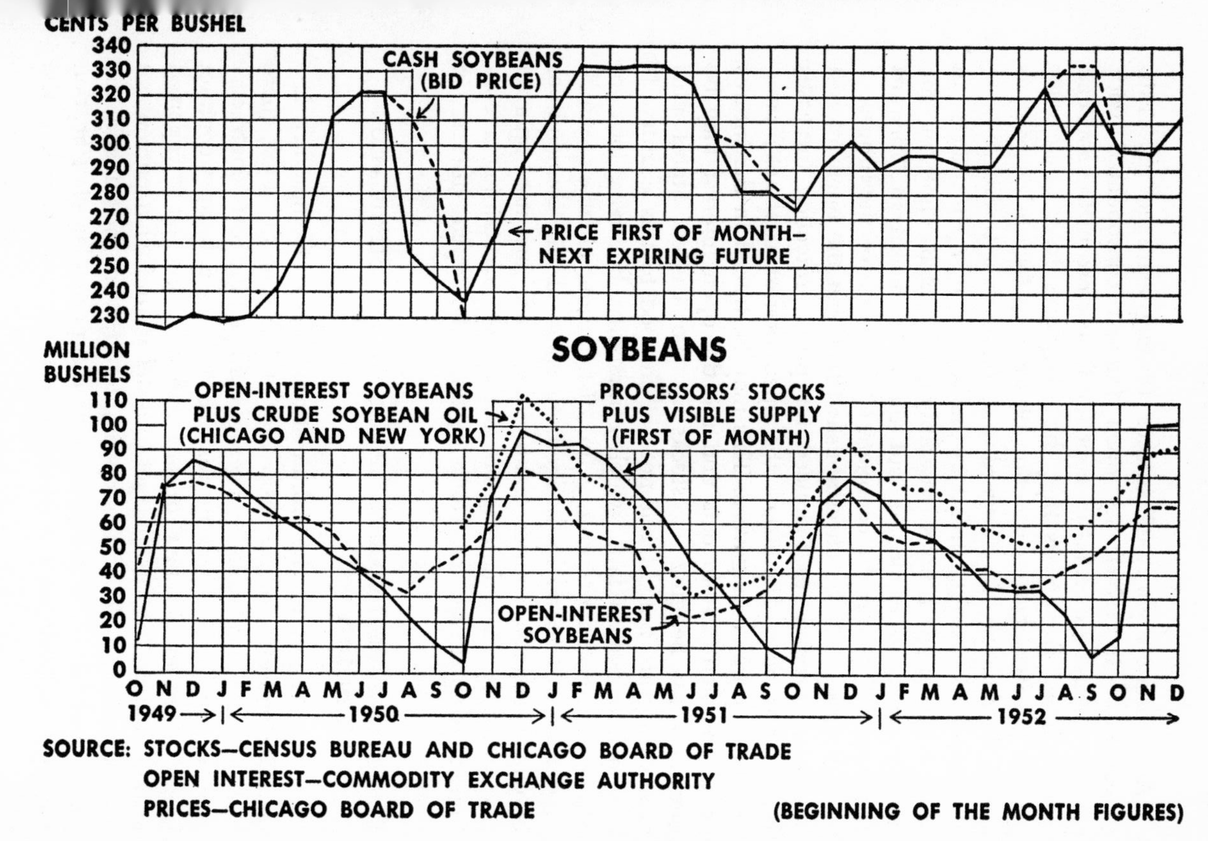

CENTS PER BUSHEL
340
330
320
310
300
290
280
270
260
250
240
230
CASH SOYBEANS
(BID PRICE)
← PRICE FIRST OF MONTH–
NEXT EXPIRING FUTURE
SOYBEANS
MILLION
BUSHELS
110
100
90
80
70
60
50
40
30
20
10
0
OPEN-INTEREST SOYBEANS
PLUS CRUDE SOYBEAN OIL
(CHICAGO AND NEW YORK)
PROCESSORS' STOCKS
PLUS VISIBLE SUPPLY
(FIRST OF MONTH)
OPEN-INTEREST
SOYBEANS
O N D J F M A M J J A S O N D J F M A M J J A S O N D J F M A M J J A S O N D
1949 → | ← 1950 → | ← 1951 → | ← 1952 →
SOURCE: STOCKS—CENSUS BUREAU AND CHICAGO BOARD OF TRADE
OPEN INTEREST—COMMODITY EXCHANGE AUTHORITY
PRICES—CHICAGO BOARD OF TRADE
(BEGINNING OF THE MONTH FIGURES)

FIGURE 12

After crude-soybean-oil futures trading assumed moderate proportions (in 1950), its open interest consolidated with soybean futures exceeded or kept the total close to the soybean stock volume. It appears that the oil futures have taken over part of the risk-bearing function of soybean futures as well as replaced some of the forward-cash oil-market trading.

There is a seasonal trend in the volume of open interest in crude-soybean-oil futures resembling the chart line of the factory stocks of crude oil, but the cash market in "forward shipment oil" clouds the complete effectiveness of the futures.

It does seem to be an established fact that the open interest in futures expands as the need for price protection increases and as this need diminishes the open-interest contracts; commercial requirements govern. This may be traced in the futures of all commodities—in oats and rye the open interest may be governed by hedging of stocks in the United States plus Canadian grain bought but not yet shipped to this country. It is also apparent in lard, which commodity, however, includes rather a constant inventory in distribution channels which cannot be systematically hedged. In some of the commodities in which there is futures trading the stocks are not reported frequently, so that there is no method of ascertaining a continuous comparison of stock against the open interest in futures.

Percentage of Hedging, Spreading and Speculation in Open Interest

In the report of the Administrator of the Commodity Exchange Authority for the crop year ended June 30, 1950, there was a table of semi-monthly averages of open interest (contracts) from which Table I was made. Inasmuch as a futures contract is one of either purchase or sale and open interest is reported as only one side of the contract in order to find what percentage one classification is of the open interest, you should add the "long" and "short" commitments of the particular classification together and double the open-interest figure to calculate the percentage. In this table only the reporting trades are given in separate classifications—hedging, spreading, and speculative —making up the total of all reporting trades.

The reporting traders had a combined total of 96,249,000 bushels of long and short positions in wheat, which was 56% of the total long and short trades for all traders. In corn the combined total was 51,158,000 bushels, or 52%; in soybeans it was 51,012,000 bushels, or 48%; and in cotton it was 2,078,000 bales, or 43%.

Hedging Percentages.—Of the 96,249,000 bushels of wheat-reporting traders, hedging made up 54%, spreading 29%, and "long" and "short" only 17%. Corn hedging made up 47%, spreading 32%, and "long" and "short" only 21%. Soybeans hedging made up 46%, spreading 40%, and "long" and "short" only 14%. Cotton hedging made up 57%, spreading 34%, and "long" and "short" only 9%. While these percentages of each classification are the percentages of only the reporting totals, they are probably somewhat representative of each classification in the whole total of "long" and "short" positions in the open interest.

From studies made in 1934 of all the open commitments on the Chicago Board of Trade, "long" and "short" hedges in wheat are listed totaling 147,333,000 bushels out of 314,634,000 bushels combined "long" and "short" trades for all traders. This was 47%. In corn the hedging percentage was 45%.

Table II contains many interesting facts of the open commitments in wheat and corn for that date. In this table the "Foreign & Miscellaneous" groups contain some hedging accounts, though as a group they are apparently predominantly speculative; however, they would add something to the percentage of hedges if they were completely classified. Another statement accompanying this table is that speculative trades include spreading trades. Also, the "long" hedging accounts average 22,000 bushels, which eliminates them from the necessity of reporting (at present), and the average "short" hedging amount is 420,000 bushels.

Another reference can be found in the administrator's re-

TABLE I*

Open-Interest Semi-month Averages, 1949–50

	Reporting Traders				Non-reporting Traders, Speculative & Hedging	Total Open Commitments
	Long or Short Only	Spreading Long & Short	Hedging	Total Large Traders		
Wheat (1,000 bu.)						
Long	14,145	13,633	17,873	45,651	40,226	85,877
Short	2,697	13,633	34,268	50,598	35,279	85,877
Total	16,842	27,266	52,141	96,249	75,505	171,754
Net	11,448	*none*	16,395	4,947	4,947	*none*
Percentage of reporting	17%	29%	54%	100%		
Corn (1,000 bu.)						
Long	7,541	8,213	4,762	20,516	28,890	49,406
Short	3,115	8,213	19,314	30,642	18,764	49,406
Total	10,656	16,426	24,076	51,158	47,654	98,812
Net	4,426	*none*	14,552	10,126	10,126	*none*
Percentage of reporting	21%	32%	47%	100%		

SOYBEANS (1,000 bu.)						
Long	6,068	10,235	6,181	22,484	31,016	53,500
Short	1,145	10,235	17,148	28,528	24,972	53,500
Total	7,213	20,470	23,329	51,012	55,988	107,000
Net	4,923	*none*	10,967	6,044	6,044	*none*
Percentage of reporting	14%	40%	46%	100%		
COTTON (1,000 bales)						
Long	136	358	565	1,059	1,315	2,374
Short	41	358	620	1,019	1,355	2,374
Total	177	716	1,185	2,078	2,670	4,748
Net	95	*none*	55	40	40	*none*
Percentage of reporting	9%	34%	57%	100%		

* *Report of the Administrator of the Commodity Exchange Authority, 1950,* U.S.D.A., Oct. 20, 1950.

port for the fiscal year of 1948, wherein reporting traders' hedging month-end commitments averaged 57% of the reporting total. The speculative "long" and "short" share was 11%. The balance of 32% was spreading trades. Average commitments are shown in Table III.

The Commodity Exchange Authority's report for July, 1950, through June, 1951, contained the open-commitment figures shown in Table IV.[1]

There are several considerations to bear in mind. First, when reporting and non-reporting traders' commitments are considered together, the hedging percentage is a smaller percentage of the total than when consideration is given to the reporting hedges as compared with the total reporting commitments. In other words, a larger percentage of the reporting trades are hedges than the percentage of hedges in all open commitments, but the percentage is not greatly larger. For example, for wheat in the 1950 table (Table I) the reporting hedging percentage was 54%, for the 1948 fiscal year (Table III) it was 57%, and for the 1951 fiscal year 58% (Table IV). These are all the percentages of combined "long" and "short" reporting hedges included in reporting traders' commitments. But on September 29, 1934 (Table II), for all open contracts the hedging percentage figured 47% (but did not classify foreign accounts which contained some hedges).

The second consideration is that commitments of hedging are compared with total commitments including spreading trades. Inasmuch as spreads are traded from a different point of view from open speculative "long" and "short" positions, a comparison may be made between hedges and open interest minus commitments classified as spreads. This would considerably raise the percentage of hedging over the percentage of the total including spreading trades. For the 1950 report (Table I) it would raise the reporting hedging to 75% of the reporting

---

[1] U.S.D.A. Commodity Exchange Authority Statistical Bulletin No. 107.

TABLE II*

Occupation Analysis of Accounts
With Open Commitments in Wheat and Corn Futures
Chicago Board of Trade, September 29, 1934
(In 1,000 bushels)

CLASS	NO. OF ACC'TS	GROUP TOTAL COMMITMENT		GROUP NET COMMITMENT	
		Long	Short	Long	Short
WHEAT					
Farmers	1,492	6,068	695	5,373	
Housewives	802	8,364	1,016	7,348	
Clerks, Small Merchants, etc.	6,237	44,403	6,462	37,941	
Executives, Financiers, etc.	3,068	56,071	19,253	36,818	
Speculative Corporations	39	3,725	240	3,485	
Total speculative	11,638	118,631	27,666	90,965	
Elevator Hedgers	738	11,577	76,949		65,372
Processor Hedgers	309	7,529	51,278		43,740
Total Hedging	1,047	19,106	128,227		109,121
Foreign & Miscellaneous	509	19,580	1,402	18,178	
Grand Total	13,194	157,317	157,295	22	
CORN					
Farmers	1,047	3,326	932	2,394	
Housewives	496	4,237	765	3,472	
Clerks, Small Merchants, etc.	3,730	23,145	6,535	16,610	
Executives, Financiers, etc.	1,876	29,681	9,148	20,533	
Speculative Corporations	27	5,825	417	5,408	
Total speculative	7,176	66,214	17,797	48,417	
Elevator Hedgers	572	4,664	63,730		59,066
Processor Hedgers	122	4,887	7,209		2,322
Total Hedging	694	9,551	70,939		61,388
Foreign & Miscellaneous	219	13,886	779	13,107	
Grand Total	8,089	89,651	89,515	136	

* *Grain Prices and the Future Market: A 15-Year Survey, 1923–1938*, U.S.D.A. Technical Bulletin No. 747.

total. For 1948 (Table III) it would raise the hedging proportion to 84%, and to 83% in 1951 (Table IV).

If this were pursued further, recognition would be given to the amount of spreading trades included in the open speculative "long" and "short" positions, which are one side of a spread against a different grain or commodity in the same market or a different grain or commodity in another market. The Commodity Exchange Authority, in their classification of spreads, does not include these trades as spreads. As there is a considerable volume of these trades included in the open interest, a reclassification of such trades and elimination of them from open commitments for a comparative purpose would further raise the percentage of hedges as compared with total open commitments. This would also reduce the percentage of commitments presently classified as "speculative long and short only."

The Commodity Exchange Authority includes in the spreading classification spreads between "odd" or "job" lots, which are contracts in units of less than 5,000 bushels of grain, and "round" lots (units of 5,000 bushels) in the Chicago market, when they are in the same futures delivery month. This may amount to a large number of bushels. This spreading is of the utmost importance in providing liquidity for trading in odd lots. Not only do spreaders make many trades with brokers who

TABLE III

Average Month-End Commitments in 1948

	Long	Short
SMALL TRADERS' COMMITMENTS	47,055	36,845
LARGE TRADERS' COMMITMENTS		
Speculative	9,127	2,505
Hedging	21,173	37,984
Spreading	16,699	16,699
	94,054	94,033
TOTAL OPEN CONTRACTS (long & short combined): 188,087		

TABLE IV

Open Commitments in All Contract Markets Combined:
Semi-monthly Averages
July, 1950–June, 1951

	Reporting Traders				Non-reporting Traders	Total Open Commitments
	Long or Short Only	Spreading Long & Short	Hedging	Total Large Traders		
Wheat (1,000 bu.)						
Long	11,624	17,857	20,405	49,886	47,657	97,543
Short	2,919	17,857	49,961	70,737	27,806	97,543
Total	14,543	35,714	70,366	120,623		
Percentage of reporting	12%	30%	58%	100%		
Corn (1,000 bu.)						
Long	11,488	8,317	6,317	26,122	28,798	54,920
Short	3,638	8,317	25,439	37,394	17,526	54,920
Total	15,126	16,634	31,756	63,516		
Percentage of reporting	24%	26%	50%	100%		
Soybeans (1,000 bu.)						
Long	2,810	8,719	6,883	18,412	21,314	39,726
Short	1,813	8,719	5,676	16,208	23,518	39,726
Total	4,623	17,438	12,559	34,620		
Percentage of reporting	14%	50%	36%	100%		

fill the odd-lot orders for customers, but they also offset opposite positions in the open interest of the odd-lot traders. They are the link between odd-lot and round-lot contracts.

The liquidity of a futures market is aided by the initiation and removal of all these spreads, making it possible for buying and selling orders to be filled with smaller fluctuations between trades than might otherwise be possible.

When trading in a new futures month is started there may be orders to either buy or sell but no traders willing at the moment to trade at that price in an opposite position. The price of the new future is more likely to induce a trader to enter the market in the form of a spread rather than at the outright price. Each newly quoted futures month bears a price relation to the ones which are already established on the relative potential plentifulness or scarceness of supplies for the time of delivery and the area which they represent. Professional traders are likely to appraise the value between the different futures more readily than the outright price; therefore, they are more inclined to trade in spreads than at a flat price when a new futures month is quoted. Or they may consider there is greater opportunity for changes in spread differences because newly quoted futures have less liquidity; therefore, these traders make spreads with the idea of having greater chances of securing profits. In well established months, in addition to the spreaders who take a position there are the scalping spreaders who operate to offset quick price changes from large buying or selling orders that temporarily put one month or market out of line with the ruling price of other months or markets. Then there are traders who consider the speculative risk is less if they trade in spreads between grains rather than in open "long" or "short" commitments.

Spreading trades are retained during either an advance or decline in the price of grain and are liquidated only because the spreading difference changes. Trading in spreads helps to provide liquidity in the market and uniformity in the immediate price movement of the different futures months and in the different markets. Because they are retained on price advances and declines, spreads are not necessarily an offset to new hedges or to the removal of old hedging commitments in the same direct manner as open "long" and "short" commitments. "Long" and "short" speculative positions are directly affected by changes in price upward or downward, which are likely to cause these traders to liquidate their "long" positions or to cover their "short" positions so that new speculators must enter the market to take their place so long as hedging commitments remain. This is not the case with spreaders who do not unwind their spreads for the same reasons. Spreaders do, however, provide liquidity in a market for "long" or "short" speculators as well as for hedgers.

Hedges constitute a large percentage of open futures commitments, and speculative commitments constitute a small percentage.

Speculative Percentages.—In the 1950 report (Table I), 17% of wheat-reporting trades were speculative, and 21% of the corn, 14% of the soybean, and 9% of the cotton. If we should eliminate the spreads in reporting commitments it would raise the percentage of speculative "long" and "short" wheat trades to 25%, corn 31%, soybean to 24%, and cotton to 13%. A complete report of non-reporting and reporting commitments would probably show that speculative "long and short only" percentages were larger than in reporting trades alone.

In the 1948 report (Table III) for reporting trades only the speculative "long" and "short" wheat trades constituted 11% of the reporting total. If spreads should be eliminated the percentage would be 16%.

Hedges vs. Speculation.—An examination of wheat hedges in the reporting trades in the 1950 report (Table I) shows that 34,268,000 bushels of "short" hedges have an offset of 17,873,000 bushels of "long" hedges. The net is 16,395,000 bushels of "short" hedges, which has an offset in 11,448,000 bushels of net "long" in speculative "long and short only" commitments. The balance, of course, is found in the rest of the open commitments, in non-reporting trades, and in spreads in both categories.

Corn "short"-reporting hedges of 19,314,000 bushels were partly offset by 4,762,000 bushels of "long" hedges, and the net 14,552,000 bushels had a net offset of 4,426,000 bushels "long" speculative reporting trades.

Soybean "short" hedges of 17,148,000 bushels and "long" hedges of 6,181,000 bushels or net of 10,967,000 bushels short hedges are partly offset by 4,923,000 bushels of net long speculative trades. The balance of the offsetting trades is in the combination of reporting spreading trades and the trades in the non-reporting hedging and speculative classification.

Inasmuch as the September 29, 1934, report (Table II) stated that "long" hedges averaged 22,000 bushels and "short" hedges 420,000 bushels (wheat and corn) there probably always tends to be a larger total of "long" hedging commitments in the non-reporting commitments than "short" hedges in this category. This would be a further balance against trades for hedging within the reporting-trades-for-hedging group.

As of March 27, 1950, the Commodity Exchange administrator made a survey of all accounts having soybean open commitments, in part it was as follows:

	Bushels "long"	*Bushels "short"*
Speculative	50,800,000	40,084,000
Hedging	14,658,000	25,356,000

Inasmuch as the speculative commitments include spreads which may be one third to one half of the 50,800,000 bushels speculative "long" amount, when reduced to the position of outright "long" they may not be far in excess of the 25,300,000 bushels of "short" hedges. And the same number of bushels taken off the 40,000,000 bushels of speculative "short" trades would also leave outright "short" speculative trades not far in excess of the 14,600,000 bushels of "long" hedges.

The foregoing presents some analysis of the open interest in futures. Hedges, as might be supposed, represent the main load, being large percentages of the "short" side of the commitments and impressive on the "long" side. There are important amounts of "long" speculative trades which might be considered as substantial offsets to "short" hedges, and there are moderate amounts of "short" speculative commitments which might be considered as a partial balance against "long" hedges. Spreading trades balance inequalities so that each independent buyer or seller of each futures delivery month has, as is necessary, an opposite party to his "long" or "short" commitment. There is no identification possible of one segment of the open interest against another as it is the result of the myriad of trades made by the varying interests which use the futures markets. The market "long and short (only)" positions of large traders identified as groups in the annual reports are considerably smaller than the hedges, so that it is mostly the small traders' positions that offset hedges.

Exchange Floor Trading

There is no identification of opposite parties to a futures contract beyond the moment the trade is made in the pit. Each customer-principal to a trade is responsible to the commission merchant through whom the transaction is carried. One customer may retain his market position for months while the other party may offset his trade an instant after entering into it.

Many of the floor traders who make their own trades in the pits are fairly active on each turn in the price. Most of this type of traders pay little attention to the trade news. Their trading revolves around the activities in the pits.

Some of these traders are referred to as "scalpers" who try to buy at the "bid" price to take advantage of the smallest price advance or to sell at the "offered" price with the idea of "buying in" on the smallest decline. There are but few of this type of traders nowadays, but formerly when price ranges during a day were less and a larger volume was traded at each price the scalpers predominated among the floor traders.

Traders who fill their own orders in the pit and who assume all the risks of the trades' "checking" with the other party to the contract have a special low rate of commission, and when quantities are bought and sold at the same price on the same day they can "scratch" the trades, paying only a nominal commission. These low rates of commission allow a margin of profit on a favorable minimum fluctuation in the market. Some floor traders are members of the Clearing House; thus, provided their volume of trading is large enough to cover the overhead expenses, their trading costs are further reduced.

Many floor traders try to follow the turns in the market, anticipating fraction-of-a-cent advances or declines and possibly changing their position several times a day. Others endeavor to follow a trend either upward or downward and, if successful, to "sell out" on small advances and reinstate their position on minor dips or to buy when they believe the market is about to advance further. If they believe the trend will be downward, their market operations are to sell "short," and if successful to "buy in" on dips, etc.

If floor traders have acted wrong on the market they normally even up quickly, theorizing that taking a quick loss permits a fresh start for the chance of a profit. Customarily this type of floor traders evens up on all their trades by the close of the session.

There are traders who watch price movements of many commodities and trade in the various pits throughout the day, although they may concentrate on one commodity more than others. They follow the news as it comes from different sources in the belief that the market will respond to these influences. Their position is likely to be reversed as the tenor of the news changes. Such traders usually carry a market position from one day to the next.

There are some traders who specialize in spreading, although many floor traders are in reality spreaders because they endeavor to reduce their risk by offsetting many of their purchases or sales with an opposite position in another commodity. These traders almost always carry spread positions from one session to the next and usually have sizable spread positions open. In each pit there may be several active "scalpers" in inter-delivery spreads (between different months in the same grain) who trade in and out during a market session, making their trades with brokers filling spread orders for customers or trading with other spreaders, and working their own spreads by trading between delivery months.

Another type of spreading is that in which traders make inter-grain spreads after a decided price movement in one grain and a lag in another, believing that there will be a tendency for a correlating price move unless there is a special consideration why the grain which had lagged should not catch up.

It is rather believed, but without substantial statistical proof, that the floor type of traders account for about half to three fourths of the volume of the trade. They become more active in total volume as commission-house participation increases or as commercial clearing firms use futures in protecting their cash business. As orders reach the pits, brokers filling orders for others are always able to trade without a moment's delay. Large quantities are often bought or sold between one broker and one pit trader without a change in the price. But if it takes the trading volume of several pit traders and by brokers with opposite orders or a small or large change in the price to equal the volume of the broker's order, the order can nevertheless be filled quickly. The floor traders' participation probably adds greater liquidity to the market than any other phase of the business does. Because of this liquidity, fluctuations are reduced, although a price trend is not impeded. The market goes its way as conditions dictate, but in the day-to-day trading "local" traders' pit activities aid in filling orders without unduly changing the price. Without this balance wheel, a buying order would advance the price, and if followed by a selling order, a rapid decline would follow, or vice versa.

Off-the-Floor Customer Activities

The rapid dissemination of quotations through the ticker service, price changes flashed over the private wires, and the slower but widespread news service and radio broadcasting keep the traders at great distances from the markets informed on fluctuations. It is a matter of only seconds before some off-the-floor traders know of a market move. Not much later the ticker records the fluctuation to hundreds of locations in this country and Canada. Speculative traders can get orders to the pits from any private wire location in short order. Commercial interests basing cash transactions on futures prices may act as quickly as speculators and place or remove hedges. They may make cash trades too that do not require the use of futures, but the futures quotation is the means of establishing the price between buyers and sellers. Country-elevator offerings of "to-arrive" grain increase on "bulges" in the market, bringing hedging from the cash buyers. Exporters having foreign bids in hand or processors selling their products can send futures-buying orders to the pits on "breaks" in futures. Any of these forces are likely to become active at any time during the day. There is no warning of their coming, but the market is always ready for any eventuality. It is the continual crosscurrents in the grain trade converging on the futures market that stimulate it. Prices do not become "set" for long.

When prices of futures move down, they are most likely to meet a demand for the actual grain that absorbs the offerings. There is also a tendency for producers to offer less grain for sale into commercial channels. Export sales enlarge and hedges are lifted, thus offsetting sales of futures, from whatever source. Spreaders between markets become active. It was common before World War II (when all markets were open) that large spreading between Chicago, Winnipeg, and Liverpool would result when any one of the three markets became out of line with the world's level of the other two. On breaks in futures new "long" speculators enter the market.

When there is a "bull" move in the market it is met by the sale of cash grain, which brings "short" hedges into the market. The professional trader who is not afraid of a "bear" position will take the "short" side on such a move. Spreaders "sell the high market." Here again when there were futures markets throughout the world prior to the war, Liverpool might lag because of Canada, Argentine, or Australian pressure so that Chicago would be sold and Liverpool futures bought.

The speculators stand ready at any moment to take the risks transferred to the futures market which are not offset by opposite hedges. Hedges usually but not always predominate on the "short" side of the market; therefore, speculators "on balance" are more often "long" than "short." Their service to the market is one of providing protection to commercial interests, although their motive in trading is to secure a profit.

Behavior of the Market

Economists have observed the behavior of markets for commodities in which there is futures trading and have found that their prices fluctuate in a pattern common to other agricultural products in which there is no futures trading.[2] The way farm products are marketed has considerable bearing on their pricing methods. Corn goes to market on the hoof, as 85% of its production does not leave the county in which it is grown in the form of grain, and rice goes to market either by private negotiation between buyer and seller or by sealed-bid auctions; yet both these commodities follow closely the price-chart curves of wheat and cotton, the two major raw materials sold through futures exchanges. Peanuts used for industrial oils and marketed chiefly in Virginia, and beef, wool, etc., all unrelated in market-

---

[2] Dean W. Malott (Chancellor, University of Kansas), *Does Futures Trading Influence Prices?* Feb. 2, 1950.

ing, follow the same price trends as grains, differing temporarily as any commodity might when special supply-and-demand conditions cause deviations.

Futures follow the cash value of the commodity, with an allowance of time for reconciliation of prices with conditions. Thus the futures are a reflection of the conditions expressed in terms of a price that will balance supply and demand. Trading in futures makes possible the registration of prices far in advance of cash transactions, and through speculation, advantage may be obtained from price changes. Whether or not speculators secure a profit or stand a loss in their trading depends upon their individual ability to estimate the commercial value. They are not trading in the unknown, for the risks assumed are already existing and must be borne by someone. Their trading has an economic value in serving producers, merchants, processors, and consumers of the commodity in which they operate.

Studies of futures trading have not disclosed that speculative activity has either a depressing or a buoyant effect on prices.[3] Large traders' activities within a comparatively brief period of time may cause the price to move with their buying or selling, but the price effect may be in part or wholly offset by small-scale trading if it is sufficiently vigorious and timely.[4] Other observations have indicated that the general public has come into the market in such numbers as to take full control from the so-called big traders.[5]

Trade historians have identified the "birth" of futures trading with the expansion of production in the United States, and with this facility, merchants and millers were able to work on a much smaller margin of profit.[6] Trading in futures has been found to have reduced the fluctuations on the market, as it

---

[3] *Ibid.*

[4] *Grain Prices and the Futures Market: A 15-Year Survey,* 1923–1938, U.S.D.A. Technical Bulletin No. 747, Jan., 1941.

[5] Dr. Alonzo Taylor (Director, Food Research Institute, Leland Stanford University) in Stamp Commission Report, 1931 (see note 7).

[6] *George Broomhall's Corn Trade News,* Liverpool, Oct. 17, 1951.

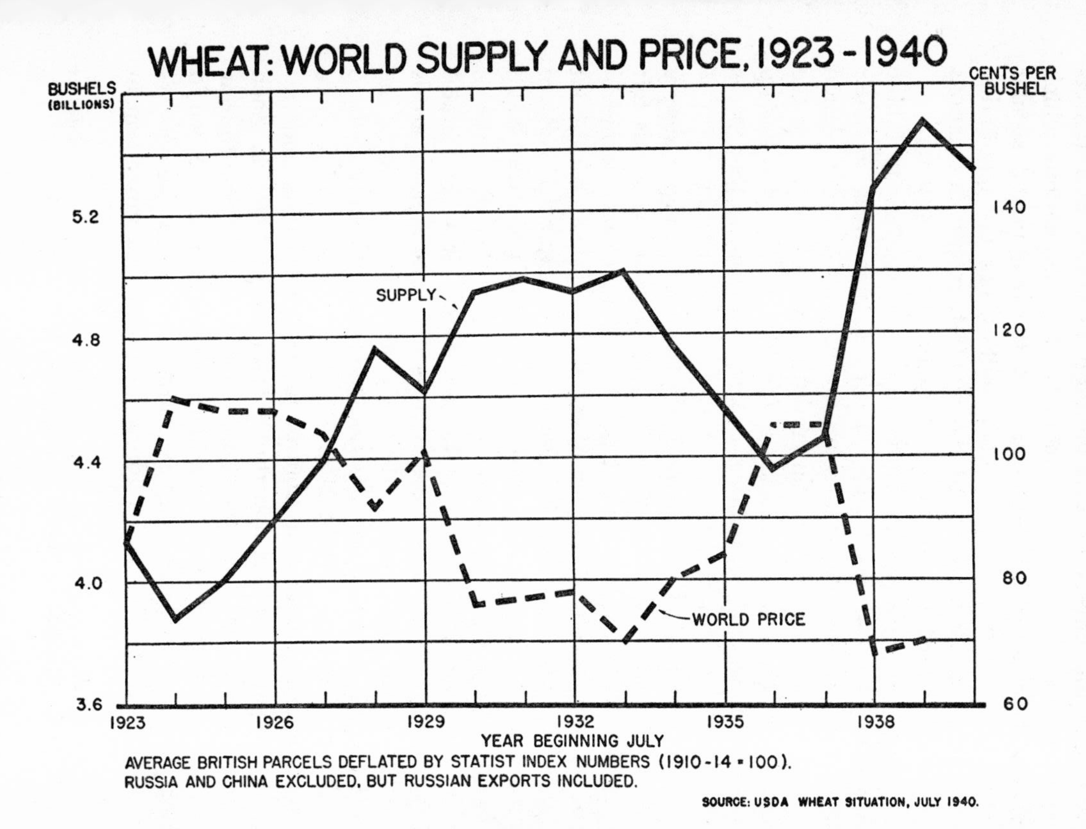
WHEAT: WORLD SUPPLY AND PRICE, 1923 - 1940
BUSHELS (BILLIONS)
CENTS PER BUSHEL
5.2
4.8
4.4
4.0
3.6
140
120
100
80
60
SUPPLY
WORLD PRICE
1923
1926
1929
1932
1935
1938
YEAR BEGINNING JULY
AVERAGE BRITISH PARCELS DEFLATED BY STATIST INDEX NUMBERS (1910-14 = 100).
RUSSIA AND CHINA EXCLUDED, BUT RUSSIAN EXPORTS INCLUDED.
SOURCE: USDA WHEAT SITUATION, JULY 1940.

FIGURE 13

evens out the effects of varying crop prospects and reflects the economic price in world markets. The fluctuations which economists claim are lessened are not the long-period secular trends of price shared by all commodities, nor the day-to-day oscillations of the market, but the month-to-month fluctuations in particular, and the year-to-year fluctuations in general.[7]

The prices registered in futures markets are free to follow supply-and-demand conditions of the commodities, as their use is open to all and no interests are favored or manipulation permitted; also, the deliverable grades are representative of the commercial quality. The market is sensitive to changes in crop or economic conditions, political events, and laws, so that prices are a guide in production efforts and in distribution.

The fundamental task of the grain trade is to keep a supply of grain in trade channels at an "economic price" which is fair to producers and consumers. It has been found that the mean-price line in each year when there was competition without restrictions rose and fell in general conformity with relative increase or decrease in the total world supply (of wheat) and changes in the value of money.[8]

The Bureau of Agricultural Economics of the United States Department of Agriculture charted the curve of British-parcels average price per bushel (deflated) as compared with the world supply of wheat for a period following World War I up to the outbreak of World War II. During these years there were political measures to control prices, production, and imports in many countries and droughts in North America. Each country participated in the international trade or withdrew from it as their internal conditions dictated, but the world supply in the aggregate had its normal affect on the world's price. The United States withdrew largely from competition in

[7] Canada, the Commission to Enquire Into Trading in Grain Futures (G. C. Stamp, Chairman), *Report* . . . April 29, 1931.

[8] *Ibid.*

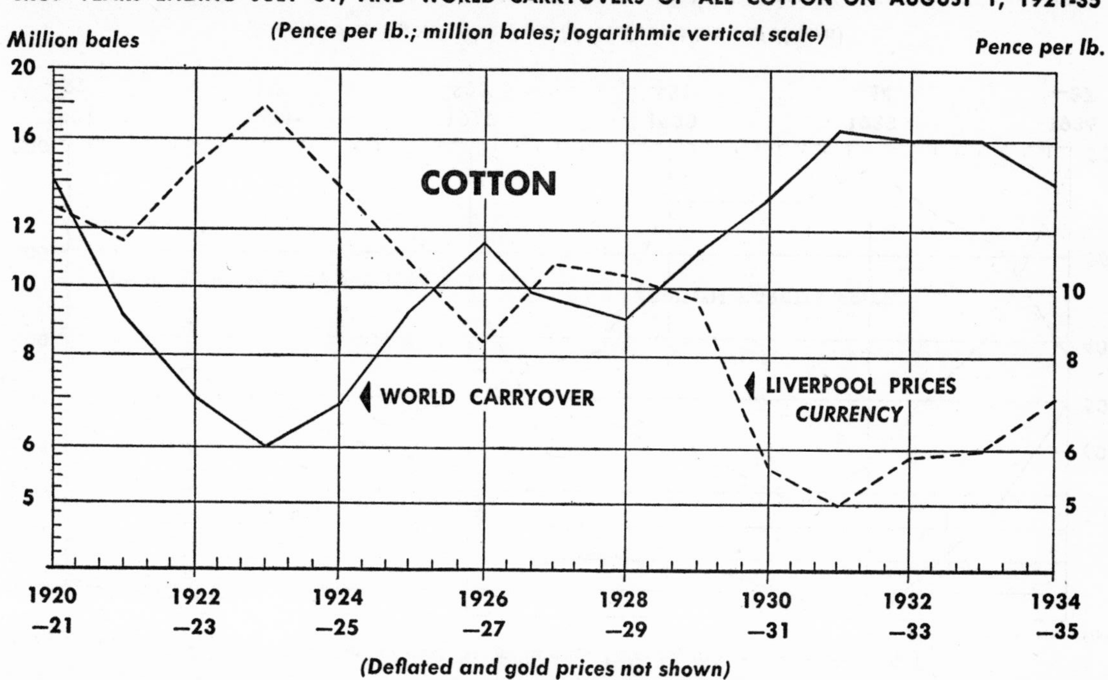

V. P. Timoshenko, in *Wheat Studies* (Food Research Institute, Stanford University), Vol. XIV, No. 7, April, 1938.

FIGURE 14

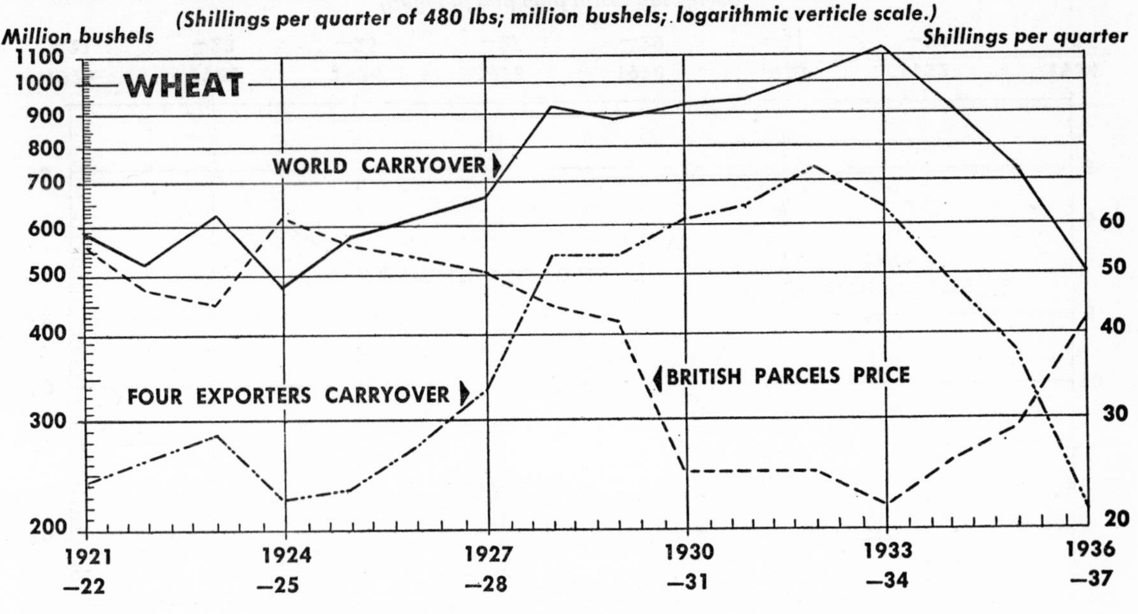
AVERAGE ANNUAL BRITISH PARCELS PRICES OF WHEAT, AND YEAR-END WHEAT STOCKS IN
THE "WORLD" EX-INDIA AND IN THE FOUR CHIEF EXPORTING COUNTRIES, ABOUT AUGUST 1, 1922-37.
(Shillings per quarter of 480 lbs; million bushels; logarithmic verticle scale.)
Million bushels
Shillings per quarter
WHEAT
WORLD CARRYOVER
FOUR EXPORTERS CARRYOVER
BRITISH PARCELS PRICE
1100
1000
900
800
700
600
500
400
300
200
60
50
40
30
20
1921 –22
1924 –25
1927 –28
1930 –31
1933 –34
1936 –37
(Deflated and gold prices, world total supplies, not shown)
V. P. Timoshenko, in *Wheat Studies* (Food Research Institute, Stanford University), Vol. XIV, No. 7, April, 1938.

FIGURE 15

some years and actually became a net importer in the drought years. (See Figure 13.)

A correlation has also been made between year-end carryovers of commodities and the price during the previous year. A carryover is a balancing item between the total supply and its utilization during the past crop year. Cotton was found to follow close to perfect curves. (See Figure 14.)

A chart of British-parcels prices which represents the selling participation of all the leading wheat-exporting countries (but not unduly affected by special conditions in any of them), compared with the carryovers, is shown in Figure 15.

CHAPTER XIII

Spreading

As a Gauge for Distribution

Spreads might be termed the grain market's gauge in the distribution of supplies. The price level of a commodity is governed by the prices of all commodities in general with special consideration for the conditions prevailing in the particular commodity. And this in general is the basis that prevails in grain spreads. When grain supplies are large they weigh upon the spread difference, sending the "near-by" grain to a discount; when supplies are small, the "near-by" goes to a premium.

Probably the fundamental basis of measurement of a spread difference within a market is the amount of grain that will come on the market relative to the demand until the next future delivery. When the "near-by" is at a discount, it encourages carrying of grain in a hedged position; but when the "near-by" is at a premium, the amount of the premium adjusts demand to the available supply. In this way spreads gauge the distribution of the supplies. If this were not so, extravagant uses of supplies in the early part of a small production year would reduce the remaining supplies to an amount below the requirements for later in the season. As withholding of stocks occurs when supplies are small, the development of a premium price for the "near-by" acts as a deterrent for carrying large stocks except by those who have a definite need for the grain. The premium advances to a limit which curtails demand of lesser importance so that the grain which is available satisfies the more urgent requirements. If more grain is put on the market than is currently needed, the spread premium narrows and discourages selling or encourages demand until a proper supply-and-demand balance results. In this manner so far as is possible a small crop is stretched over the uses for an entire season.

It would not happen that in a year of small supplies the deferred futures months would simultaneously sell higher than those maturing earlier, the reasoning being that as supplies became scarcer the grain would be worth more money. Whether or not the flat price of grain later in the season is higher, it is not so in spreads. When supplies are small the more urgent type of demand keeps storage stocks low and buyers are willing to absorb the cost of carrying the grain in order to have some available as it is needed in their business. Premium prices are paid by elevator operators for a working stock of grain which they believe they can merchandise at a profit, but the quantity is limited to this amount. Processors may have to carry relatively more grain at the risk of a loss in order to keep their processed brands before the public or to have a stock sufficient to maintain minimum operations in their plant.

Spreads are at a discount price for the "near-by" when supplies are ample. Under such conditions people are willing to carry hedged grain provided they can secure a profit from the storage of the grain—in other words, if they can earn "carrying charges." Sales are made at a discount to those people who will carry the grain. This is so because there is a cost to absorb in carrying the grain no matter who the owner may be.

Market Adjustment to World Levels

Spreads do not directly affect the price of grain, because that is governed by dependence on the world's level—in the case of wheat, if the country has a surplus to sell. But when such a country has no surplus for sale in the export market its price advances above the world's level and remains there so long as this supply condition lasts. No export country normally stays at the world level even during a whole season. When a country has sold its surplus its prices temporarily advance relative to those of other countries. This cuts off its export outlet. Some other export nation becomes cheaper, at least for a while. Spreads gauge the demand for the supply that is considered to be a surplus. If an old crop surplus has been exhausted or the unharvested crop is unpromising, the whole country's price level may rise above the world's level. However, if an old-crop surplus remains, carrying charges may continue in the futures market even though the old and new crop combined may not provide an export surplus. On the other hand, if the old-crop surplus is sold and the new-crop outlook is good so that a surplus will exist at harvest time, the new-crop futures will be at the world's level and there will be "inverse carrying charges," with old-crop futures at a premium; that is, the near-by price will be higher than the world's level.

Degree of Scarcity Governs Inverse Carrying Charges.— It may also be that export business continues when there are inverse carrying charges, provided the foreign demand is strong enough to maintain premiums and to induce holders of grain in the export country to draw upon their stocks, thus reducing the carryover to below a normal amount. A very strong export demand may cause a severe reduction in the carryover and justify a high premium or a large inverse carrying charge to induce holders to part with their grain.

A strong domestic demand results in the same inverse carrying charges as result from export sales, even to the extent of attracting imports.

When there are inverse carrying charges, the degree of scarcity of supplies governs the premium to which demand will force the near-by prices. As an inverse-carrying-charge spread widens it not only draws grain from holders previously unwilling to sell, but it reduces the demand. Those consumers who can wait for a later shipment which they can simultaneously buy at a cheaper price may do so and reduce their working stocks during the interim.

During a delivery month, owners of grain who are still short the current futures must decide whether to change over their hedge at a discount or put the grain on the market. It is not only grain held in the delivery center but also grain elsewhere that satisfies demand which is effective in offsetting a tight inverse-carrying-charge position. The hedging or speculative longs may gain from forced buying by shorts who cannot deliver, but they must also evaluate their chances of receiving grain on delivery and having to find buyers at the existing premium over the deferred futures. Grain received and not sold but carried to the next delivery month not only loses the inverse premium but also has storage, etc., assessed against it. Longs may take advantage of a technical condition when delivery stocks are light and retain their position until deliveries threaten, and then sell their holdings; they may take delivery when they believe they will own a stock of grain that can be profitably sold; or they may take large amounts on delivery when it seems likely that further large amounts will not be forthcoming later to compete with their holdings.

Judgment must be exercised by both sides: those who own grain, including the farmers, not to overstay the market; and the various interests representing consumers to make provision for their requirements. From the nature of the market structure—inverse carrying charges representing limited supplies—many short hedgers avoid keeping their futures commitments in delivery months that mature before they are likely to sell or use their present stock of grain. However, for grain likely to be sold earlier, inasmuch as the cash sale price will be based on the near-by or the current future, they have less risk in carrying hedges in such future. In gauging the prospective demand, cash-grain owners may change over short hedges at a discount on grain likely to be merchandised after the expiration of the current future, but in their judgment on only the amount of grain that will be merchandised before the cash basis declines relative to the new hedge.

Processors may change over hedges in order to retain a stock of grain needed to continue their activities. The retention of the grain gives processors a convenience stock from which to sell products on a price basis at which they can replace the grain or meet competition of others having to enter the cash market to buy grain for processing even though knowingly they are likely to sustain a loss on the cash basis. They must consider that if they sell the unprocessed grain and take in the hedge they will be without supplies and will be unable to carry on processing activities, or that if they have to re-enter the market for processing supplies the cash basis might even be higher than their previous sale price.

References.—Economists of the Food Research Institute in their studies have said:

> It has not been possible to find any measurable persistent relation between the size of the new winter-wheat harvest and the spread between the May and July futures at Chicago. . . . In general, expectations regarding future developments affect the price of a near future if not quite as much as they affect the price of deferred futures. Indeed, it may be added, they tend to affect cash wheat prices nearly if not quite as much as they affect the price of futures. This being the case, it follows that most expectations regarding future developments have no important effect on the relations between the prices of near and distant futures. . . . The pertinent conditions are chiefly those related to scarcity or abundance of supplies that will be available for use during the interval between the time of expiration of the nearer future and the time of arrival of substantial supplies from a new source.
>
> If the supply is large, the distant futures tend to stand at a premium (or "carrying charge") over the near. If the supply is small, the near future tends to be at a premium, and the amount of the premium tends to be in direct relation to the degree of scarcity. The supply that is chiefly important from this standpoint is not merely that adjacent to Chicago, nor even the total supply in terminal markets, but the whole supply in the country, including stocks on farms. Stocks removed from normal availability for commercial use, such as those held by the Grain Stabilization Corporation in 1930–31 and by farmers under government loans in 1938–39, however, seem to count for little in determining spreads between old-crop and new-crop futures in Chicago.[1]

[1] Sidney Hoos and Holbrook Working, in *Wheat Studies* (Food Research Institute, Stanford University), Vol. XVII, No. 3, Nov., 1940.

Relation to Government Program

It might be stated in relation to spreads and also to market prices of cash grain and futures that, since the Government-support program in its present form started in 1938, grain-trade merchandising and futures markets have absorbed free offerings of producers' grain in amounts equal only to domestic and free export requirements plus a surplus of less than a normal carry-over. The balance of what might be considered a normal carry-over plus excessive stocks has rested with the Government agency which carried the risk. It has been necessary at times for old-crop futures to remain at "redemption" levels that permitted producers to redeem their grain in the loans from the Commodity Credit Corporation and to sell it in the open market, while at the same time the new-crop futures have been lower than the new-crop loan price. Elevators, acting as warehousemen, have stored large amounts of grain in excess of commercial needs, but the grain has been owned by producers or the Government.

Handling Spreading (Changing Hedges)

It is the task of the grain man, usually the elevator operator or the executive who handles futures trading for a processor, to try to carry his hedges in the most advantageous futures month or in the month that exposes them to the least risk from adverse changes in spreads. This is a matter of judgment and is by no means an exact science. Carrying(or inverse-carrying)-charge spreads do not normally fluctuate as much as the flat price of the market, but they are governed by changing conditions which cause the spread differences to vary.

Those firms having warehouses at delivery points, whether they are for grain, lard, or oil, can deliver the commodity on their futures contract or change over the hedge and retain the commodity in their warehouse. Those who are in this favorable location can therefore wait for an opportune time to act. Others not so fortunately located may have to arrange for the sale of their commodity if they do not wish to change hedges over at inverse carrying charges (buying the near-by and selling the deferred at a lower price). Even firms having warehouses both at delivery points and elsewhere must be cautious in the handling of their hedges against stocks in outside positions. Sometimes they can ship the "outside position" commodity to the delivery point, but this is not possible for that which is out of position, and it is not possible if their delivery warehouse is otherwise occupied. It is prudent to sell stocks located in outside positions if large inverse carrying charges prevail, but when the penalty is not severe, hedges are often changed over.

At times hedgers find themselves in a difficult position, notably processors who have difficulty in accumulating or replacing their raw materials and need the stocks for continuing plant operations or those who have paid premiums over the futures for quality. Often this condition induces the firm to put hedges in the most distant future at the time the cash grain is purchased. But firms which buy grain and sell grain as such (not products) have no hesitancy in divesting themselves of grain which cannot be carried with normal risks. This tends to direct the grain in commercial channels toward those who need it.

Trading in spreads speculatively entails a greater risk than is borne by some of those who use futures as a hedge and have to deal with spread differences in placing and changing hedges. The short hedger may be able to ship his grain to market for delivery or to sell his hedged grain during the delivery month. Also, if his grain is in a deliverable position he can wait until near the end of trading before deciding to deliver or he can change over the hedge. The "long" hedger may wish to take delivery and carry the cash grain instead of changing his hedges to a later month. In other words, he carries cash grain as a hedge against a sale instead of carrying futures. This cash grain held in the delivery position may later be sold at the time the identical grain in suitable position and of desired quality needed to fill the cash sale is procured. It must be considered that delivery grain, although of commercial quality, does not always fill the processing requirements, especially in the wheat-milling trade.

The speculator in spreads has futures contracts carrying the same obligations as the hedger and is subject to the same variations in spread differences, but he lacks the cash-grain stocks or cash contracts which may offset adverse conditions. His motive, being entirely profit and not hedging protection against market fluctuations, permits him to spread for either narrowing or widening spread differences. This gives him more flexibility in his spreading operations than the hedger, but the speculator lacks the advantage of being able to deliver the cash grain if he has judged the spread wrong.

Odd-Lot Spreading

In the Chicago grain-futures market the "odd lot," or "job lot," contract, as it is commonly called, is for 1,000- or 2,000-bushel units but of the same terms as the "round lot" contract for 5,000 bushels. Odd-lot contracts cannot be applied against round lots in trading. However, delivery may be taken on one and redelivery made on the other provided rules governing grade and location minimum requirements are observed; or on the last delivery day one contract may be applied against the other on prescribed terms.

In pit trading the execution of any order whether it is a round lot or an odd lot depends upon locating an opposite buyer or seller. Odd lots are not automatically executed at a fixed difference compared with round lots. There are not always opposite odd-lot orders in sufficient volume to permit brokers or traders to trade at a price equal to the round-lot price. This creates a market for spreaders to meet the odd-lot brokers' or traders' needs. Spreaders in job lots against round lots trade in the same delivery month of both, keeping the prices about in line with each other but at a changing difference. In a market of good volume, but not a widely fluctuating market, spreaders keep the odd-lot and round-lot contract prices close to each other. When odd-lot trading is not very active, so that spreaders cannot simultaneously trade in equal quantities of the two contracts, they widen the difference at which they are willing to trade, because in addition to spreading they have to speculate on the unequal amount. When fluctuations are rapid and one side of the spread is elusive, spreaders also try to work on a greater spread difference. However, competition from other spreaders and from straight buying or selling of odd-lot orders limits odd-lot-spreading differences. Any trader is potentially an odd-lot spreader if it is remunerative for him.

Large amounts of these spreads are accumulated by professional traders, especially in a running market when odd-lot speculators tend to trade on the same side of the market. Odd-lot–round-lot spreading is essential to a market, because odd-lot market positions may make up an important part of the open interest.

Execution of Orders

The "execution of inter-delivery spreading orders" and "changing orders for hedges" is the same pit operation. The broker must buy one future and sell the other as he judges the opportunity for filling the order (in part or all of the order at one time) at the guaranteed spread difference. There may be an opportunity to trade with a spreading trader or another spreading broker filling an opposite order, in which case the broker's task is simplified; but spreading nevertheless is a difficult pit operation and entails considerable risk to the pit broker. He is obligated to execute the order at the spread difference stated in the order so that any errors in judgment in filling one side first and not being able to trade successfully in the other side may result in a loss to the broker. However, even though simultaneously quoted prices of each month make it appear that a spread should be executed it does not bind the broker. As in all pit trading, the spreading broker must be able to fill the order in the open market or he is not liable, except in the case of negligence.

The same method of trading is followed in filling inter-grain and inter-market spread orders, but the latter (because of exchange rulings) may not be offset against an opposite order.

When there are large quantities of spreads to be executed or hedges to be changed, customarily the principal enters portions of the amount one at a time over a period of time—possibly weeks. These orders are necessarily priced at varying spread differences following the market changes.

The seasoned trader thinks of spreads as readily as he thinks of buying or selling, knowing how to enter his orders to endeavor to accomplish the desired results from changing spread differences. It does take some training, however, in order not to be confused when entering spread orders. At the outset it is usually not a consideration that the whole market should either advance or decline for spread differences to change as the trader anticipates.

An inter-grain spread is quite understandable. The spreader buys a grain that is considered to be underpriced; or if he believes a grain is overpriced, that is the one to be sold, and consequently an opposite purchase or sale is made in the other grain. Even though his judgment of price level is wrong, provided the grain bought advances more than the other grain sold the trader has correctly analyzed the spread; if the grain bought declines less than grain sold, he was also right. What counts is that the profit on one grain is greater than the loss on the other. The net profit (or loss) accrues from the price changes in the combination of the two grains.

Inter-market Spreads

Inter-market spread orders seldom carry a market-level consideration. However, the spreader has the same ideas in mind as he might have for inter-grain spreads. When free market supplies are large in the Southwest, Kansas City futures are likely to be under pressure and that market is sold against the purchase of Chicago with the expectation that the Kansas City price will decline compared with Chicago's. This is like selling the near-by future in a carrying-charge spread—you sell the market near the supplies. Small crops in the Southwest or the near market (Kansas City or Minneapolis) just as small supplies in an area point to inverse carrying charges in an intra-market spread—so the near is bought and the distant is sold.

One difference between inter-market and inter-delivery spreads is the consideration that the natural direction of movement of grain is toward the eastern consuming area; therefore the freight rate from one market to the other is a factor. Another is the difference in deliverable grades, if any. Some consideration is given to available storage space in Chicago, where the grain would potentially be shipped, and to the time element in moving grain from one market to the other. While all the factors would be pertinent if shipment between markets should be contemplated, it is seldom that the spreads widen to the full shipping difference to permit actual shipment. Substitution of shipments to areas to which Chicago might ship by the movement of winter wheat from the Southwest or spring wheat from the Northwest relieves the tension in the Chicago market so that actual shipment to the Chicago market is rarely resorted to to relieve a tight situation. These markets have favorable freight rates to many areas that permit them to sell to such destinations cheaper than Chicago could sell after paying the full in-freight and reshipping to the same places. Shipment might originate at some intermediate market such as Omaha, which does not have futures delivery or at a mill location taking advantage of the relatively high Chicago price. When wheat moves to Chicago from either the Southwest or the Northwest other than at a premium for milling or merchandising purposes it is usually for a short time during the harvest season in order to relieve elevator congestion in Kansas City or Minneapolis. At such a time cash-basis discounts are large and make up any deficiency in the spread to put the wheat on a Chicago futures-delivery basis. Usually the principle involved in these inter-market spreads is the relative supply-and-demand condition.

The Kansas City–Chicago spread normally stays at a difference representing part of the freight cost to ship the wheat from the Southwest to the Chicago area. Minneapolis may be lower than Chicago for the same reason, but in years of spring-wheat scarcity it sells higher than Chicago. It takes an unusual set of conditions to put the Kansas City price to a premium over Chicago, but actual or artificial scarcities created by Government-support loans in the Southwest, where there is ample storage space to take the loan, compared with large soft-red-winter-wheat supplies in the East, where the loan is not always so generally taken, have caused such a spread condition to exist.

When it is necessary to move wheat to Chicago to supply grain for delivery purposes, grade, storage-space, and time problems may be overcome by a cash trade with a Chicago elevator firm. The classes deliverable in both Kansas and Minneapolis are applicable on Chicago futures but all the numerical grades are not. Chicago does not permit number-two spring or number-three winter wheat to be delivered. Storage space and time element are more easily solved by the Chicago elevator firm which buys the cash grain rather than by the out-of-town spreader shipping the grain and making the futures delivery himself.

Kansas City delivery grain cannot be delivered in Minneapolis because one is a winter-wheat delivery market and the other a spring-wheat market. When spring wheat is scarce because of a small crop the Minneapolis market has to work out its own spread problems, as there is no other area that can supply wheat that is deliverable on the Minneapolis futures. The costliness of spring wheat in such years attracts winter varieties to many consuming places, including Minneapolis, in substitution for spring wheat. But there is some demand for spring wheat outside the production area that apparently cannot be substituted no matter how high the price goes. When spring wheat is plentiful and the spread is wide (under Chicago) it is often shipped into the Southwest hard-winter area to the mills for domestic use or sent via Gulf ports for export. The lowest-priced wheat, quality considered, replaces other classes.

When either of the outside market's prices (Kansas City or Minneapolis) are close to the freight differential under Chicago prices, or if Kansas City is weak compared with Minneapolis, the weakest market has an enlarged area in which to sell its wheat. The relative weakness of a market is the result of large supplies compared to the supplies available for the other market. This is the same as the basis for carrying charges in inter-delivery spreads. When supplies are small, the price of the respective market is strong compared to the other markets. This limits the areas to which the stronger market can ship its grain.

It is considered desirable for mills, for elevators, and for exporters who handle any volume of business to carry part of their hedges in Chicago because of its volume of trade and liquidity. Even when this is not regularly done, they are likely to buy Chicago futures when making a large cash sale, because of greater convenience, and then gradually to change the long hedge to Kansas City or Minneapolis. Because of this, there is always spreading interest between these markets and Chicago.

When there is a widening of the trading difference (Kansas City or Minneapolis selling at a greater discount under Chicago) before cash-wheat stocks have been accumulated, it affords an opportunity of making a spread with the short side of the spread in Chicago. Then, as cash wheat is bought, the long Kansas City or Minneapolis futures are sold out, leaving the short side as a hedge in Chicago against the cash wheat located in the Southwest or the Northwest.

Minneapolis wheat, because of its lake-freight advantage via Duluth to the East, and Kansas City, because its wheat is considered to be of a higher bread-baking quality than Chicago-area varieties, both normally sell somewhat closer to Chicago than the "freight differential." The advantage of Great Lakes transportation of spring wheat over the railroad rates to the East and the fact that both are less than Kansas City rates to the East normally permits Minneapolis wheat to sell higher than Kansas City wheat. This tends to equalize the delivered prices of flour in the densely populated eastern part of the country.

Foreign Inter-market Spreads

Formerly, the Chicago wheat-futures market's spread against Winnipeg changed as the United States and Canada vied for export business. In order to be in a competitive position to export heavily following the United States winter-wheat harvest, the Chicago prices representing shipments during the summer and early fall months were normally relatively lower than Winnipeg's. Later in the fall Canadian wheat represented by the Winnipeg October future became cheaper and gained the export advantage over United States wheat and resulted in large sales to Europe. It was the habit of spreaders at this time of the year to buy Winnipeg and sell Chicago. This buying power aided in carrying hedges on Canadian wheat, and the selling in Chicago, coming when the crop was all gathered and hedging was light, helped balance United States market operations.

This spread was based on the assumption that Canada would sell a good share of its surplus and that United States wheat would again compete in the export market. For that reason the spread was made only when United States supplies included a surplus over the domestic requirements and when there was potentially a normal carryover. Therefore, the Chicago market in most seasons when this spread was attractive was at a carrying charge between its futures. The spreader who was short in Chicago could change over to later futures at a premium, thus improving his spread position. In the fall of the year Canadian wheat shipments down the lakes for winter storage in the East depleted the Fort William stock of grain. This caused inverse carrying charges, putting the Winnipeg December to a discount under the October futures. The spreader then had the opportunity of changing the long end of the spread (Winnipeg October) to Winnipeg December futures at a discount. Later the Winnipeg December was changed to May, which, although it was at a carrying charge over the December, was no greater penalty than the gain from October to December. Historically such spreaders had the advantage of some inverse carrying charges in Winnipeg and carrying charges in Chicago, and they based their reasoning for the spread upon the probability of the two countries' competing for export business.

Meanwhile, the prices of each of these countries fluctuated against Liverpool futures. This brought spreading opportunities. One spread was the expectation that when one country's prices were less than a shipping difference to the foreign market they would have to be adjusted. Another spread was the opposite, the expectation that when at a shipping difference they would sell enough to relieve the pressure on their market and their supremacy would be challenged by other exporters becoming cheaper.

Spreading tended to even out some of the hills and valleys in futures-market fluctuations in the anticipation that each country needed an export outlet for its surplus wheat.

Importing Spreads

Through the use of futures, importers may accumulate a reservoir from which to furnish feed distributors and industrial users with grain supplies as they require them. At the same time, even though importers carry sizable stocks of these grains they limit their activities to merchandising risks.

Canada in most years raises surplus quantities of oats and in many years more rye than they can consume domestically and export overseas; also, their barley crops often provide a surplus. Canada's prices therefore approximate those of United States grains in a similar geographical location relative to the deficit grain-producing area of the eastern United States. While there is a United States duty to overcome on imported Canadian grain, the quality of Winnipeg's futures-delivery grades normally commands a premium over similar numerical grades of United States standards to partially overcome this charge. Canadian oats contain two pounds per bushel more than ours, so that at an equal price per respective bushel they are about 6% cheaper in United-States-bushel measurement.

Imported Canadian oats are consumed mostly in New England and in states south thereof close to the Atlantic seaboard, although at times buyers in the Central States and the Southeast find these oats priced competitively with home-grown varieties. The rye may work to distillers, who can draw this imported grain from Buffalo or Chicago. Barley goes largely to maltsters via Lake Michigan ports. Barley, however, is a direct commercial trade between Canadian sellers and United States buyers without the aid of futures in this country, although it is not independent of Winnipeg futures as a basing price.

Great Lakes boat-freight rates from Fort William to Chicago are approximately the same as the rates from either of these ports to Buffalo, so that imported grain costs about the same at either Chicago or Buffalo. Thus, when Canadian grain (United States duty paid) can be shipped to Buffalo at a price equal to a like quality of United States grades, it becomes competitive with shipments from Chicago and similar United States shipping points. At this price comparison it offers a merchandising risk for importers to buy Canadian grain, ship it to Buffalo, and hedge it in Chicago futures. This, therefore, does not provide full protection to the hedger, because the grain is out of position for delivery on the Chicago futures. But it assumes the same merchandising risk as shipping grain from Chicago to Buffalo in contemplation of making merchandising sales.

Occasionally there are seasons when Canadian prices decline to a level which permits the purchase of the grain for shipment to Chicago on a futures-delivery basis. This grain then can be safely hedged for delivery purposes and cannot, except possibly for a heavy harvest run, be underpriced by United States grades moving to Chicago. At the same time Canadian oats shipped direct from Canadian ports to Buffalo are lower in price in the East than oats transported from Chicago to Buffalo.

This business begins with the purchase of oats futures in Winnipeg and a simultaneous sale of futures in Chicago when the spreading difference brings the relative values into line for importation. The spreading may start in small units and be held in the form of futures spreads. But as the amount enlarges and the quantity becomes equal to the size of vessel-shipping lots, Winnipeg futures may be exchanged for cash oats and oats shipped across the lakes. Or delivery of the oats may be taken in consummation of the futures contract and shipment arranged thereafter. Simultaneous with the futures spreading, forward sales of cash oats can be made to buyers in the eastern part of the United States or elsewhere. If the grain is not sold before it is imported it may be held in storage and disposed of as buyers need supplies.

It would be difficult to handle this business without the use of futures, because importation may be arranged for at a time not corresponding with sufficient demand from cash buyers in this country. Futures anticipate a later need for the cash grain and act as a holding medium awaiting consumer purchases.

This kind of spreading is not dissimilar to actual hedging of grain originating at a location which permits shipment to the futures-delivery location or grain that may be held for merchandising in an outside or out-of-position location. In fact, as soon as cash is substituted for futures in Canada the operation is one of actual hedging. The import business originates because of spreading possibilities which, like hedging, put value into the grain because it is where it is wanted when it is wanted. This is possible only because the importer buys the grain regardless of his opinion of price changes. Even though he may think the flat price will be lower later, he is able to hedge and eliminate the price risk from his commercial dealings.

As the imported grain is merchandised, short hedges are

bought in, as is the customary practice. Sometimes this grain is sold for export and may even be held in bond in vessels or in elevators in the United States and re-exported on the original Canadian inspection certificate.

Grain vs. Products

There are changing values between grains and the products of their manufacture, but not many spreads can be made between these, because of the lack of futures markets for the products. Because flour prices follow wheat fluctuations, there is little need for flour futures; Kansas City millfeed futures hold a measure of protection for the balance of the wheat products but are not representative of the trade in all locations. Products of other grains—corn, oats, rye, barley—largely follow influences differing from those affecting the raw grain itself and have no futures available for hedging or spreading purposes. Soybeans are naturally closely related to the products soybean oil and meal, but each moves within its own sphere from influences affecting one and not necessarily either of the others. As a consequence, product values change in relation to soybeans and the proceeds of oil sales vary against the meal. In times past, oil from a bushel of soybeans has brought about twice as much as the meal and at other times the meal twice as much as the oil. The combined value of oil and meal fluctuates against the soybeans anywhere from being below the cost of soybeans without any provision for conversion costs to a sizable manufacturing profit over costs. This permits satisfactory functioning of futures markets in each soybeans, oil, and meal.

Each of these futures markets follows the dictates of carrying-charge (or inverse) influences as required by supplies relative to demand within each trade. Soybeans reflect the overall demand for exports of soybeans and the need for soybeans for conversion to products. In the course of merchandising, hedges can be placed in the futures market representing the product in which the risk lies and in the delivery month judged to offer the greatest price protection. Speculative opportunities exist in correctly analyzing the commercial potentialities. Soybean-oil futures may be spread against its foremost competitors —cottonseed oil and lard. The parent crops (soybeans, cotton, and hogs) of all three of these are produced for different purposes and are influenced by different conditions; yet these products are the three most important in the edible-fats-and-oils economy of the nation.

Price comparisons between grains and products when pertaining to feeding are referred to as "price ratios." It is the ratio that determines the tendency of farmers to sell their grain for cash or to feed it to livestock. Price ratios may be good or bad at a high or a low price for grain. Some farmers feed their grain every year regardless of the ratio and take the bad years along with the good. Other farmers and feeders feed as it is profitable, expanding or contracting their activities or stopping them entirely.

The ratio at which a feeding operation becomes profitable changes with genetic improvement in the breeding of livestock and the quality of the feed in particular, but there are other contributing factors. Progress in formula feeds with the addition of vitamins and antibiotics, together with selection, inbreeding, and crossing of livestock, have reduced the amount of feed required to produce a given weight of livestock. Hybrid chickens, more milk per cow, sanitation, etc., continually aid the feeding industry. Another consideration in feeding is the relative cost of shipping the grain to market as compared with the freight on livestock which the same amount of grain will feed. Shipping costs to market are less for the livestock than for the required grain, and establishment of packing houses in diversified locations has further aided the livestock feeder.

The effect of scientific progress on price ratios is more gradual than the year-to-year changes in ratios because of price changes of grain resulting from varying crop production or the prices of the end products—meat, eggs, milk, etc. Grain prices usually exert the greatest short-term influences on ratios, even more than the demand for meat, which is tied to general economic conditions having a longer cycle or affected by different individual conditions in livestock or products.

The largest feed-grain crop is corn, and more corn is used to feed hogs than for any other use in the United States. Therefore, the price ratio watched most closely is the hog-corn ratio—the number of bushels of corn that equals the price of 100 pounds of hogs, live weight. The Chicago ratio is calculated weekly and is readily available in the trade news. The ratios for the United States and for sections of the Corn Belt states are published frequently. Other price ratios include beef-steer–corn, butterfat-feed, milk-feed, egg-feed, chicken-feed, and turkey-feed.

Corn and other grains compete against each other in household and industrial products. Cane sugar and corn sugar are competitive; lard competes with soybean oil (one is derived from the feeding of corn combined with soybean meal and other ingredients and the other is the product of soybeans); cottonseed oil goes into some of the same uses as lard and soybean oil, and the latter goes into competition with drying oils such as linseed oil. Millfeeds, the price of which is a factor in the pricing of wheat flour, are a livestock feed. The same is so of other by-products feeds, tankage, meat scraps, distillers' and brewers' dried grains, corn-gluten feed and meal, dried-milk products, etc., as their prices have some effect on the sale prices of the products from which they are derived. Declining prices of by-products tend to increase the necessity for higher prices of the other products derived from the same source to obtain the same total proceeds, and advancing by-product prices have the opposite effect.

There is a tie-in of intended acreage, crop production, feed-grain prices and economic conditions all relating to price ratios. Price changes of different commodities cause substitutions, curtailing the use of some and favoring others, so that lower-priced materials find the greater use. This follows the same theory of spreads in grain between countries, markets, or months in the same market. When supplies are plentiful the marketing op-

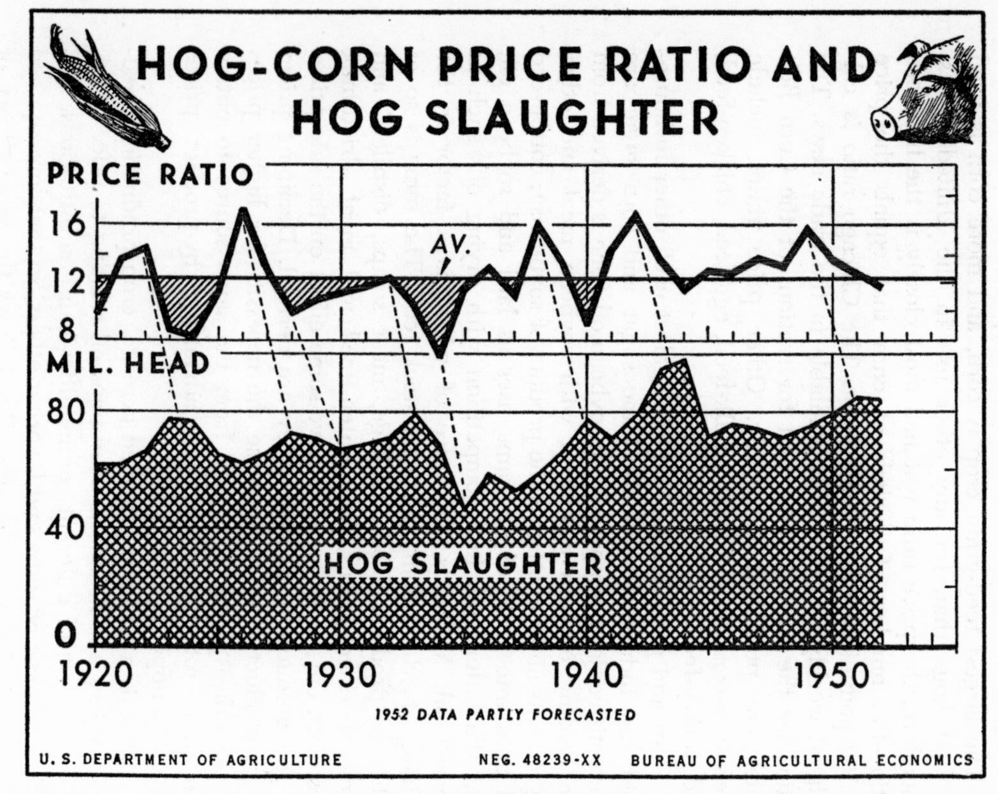
HOG-CORN PRICE RATIO AND HOG SLAUGHTER
PRICE RATIO
16
12
8
AV.
MIL. HEAD
80
40
0
HOG SLAUGHTER
1920
1930
1940
1950
1952 DATA PARTLY FORECASTED
U. S. DEPARTMENT OF AGRICULTURE
NEG. 48239-XX
BUREAU OF AGRICULTURAL ECONOMICS

FIGURE 16

portunities expand, and because of lower relative grain prices it becomes a buyer's market, as in the case of carrying charges. When grain is scarce the prices advance and a seller's market prevails, as in the case of inverse carrying charges. This is similar to paying a premium or having to buy accessories for early delivery of an automobile when they are scarce or getting an extra allowance for a used car when new cars are relatively plentiful.

The pricing system is one of relativity. Each commodity bears a certain proportionate price to other commodities, getting out of line because of individual supply-and-demand conditions. Prices do not long continue in an unnatural trend—for example, corn being priced equal with wheat, which we have seen, or corn being too high relative to the price of hogs. The economic balance returns each commodity to its true value. It is not always possible to take speculative advantage of corrections in prices through spreading actions, because the overpriced grain that you would sell may be cheaper for the deferred position through inverse carrying charges and an underpriced grain may correct its price level by carrying charges.

CHAPTER XIV

Summary

SERVICES

The grain trade embraces a number of interrelated businesses. Some of these are inseparable from the purpose of handling grain, and others perform auxiliary services to the trade. Some of the inherent services have been scientifically and mechanically developed to a high degree. Many men devote their careers to the practical side of the business—the handling or inspecting of the grain—and others to the operational functions of trading or merchandising.

The great bulk of grain moved and stored has created problems to be overcome. In its handling after it leaves the farms the grain must be segregated according to its quality factors. Elevators are designed for speed and efficiency so that the grain can be economically handled and, while it is in storage, the quality improved by the use of intricate machinery. Stored grain is watched for presence of insects or factors that will cause it to deteriorate. The development of chemicals to treat grain and machinery to handle and clean it tax the abilities of chemists and engineers and employ many men in their manufacture.

The grading of grain starts from the time it reaches the country elevator, but the farmer before this must take care in the selection of the seed, cultivation and harvesting of the crop, and its storage on the farm to maintain its quality. Endless and painstaking research guides those who grade the grain. This not only permits the selection of suitable grain by the processors without inspection of samples, but assures each handler that the quality of the grain is equal to its contract specifications. Even though there are strict rules for grading grain, some quality factors are left to the judgment of grain inspectors, but they are skilled in the application of the grading rules.

Elevator superintendents must have complete knowledge of grading standards and all storing and handling operations of the elevator under their care. It is they, with the co-operation of the merchandisers, who have to segregate the grain for storage so that its full value is realized upon resale. Wasted bin space in elevators or loss of identity of valuable grading or protein factors reduces profits. Judgment in turning and treatment of the grain prevents losses. Knowledge of blending and conditioning adds to the profits. These are some of the duties with which elevator superintendents are charged.

The merchandiser for a firm is directly responsible for the purchase and sale of the grain, but he must also work with all departments—traffic, banking, futures, etc.—in addition to elevator operators.

Transportation service for the grain interests is provided by truck, railroad, barge, and steamship lines as it is required, and these agencies work closely with grain shippers, exporters, and port grain handlers.

The grain trade relies upon the availability of all the established services for the regular conduct of its business. On each transaction it is necessary to arrange for the use of some of the facilities, but other facilities are always available in the regular course of grain handling.

Services Used and Operations Performed

By Country and Terminal Elevators.—Country elevator operators engage in portions of the physical, trading, and merchandising branches of the business as well as contacting the railroads, truckers, and bankers. Their business necessitates the use of grain-inspection services as well as weighing services when the grain arrives at its destination. It is essential that country elevator operators be familiar with the grading of grain so that they may purchase it on the basis of its moisture content, test weight, damage, or any of the other factors which the official inspector recognizes at the terminal market. Inasmuch as processor terminal buyers have their end product in mind, the same as sub- or terminal elevator buyers who later sell to processors, the grain is discounted on its arrival at destination commensurate with its intrinsic value. If the country elevator operator does not buy in accordance with the grain's physical features he finds that the truck lots purchased from the farmers exceed the value of the grain when his terminal-account sale reaches him. The same kind of invisible loss reduces profits unless the country elevator's scales are accurate, because any shortage shows up when the grain is weighed at the terminal. Terminal elevators have official weights, with the weighing supervised by boards of trade, Chambers of Commerce, or other recognized bodies.

Grain that comes from farms may have admixtures of foreign material, some of which is readily separable and may be termed dockage in some of the grain; it is not paid for as grain but does not lower the grade. Other foreign material results in the lowering of the grade. Mechanical devices remove these impurities from the grain, but to different degrees in accordance with the type of handling. The country elevator ordinarily has little cleaning machinery; because terminal elevators work for a grade of grain, they remove only material the absence of which improves the grade to a commercial standard; the processors' requirements are more exacting, but even they watch the point at which cleaning would reduce profits. Anyone of these handlers blends the grain passing through his hands to give the best financial returns.

The country operator must secure the co-operation of the railroad on which his elevator is located to get boxcars to load the grain with the minimum of delay when farmers are selling freely. The cars must be in good order, coopered, and the grain doors securely installed so that there will be no undue loss of grain in transit. Terminal elevators may use their empties from grain received to load out grain for shipment or they may have to order cars from the railroad that is hauling the outbound shipment.

The country elevator operator is little concerned over railroad routing or billing except to carry out his buyer's instructions. The terminal elevator operator and the processor, however, must watch both of these railroad requirements very closely, as they make up one of the most important features of their business.

Trucks carry grain from country elevators and direct from farms at the direction of the country grain dealers in an increasing percentage of the national total of grain handled. Therefore, grain operators must stay in close contact with this business. Terminal elevators receive considerable grain by truck, but except in some areas do not ship out much by this method of transportation. The area in which a processing plant is located may also govern its use of trucks in transporting grain or products to the final destinations.

Barge and vessel uses are limited to those grain firms in position to handle this business, but grain must be routed from its origin to take advantage of vessel-shipping services. Trucked or barged grain or grain moving to Chicago on the special railroad "lake rates" can move out via lake steamers without any loss of incoming freight, but the several cents per bushel paid out on "Illinois proportional" billing is lost if the grain does not move by rail to the eastern part of the country. Likewise, shippers anywhere in the country have to know the points at which their billing will transit and be guided in their grain purchasing accordingly.

The country banker usually intimately knows the elevator operator who uses his bank's services, handles draft collections, and provides credit for conduct of the elevator business as it is needed. Terminal-elevator men and processors normally borrow large sums of money on collateral, at times on open credit, and are in daily contact with their bankers. Bankers know that it is the practice of most of these firms to hedge in futures and are likely to require it, especially where capitalization is limited. It is probably the exception when financially strong firms requiring the use of bank funds do not hedge. Many firms can borrow up to 85% to 90% of the collateral value of hedged grain from banks at a low rate of interest. Loans are easily negotiated because bankers know the firms or individuals handling this grain are not subjecting themselves to the risk of fluctuations of the market.

The country man at the average elevator with possibly one assistant is his own grain inspector; he handles the railroad traffic, the banking, the weighing of the grain, the operating of the elevator (including what blending is done), all the buying and selling of the grain, and the purchase of staples which he sells to the farmers. For the larger elevators it takes more specialization of duties according to elevator facilities and operations.

By Moderate-Sized Firms and Dealers.—Firms with more diversification in one area, operating a sub-terminal elevator or a terminal elevator, or using semi-public and public elevator space divide the operations within their organization, but act as a unit. They may be guided in their activities by the producer-selling of each grain as it is harvested and by the amount of grain and for the length of time they are required to hold it in storage as regulated by the demand. Some firms specialize in a certain grain, but in its periods of off-season movement and for excess storage space handle other grains. Having limited storage capacity, their opportunity for profit lies in turning over their stock of grain many times during the year. The firm as a whole tends to concentrate on the grain being handled in predominant quantity.

Dealers who do not have elevators or who use others' space only occasionally are similar to brokers, except that they do not drop out of the transaction by disclosing the principals to each other. In many cases they have immediate buyers for the grain which they purchase or sellers for the grain which sudden downturn in the futures market; but except for changes in the cash basis the prices of cash grain and of futures follow each other.

There is no compulsion in the use of futures; in fact, many who hedge do not have the grain in a location to make delivery on the futures contract which protects it from fluctuations. They know, though, that the price of grain in the part of the country east of the Rocky Mountains fluctuates largely as one unit. They prefer to hedge, however, and forego the possibility of making a speculative profit in favor of earning an expected normal merchandising or service charge through the efficient operation of their respective businesses.

All the actions that influence production, distribution, and consumption culminate in the futures market. These are the successive actions of the farmer or, even before him, the influences that encourage production of one crop or another, and they progress step by step throughout the trade to the consumer. Everything of importance registers its influence on the price of futures.

There are risks that may be assumed on either side of a trade—those risks that go with a purchase or the risks of a sale. As there is no compulsion in the grain trade that you must buy before you sell, either obligation may be contracted first. At any time, however, this burden of major price changes for buyers or sellers of grain may be transferred to the futures by hedging.

Even before the farmer plants his grain, a consumer in this country or abroad may influence prices upward by buying futures in anticipation of his later needs, or it may be on the keener judgment of a speculator that a purchase is made in the consumer's stead. In either case, it is trading actions based on judgment of conditions that are likely to prevail during a later period. Futures prices may currently advance because of some bullish condition at a distant location or because of an event that will affect supplies at a later date. At the same time, during the period at hand cash-grain operators in the vicinity of the futures market may be troubled with a surplus. Or a surplus elsewhere or a forecast for a surplus at a later date may lower futures-contract prices at a time when a local scarcity exists. A modifying effect is continually registered throughout the world because all the influences converge in the futures market.

The contracts, working agreements, and customs of trade of the exchanges and trade organizations which the grain trade has for its protection give it security, in a business sense, which does not differ from that of business in general. But the added price-risk-transference feature available through hedging eliminates a risk and gives increased selling prices to producers and lowered costs to consumers. No charge is made to those who use this service and no premium is paid to the agency (the speculator) furnishing the service. Once price risks are assumed in general business, they cannot usually be dropped at will, and if losses threaten, the only course is to see them through even though bankruptcy follows. Adverse price changes of cash grain covered by contracts need not threaten the stability of buyers or sellers, because of the availability of the futures hedge. At any time in the life of a cash contract or while carrying a stock of grain, the price-transference feature through the use of futures may be invoked. There are times and conditions under which price protection is not needed; it is, however, available to tradesmen handling such business. These times occur in the concentration of grain purchased from producers by independent elevator operators or in the final retail distribution of grain or grain products to consumers. The price risk is of short duration and on a minor quantity, and a larger handling fee is charged; therefore, a hedge is not customarily applied. The country-elevator man also uses the "to-arrive" market for quick sale to offset his purchases. For the main part, when any volume of cash grain is handled the unit of profit on merchandising is so small that the use of futures is indispensable.

Index

Agriculture (*see also* Farming)
development of, 6
inventions in, 9
Areas
equilization of, 54
harvests in wheat, 60; in corn, 72
Argentina
exporting of, 247
harvests of wheat in, 60, 72
as producer, 6, 59
Australia
exporting of, 247
harvest of wheat in, 60
as producer, 6, 59

Banks, 170, 257, 335, 341
Barley, 77
classes of, 170
futures, 78
international trade in, 71
malting, 77, 202
Orient, imports of, 248
pearling, 205
purchasing and processing of, 202
Behavior of market, 276, 303
Brewing, 205
Bucket shops, 16
Business Conduct Committee, 18

Canada
export ports of, 262, 268
inspection in, 172
news and statistics in, 235
production growth in, 6
as surplus producer, 59
Carrying charges, 53
changing, 315
inverse, 48, 311, 313
Carryover
cotton, 309
export relationship of, 245
wheat, 309
Cash basis, 44
cannot hedge, 43
Cash grain, 40
consignment of, 181
hedging of, 313
risks of, 42, 43
sales of, to terminals, 101
scope of, 40
"to arrive," 182
when bought, 47
when sold, 48
Chicago Board of Trade, 12
appeals in, 24
arbitration in, 24
charter of, 17, 23
deliveries at, 66, 69
departments of, 24
early days of, 13
floor trading at, 299
inter-market spreads at, 319
odd lots at, 317
organized, 13
partnerships, corporations and, 24, 27
quotations at, 229
relation of, to other markets, 38
rules and regulations of, 23
spreads at, 314
Clearing. *See* Futures
Commission merchant and
cash grain, 101
consignment, 102, 181
export, 274
futures, 28
purchasing, 180
"to arrive," 180, 182

Commissions
  export, 274
  freight, 129
  futures, 27
Commodity Exchange Authority, 17, 26
  classification speculation, not spread, 292
  deliveries, 70
  delivery grades, 75
  odd lots as spreads, 294
  open interest, 280
  open interest, hedges, speculation, spreading. 288
  penalties, 234
Competition, 49
Corn, 71
  cattle and, 74
  Chicago receipts of, 74
  classes, grades of, 170
  cribs, 14, 133, 139
  damage to, in grading, 169
  drying, 139, 144
  dry processing of, 199
  as feed, 199
  feeding percentage of, 74
  hogs and, 74
  hog-corn ratio, 329
  movement chart for, 73
  off-farm, 74
  precipitation and, 72
  weather and, 239
  wet processing of, 195
Corn Belt, 72
Cotton, carryover of, 309
Crop reports, 217
  aid shipping, 243
  procedure of making, 223
Crops (*see also* Farming; Harvests)
  sale of, 94
  world cereal, 58
Deliveries, 21, 34, 69, 70
  cash grain and, 53
  at Chicago, 69
  classes of, in markets, 66
  Clearing House relation to, 26
  conditions of, 70
  out of position for, 53
  time of, 70
  track, 22, 69, 70
Diet, 56
Distilling, 205

Elevators
  barge, 149
  country, 45, 99, 140, 277, 333
  Custodian Department, 155
  Federal, 153
  floating, 264
  harvest movement to, 96
  laws regarding, 152
  quality of grain protection at, 154, 155
  terminal, 145, 333, 337
  weighing at, 156
Europe
  agricultural production of, 3
  diet of, 56
  imports of, 6, 247
Export, 109, 245
  as balancing item, 111, 127, 236, 245
  cargoes, 258
  carrying charges and, 270
  commissions on, 274
  competition in, 270
  contracts (N.Y.P.E., N.A.E.-G.A., L.C.T.A.), 255–57
  crop reports aid shipping of, 243
  elevators, 150
  floating elevator for, 264
  fobber, 111

foreign exchange and, 257, 273
futures, 249, 251, 271, 275
inspection of, 162, 268
insurance and, 258
lighters and, 264
out-turn of, 261
parcels, 260
ports for, 262
pricing of, 273
routes to ports for, 111, 264
routine of business of, 251
selling, 269
transportation of, 126
types of firms, 253

Farming
acreage tie-in with prices and ratios, 329
advancement methods in, 92
crops reports, 217, 223
crops, sale of, 94
farm storage vs. elevators, 136
grain areas, 62
harvest movement, 96
hazards of, 89
land uses, 56
quality in storage, 184
storage, 133, 134
weather and, 238
Federal Drug Act, 168, 169
Feeding
hog-corn ratio, 329
livestock proportions, 74
other ratios, 329
Feed manufacturing, 213
Fertilizer, 91
Flaxseed classes, 171
Food and Drug Administration, 169
Freight rates, 128
Funds, customers', 19
Futures, 10 (*see also* Commodity Exchange Authority)
actually started, 15
barley, 78
brokerage, 29
buying of, in anticipation of export sales, 275
by whom used, 52
carrying charges on, 53, 107, 270
carrying charges and products, 327
changing hedges in, 107
clearing of, 25, 32, 300
commission business and, 27
commission-merchant operations in, 28
commission rates of, 27
corn, 75
customer activity in, 302
customers' accounts for, 31
deliverable stocks for, 232
delivery grades for, 66
development of, 10
example of use of, 51
execution of orders for, 35
exporting, 249, 271, 280
floor trading of, 299
floor trading, clearing of, 300
foreign spreads of, 323
give up, exchange of, 102, 271
grain-sorghum, 81
guide to price of, 22, 39, 250
hedges, 42
hedging, changing, spreading, 315
importing, 324
inverse carrying charges for, 48, 312; references, 314
lard, 82
margins, 34
oats, 76

Futures (*cont.*)
odd-job lots, 27
odd lots, 317
odd lots as spreads, 294
off-floor customers for, 302
open interest in, 18
open interest follows volume unsold grain, 342
open interest, hedging, speculation, spreading, 288
open-interest soybeans vs. stocks and prices, 284
open interest vs. stocks of grain, 280
operations, 25
orders, 29
pit trading of, 29, 35
quotations of, 22, 37, 302
relation of, to cash grain, 40
relation of, to Government program, 315
relation of, to other markets, 38
rye, 79, 194
settlement of, 32
"short" position of, 312
soybean, 85, 208
soybean-meal, 86, 212
soybean-oil, 85, 212
speculation in, 11, 341
speculative per cent of open interest, 297
spreading, 37, 310
spreads of, 316
time contracts in, 15
"to arrive," 15
trade information on, 234
transference of price risk in, 276
use of, 52, 338
value of, 302
volume of, 301
wheat, 66

Government program, reference to, 249, 315
Grading starts at country elevator or before, 332. *See also* Inspection
Grain
relation to world's food crops, 3
vs. products, 327
Grain sorghums, 80
area of, 80
classes of, 171
futures, 81
processing, 196
Grain trade
development of, 4
factions consolidate, 338
Great Lakes, 97, 119
elevators, 150
winter storage at, 151
Growing, marketing, merchandising, 89
and transportation, 130

Harvest
movement, 96
world, 60
Hedges
on breaks, 302
on bulges, 302
cash grain, 313
changing, 107, 318
changing between markets, 37
Chicago, always use for, 190, 322
of flour mills, 190
futures offset cash, 42
individual risks in, 43
open interest vs. stocks, 280
per cent of open interest, 289
processor, 103
rye, 194
"short" position, 312

soybean, 284
speculation, spreading, open interest, 288
terminal, 103
transference of risk in, 276
vs. speculation, 297
wheat, 280
when without, 45
Hogs
in Corn Belt, 74
hog-corn ratio, 329
proportion feed of, 74

Illinois & Michigan Canal, 14
"Illinois Proportional," 122
Imports, 247, 248
spreads, 324
transportation of, 126
Inspection, 158
analysis, 163
appeal, 159
Board of Trade sampling, 179
in Canada, 172
classes, vi, 22, 169
damage, 167; to corn, 169; to soybeans, 169; to wheat, 168
dockage, 167, 334
export, 268
Federal Drug Act, 168
first grading, 17
grades, 22 (*see also* classes, *above*)
grading, 66
grading factors, 164
hidden infection, 169
licensed inspectors, 159
moisture, 165
of other commodities, 176
protein, 171
purpose of, 158
sales on qualifications, 175
sampling, 161
service, 171
soybean damage in grading, 169
test weight per bushel, 165
"unfit for mixing," 168
United States Grain Standards Act, 158
Intercoastal waterways, 267
Interstate Commerce Commission, 118, 123
Inverse carrying charges, 48
changing, 315
degree of scarcity, 312
references, 314

Job lots. *See* Odd lots

Lard, 81
futures, 82
inspection, 176
Livestock
feeding proportions, 74
vs. exports, 245
"Long," 33

Margins
Board of Trade, 15, 31
C.E.A. no authority on, 20
Clearing House, 35
speculation, 341
Marketing, 89
Markets
behavior of, 303
foreign exchange, 273
growing, merchandising and, 89
inter-market spreads, 318
mechanics and behavior of, 276
prices and, 244
purchasing and processing at, 190
relation to Chicago, 38, 68
transportation and, 131
weather and, 240

Merchandising, 89, 337
  barge, 120
  buying from terminals, 108
  country dealers, 100, 336
  export, 109, 110, 269
  by farmers, 94
  by large firms, 337
  by medium-size merchandisers, 336
  sales to terminals, 101
  of soybeans, 208
  storing and selling from terminals, 104
Milling in transit, 125

News and statistics. *See* Statistics
North Dakota, storage in, 137

Oats, 75
  areas of, 76
  classes of, 170
  purchasing and processing of, 200
Ocean transportation, 127. *See also* Exports
Odd lots, job lots, 27
  as spreads, 294
  futures, 317
Oklahoma, storage in, 136
Other markets
  equalization of areas, 54
  relation of, 38

Pit, execution of orders in, 35
Precipitation
  and corn, 72
  and wheat, 64
Prices
  central, 55
  vs. carryover cotton, 309
  vs. carryover wheat, 309
  grain exchange, 229
  grains vs. products, 327
  hog-corn ratio, 329
  influences on, 23
  pattern of, 42, 342
  ratios of, 328, 329
  relation of, to other markets, 244
  relativity of, 329
  soybean open interest and, 284
  vs. supply of wheat, 306
  vs. wheat, Government supports, 283
  world, 236
  world levels of, 311
Processing
  barley malt, 202
  barley pearling, 205
  buying and hedging, 103, 184, 185
  corn, dry, 199; wet, 195
  of feeds, 196, 199
  feed manufacturing, 213
  flour milling, 188
  of grain sorghums, 196
  mill hedging, 190
  of oats, 200
  in Orient, 206
  of rye, 194
  of soybean meal, 212
  of soybean oil, 212
  of soybeans, 206
  soybean, types of, 210
Purchasing and processing, 180, 200
  of barley for malt, 202; for pearling, 205
  consignment, 181
  consumption and, 186
  corn for dry processing, 199; for wet processing, 195
  country, 180
  of feeds, 199

flour milling and, 188, 190
of grain sorghums, 196
market's relation to, 190
of oats, 200
processor, 184
rye milling, 194
of soybeans, 206
terminal, 182, 183
"to arrive," 180, 182

Quotations
exchange, 229
futures, 302

Railroads (*see also* Transportation)
Chicago, in and out of, 16; G. & C. U., 13
Illinois Central, 16
Rice, 3
Risks (*see also* Hedges)
cannot hedge cash basis, 43
individual, 43, 278
Russia
exports of, 246
production areas of, 246
rye, wheat, of, 3
Rye, 78
areas of, 78
classes of, 79, 171
futures, 194
hedging, 194
milling, 194
supply, 79

Sea routes
domestic, 125
ocean, 127
Services, 332
"Short," 33
position, 312
Soybean meal, 84
as feed, 208
futures, 86, 212
inspection of, 178
Soybean oil, 84
futures, 85, 212
inspection, 177
Soybeans, 82
areas of, 83
classes of, 171, 209
damage to, 169
exports, 209
flour, 212
futures, 85, 208
hedges, 284
marketing, 208
meal, 84
oil, 84
and open interest and prices, 284
in Orient, 206
purchasing and processing of, 206
transportation of, 210
uses of, 82
varieties of, 84
world supply of, 83
Speculation, 11, 341
before futures, 15
vs. hedges, 297
hedging, spreading, open interest, 288
percentages, 297
spreads, 316
Spot grain, 21
consignment, 181
Spreading, 230, 296, 310
adjusts world levels, 311
basic reasoning behind, 319
changing hedges, 37, 315
during delivery month, 342
execution of, 318

Spreading (*cont.*)
  foreign, 323
  futures, 316
  as gauge for distribution, 310
  handling, 315
  hedging, speculation, open interest, 288
  hedging, spreading, changing, 315
  how to operate in, 318
  importing, 324
  inter-market, 319
  odd-lots, 294, 317
  spreads, 316
Statistics and news, 217
  Canadian, 235
  Commodity Exchange Authority, 234
  crop reports, 217, 223
  crop reports and railroads, 243
  crop reports aid shipping, 243
  deliverable stocks, 232
  general, 233, 242
  Government, 227
  grain exchanges, 229, 232
  private agencies, 233, 251
  on passage, 237
  quotations, 230
  trade information, 234
  weather, 238
  world, 236
  world shipments, 236
Storage, 104, 132
  in barge elevators, 149
  in corn cribs, 133, 139
  in country elevators, 99, 140
  charges, 148
  custodian, 155
  drying in, 144
  emergency, 152
  in farm bins, 134
  farm vs. elevator, 136
  Federal, 153
  in Great Lakes elevators, 150
  in Illinois, 152
  kinds and places of, 132
  laws regarding, 152
  off-farm capacity for, 138
  quality protection during, 70, 154, 155
  terminal, 104, 145
  thermometer, 147
  tickets, 153
  Uniform Agreement, 156
  weighing in, 156
  winter, 112, 151
Summary, 332
  grain firms generally, 337
  large grain firms, 337
  medium-size grain firms, 336
  services, 332, 333
Supreme Court decision, 12, 26

Terminals, 183
  buying from, 108
  hedging at, 103
  sales to, 101
  selling at, 104
  storing at, 104
"To arrive," 15, 180, 198
  commission merchant, 182
  vs. consignment, 101
  country use of, 180, 280
  forward sales, 101
  on market bulges, 302
  origin of, 15
  sales to terminals, 101
Trading
  pit, 21, 35
  spreading, 230
Transportation, 114
  barge, 120
  commissions on, 129
  connection of, to grain conditions, 115, 130
  crop reports aid railroads, 243

export cargoes, 258
export ports, 261
exports, 126
and feed manufacturing, 216
freight bills for, 124
gateways, 116
general rates of, 128
grain movement, 125
Great Lakes, 119
"Illinois Proportional," 122
imports and, 126, 325
on inland waterways, 120, 267
Interstate Commerce Commission, 118
lighters, 264
loading cars, 124
market's relation to, 131
milling in transit, 125
ocean, 127, 243
on passage, 237
other charges for, 129
of parcels, 260
railroads, 115
railroad billing for, 118, 183
railroad gateways, 116
railroad rates, 116
of soybeans, 210
summary, 130, 334
tariffs and, 123
traffic territories, 116
transit balances, 123
trucks, 114

United States
agriculture, 4
cultivated land in, 4
weather of, 238
world-news effects on, 236

Weather, 238 (*see also* Precipitation)
corn and, 239
markets and, 240
origin of observations of, 240
Weighing, 17
at elevator, 156, 333
Weight per bushel, 128, 165
as quantity measurement, vii
test for, 165
Wheat
at Chicago, 15
classes and grades of, 169
damage to, 168
flour-milling cash-basis, 190
futures, 66
harvests, 60
hedging, 190, 280
prices vs. carryover of, 309
prices vs. supply of, 306
purchasing of milling, 188
stands freight farm to market, 65
stocks vs. hedges on, 280
weather and, 238
where grown in U.S., 62
world, 3
world classes of, 59
world levels of, 311
Winter storage, 112, 151
World
cereal crops, 58
grain and its trading, 3
grain résumé, 56
news and statistics, 236
on passage, 237
prices, 236
price vs. supply, 306
production and trade, 56
shipments, 236
wheat, 59
world's level, 311